Our planet, our health

Report of the
WHO Commission on Health
and Environment

World Health Organization
Geneva
1992

WHO Library Cataloguing in Publication Data

WHO Commission on Health and Environment
    Our planet, our health : report of the WHO Commission
    on Health and Environment.

    1.Environment   2.Environmental health   I.Title

    ISBN 92 4 156148 3   (NLM Classification: WA 30)

PRINTED IN SWITZERLAND

91/9104 – Benteli – 10 000

Contents

Foreword

The various ways in which the environment interacts with health in the context of development have never been analysed in depth at the international level. The principal objective of the Commission on Health and Environment set up by the Director-General of the World Health Organization, Dr Hiroshi Nakajima, was to fill this gap by examining knowledge and understanding of these interactions and reaching some conclusions on the relative importance of the various mechanisms involved and the kinds of action that need to be taken in the coming decades to counter their adverse effects. One specific purpose was to produce a rigorous and detailed update on these questions that could be made available to the United Nations Conference on Environment and Development to be held in Rio de Janeiro from 1 to 12 June 1992.

Not being a specialist in any of the fields the Commission would be covering, it was with some hesitation that I accepted the honour of becoming its chairwoman. However, I realized that there might be some advantage in entrusting this responsibility to someone with no specific training in matters of environment and health, but with experience in the practice of seeking advice from specialists on technical questions in order to be able to reach fully informed decisions of a political order. It is in this capacity that I have undertaken and carried through this mission, keeping clearly in mind, as a decision-maker, the questions to which we should all like to have a clear answer.

Thus, in view of the fact that health issues are not attracting as much attention as purely ecological issues in contemporary discussion of the environment and development, it might legitimately be asked whether there is some sort of incompatibility or conflict between protecting and improving the environment and protecting and improving health. The Commission's conclusions are unequivocal: not only is there no conflict between these two objectives, but the kind of development needed to safeguard health and welfare will depend on many conditions, including respect for the environment, while development without regard for the environment would inevitably result in impairment of human health.

The Commission also examined the consequences of population growth in certain countries and of rising consumption in others, the role of the production and disposal of waste, and the effects of poverty on nations and people. There can be no doubt that, for sustainable development to be achieved, the protection of the environment—and hence of health—will require a global approach to the control of these factors, each of which must be examined in the light of the local situation in any programme of development. This is a very long-term objective, and its attainment will require far-reaching and sustained changes in policies and practice at all levels, in countries where the population is stable as well as in those where it is expanding.

Such a wide-ranging review would not have been possible without the contributions made by the members of the Commission, the panels which provided them with the basic materials essential for their work, and the Secretariat, without whose help this report could not have been written.

My gratitude goes to all those who have facilitated a task that will not have been in vain if the international community, and WHO in the first instance, acts in consequence and reflects in its decisions the concerns voiced by the Commission. The state of the environment, and especially the trends that can now be observed, give few grounds for optimism in the decades to come. They should rather spur us to intensify our still far from adequate efforts towards worldwide protection of our environment through policies of sustainable development, for on this depend the health and ultimately the survival of the human race.

Simone Veil
Chairwoman,
WHO Commission on
Health and Environment

Preface

If health for all is to be achieved, a new alliance for health is called for. Health protection and promotion must be considered in their widest sense. Human health is a vital cross-sectoral issue, dependent on the continued availability of environmental resources and on the integrity of the environment. In recent years, environmental problems have acquired new dimensions. Everywhere in the world, the environment is changing, as a result of pollution and loss of natural resources—water, land, air, vegetation, and even genetic diversity. All around us we see the deleterious effects on health of environmental degradation.

The health challenges to be faced in the coming decades will require concerted action on the part of many individuals and agencies at all levels. As the directing and coordinating authority for international health work, WHO must fulfil its role as leader in such action. For this reason, in 1990 I established an independent Commission on Health and Environment, comprising internationally recognized experts in the scientific, social and political fields. The conclusions and recommendations of the Commission will help to shape WHO's programmes of cooperation and will provide the basis for a new global strategy for environmental health.

The Commission has provided an essential and timely assessment of the relationship between health and the environment, in the context of development. I am grateful to all its members for their personal commitment and dedication to such a daunting undertaking. My particular gratitude goes to Mrs Simone Veil who, as Chairman of the Commission, ensured the success of its work, and to the Vice-Chairmen, Dr Emil Salim and Professor Nikolai Izmerov, who provided guidance and inspiration. I also wish to thank the members of the four technical panels for their contributions, in particular the four chairmen whose work was vital to the success of the Commission.

The Commission's report will be an important contribution to the United Nations Conference on Environment and Development and will bring to the forefront the health dimension of the environmental and development crisis. WHO and its Member States must play a more aggressive role in protecting and promoting health as part of development and environmental protection policies in a changing world. The action required is substantial and the task will not be easy. But if we work together for human health and well-being, the integrity of the environment, and sustainable development, we shall all benefit.

Hiroshi Nakajima
Director-General
World Health Organization

Background and acknowledgements

The WHO Commission on Health and Environment was appointed by the Director-General of WHO as a fully independent body in early 1990. Composed of 22 members (Annex 1), the Commission was chaired by Mrs Simone Veil, France, Member of the European Parliament. H.E. Dr E. Salim, Minister of State for Population and the Environment, Indonesia, and Professor N.F. Izmerov, of the Academy of Medical Sciences of the USSR, served as Vice-Chairmen.

The work of the WHO Commission can be regarded as a follow-up of the 1987 report, *Our common future*, of the United Nations World Commission on Environment and Development (WCED). That report reviewed the relationship between the environment and development, and methods of assuring the progress of mankind while respecting the environment so as to make it possible to bequeath it in a healthy condition to future generations. Although the relationship with health was not considered in detail in the WCED report, concern for health underlay most of it. It therefore seemed opportune, three years later, for an independent body to make an assessment of the health consequences of environmental change, especially in anticipation of the United Nations Conference on Environment and Development which will be held in Brazil in 1992. The Director-General considers the report of the Commission on Health and the Environment to be WHO's main contribution to that Conference, one that underlines the importance of health in environmentally sound and sustainable development.

The Commission had the support of four independent expert panels appointed by the Director-General, on food and agriculture, energy production, industry, and urbanization—four areas that cover the main aspects of development. Professor E.H. Kampelmacher (Netherlands), Dr B.H. Mac-Gibbon (United Kingdom), Dr B.D. Goldstein (USA) and Mr M. Diop (Senegal) were appointed respectively chairmen of the food and agriculture, energy, industry, and urbanization panels. In the absence of Mr Diop, Dr B.W. Christmas (New Zealand) chaired the panel on urbanization. The panels held two meetings each. The members of the panels are listed in Annex 2.

Within WHO, a task force was established by the Director-General to provide technical support to the Commission. The members are listed in Annex 3.

The Commission held three meetings. The first (June 1990) was devoted to planning the work of the panels, the second (March 1991) to developing the structure of its report, and the third (July 1991) to the drafting and adoption of the report. While the Commission takes full responsibility for its own report, it acknowledges that much of it is based on the reports that the panels prepared under their own responsibility. Any discrepancy between the panels' and the Commission's conclusions and recommendations must therefore be attributed to the fact that Commission and panels worked independently of each other, the panels, owing to their mandate, taking a more sectoral approach than the Commission.

The meetings of the Commission were attended by representatives of a number of United Nations Organizations, other international organizations, and nongovernmental organizations. They are listed in Annex 1.

The Commission wishes to express its indebtedness to Mr D.E. Satterthwaite, who was responsible for the preparation of the first draft of the report and gave invaluable assistance to the Commission throughout its work.

* * *

The World Health Organization is indebted to the Governments of Australia, Finland, Germany, Italy, Japan, Norway, Sweden and The Netherlands for their generous financial contributions to the work of the WHO Commission on Health and Environment. Without their support this work would not have been possible.

Summary

Health and the environment

The maintenance and improvement of health should be at the centre of concern about the environment and development. Yet health rarely receives high priority in environmental policies and development plans, rarely figures as an important item in environmental or development programmes, despite the fact that the quality of the environment and the nature of development are major determinants of health.

Indeed, the most immediate problems in the world are ill health and premature death caused by biological agents in the human environment: in water, food, air, and soil. They contribute to the premature death of millions of people, mostly infants and children, and to the ill health or disability of hundreds of millions more. The problem is most acute in the developing countries where:

— four million infants or children die every year from diarrhoeal diseases, largely as a result of contaminated food or water;

— over a million people die from malaria each year and 267 million are infected;

— hundreds of millions suffer from debilitating intestinal parasitic infestations.

Serious environmental health problems are shared by both developed and developing countries, affecting:

— hundreds of millions of people who suffer from respiratory and other diseases caused or exacerbated by biological and chemical agents, including tobacco smoke, in the air, both indoors and outdoors;

— hundreds of millions who are exposed to unnecessary chemical and physical hazards in their home, workplace, or wider environment (including 500 000 who die and tens of millions more who are injured in road accidents each year).

Health also depends on whether people can obtain food, water, and shelter. Over 1000 million people lack the income or land to meet such basic needs. Hundreds of millions suffer from undernutrition.

It is a requirement of health that the global cycles and systems on which all life depends are sustained. Population growth and the way resources are exploited and wastes generated threaten the environmental base on which health and survival depend and transmit the growing costs to future generations. The toll they exact on human health and natural resources and systems could be enormously reduced by better environmental management.

Integrating development, the environment, and health

Health depends on our ability to understand and manage the interaction between human activities and the physical and biological environment. We have the knowledge for this but have failed to act on it, although we have the resources to meet current and future needs sustainably.

Two concerns are vital: development addressing people's needs, especially for health; and ecological sustainability so that natural resources are not depleted and natural systems not damaged or degraded. Meeting the needs of the present and future world population for food, water, and energy without depleting or damaging the global resource base, while avoiding the adverse health and environmental consequences of industrialization and uncontrolled urbanization, can be achieved only if people have the knowledge and the means to influence action. This calls for changes in the way governments plan and manage development. In agriculture, research and extension services are required that are more participatory and more responsive to the needs of poor farmers. In urban areas participatory partnerships between local authorities and community organizations need to be developed. People dependent on natural resources should be fully involved in decisions about their use and protection. All groups, including those who are living and working in the least healthy environments or are currently excluded from decisions about how resources should be used, should share in decision-making and action.

Local participation needs national and global frameworks to ensure that adequate knowledge and resources are available and that local actions do not result in an unsustainable burden on natural cycles and systems. It also requires intergovernmental agreements that limit each country's call on finite resources and its right to dispose at will of non-biodegradable wastes. For this, people are needed whose concerns go beyond the quality of their own environment; only they can press their governments' to reach the international consensus on which a healthy and sustainable planet depends.

Global challenges to health and the environment

Any discussion of health, the environment, and development must include consideration of the size of the population and its consumption level, since this combination largely determines the impact that the human population makes on the environment. It must include the distribution of income and assets, the prime concern being for people whose health is impaired by lack of them. It must also include the macroeconomic framework within which governments set their economic, social, and environmental policies. While the priority is to change the sectoral policies of governments and international agencies so as to promote health and sustainability, macroeconomic policies affect all sectoral policies.

Population

The world's population grew more than fivefold between 1800 and 1990 to reach over 5000 million; projections suggest 8000 million by 2020. In developing countries, where populations are still expanding, pressure on scarce resources has made it difficult to improve living conditions; in the towns and cities the authorities have rarely been able to provide the extra services required by the rapid growth in population. In developed countries, where population levels are largely static, prosperity has given rise to increased consumption and even overconsumption with insufficient regard being paid to their possible planetary impact: the depletion of non-renewable resources, the degradation of soil and water resources, and the emission of gases that threaten climatic stability and the stratospheric ozone layer. Such consumption levels raise the question of sustainability, especially as a growing proportion of the world's population aspires to comparable levels of consumption.

Healthier environments and lower death rates are not inconsistent with the goal of reducing population growth rates. Indeed, the steps that reduce infant and child deaths also tend to encourage reduced fertility rates: a secure livelihood, better health and education of the mothers, improved water supplies, sanitation, and nutrition, all coupled with effective family planning programmes integrated into health care systems available to all. Where serious measures are taken for a sustained reduction in child mortality, the fertility rates eventually fall. Sustaining reductions in fertility requires policies that remove the economic necessity for poorer groups to have large families. But the pressure on resources of growing populations and growing consumption levels is so severe that to wait for economic expansion to reduce fertility would be disastrous. Provision of a secure livelihood, education, and health care (including the means to control fertility) is therefore a high priority.

Poverty

At least 1115 million people were classified as poor in 1985 and 630 million of these were living in extreme poverty. Such statistics cover only those with an inadequate income. The number lacking a minimum standard of living is much higher. Those who cannot read, obtain clean water, or avoid environmentally induced disease, and who are permanently under the threat of physical violence and the effects of crime are invariably poor, whatever their income. So too are those who cannot participate in community life or expect to live beyond the age of 60. If poverty is measured by the number of people lacking a standard of living that includes adequate food, safe and sufficient water, sanitation, a secure shelter, and access to education and health care, over 2000 million people live in poverty—some 40% of the world's population. A high proportion are women and children, who are more vulnerable to environmental health risks. Within households it is generally women who look after the children, manage the household, and care for the sick; as such they suffer more from the diseases associated with inadequate water and sanitation and from the defects in the provision of basic services. Women who head households also usually face discrimination in looking for jobs and in obtaining access to public services, housing, and credit.

Resource use

The impact of any population on the environment depends on the type and level of its resource use and on its waste generation and management. Most of the world's consumption of non-renewable resources is concentrated in Europe, North America, and Japan. Per caput consumption levels in the richest countries are 50 or more times higher than in the poorest countries. The OECD nations, with 15% of the world's population, are responsible for 77% of all hazardous industrial waste. More than 80% of the gases in the atmosphere that contribute to the greenhouse effect arise from production or consumption in the developed world.

A healthy population may require a relatively prosperous and stable economy, but this need not imply the levels of income and resource consumption common in developed countries. Many communities with a relatively low level of income have made substantial improvements in health; some have achieved a life expectancy close to that of West Europe and North America with a much lower level of resource use. Improved health can be separated from ever-increasing consumption if development programmes stress the promotion of health both in the narrow sense of curing or preventing disease and in the broad sense of promoting well-being and informed participation.

Macroeconomic frameworks

Macroeconomic policies are major influences on the state of health and of the environment within all countries. But they are usually established with little or no consideration given to their health or environmental consequences. For example, trade and fiscal policy or agricultural or energy pricing may influence health either by their effect on income levels and distribution or by the effect on the quantity and quality of land, air, and water resources. Macroeconomic policies influence the extent to which health care and health-related services are funded. They also affect the size of household incomes, and hence the quality of food and housing affordable.

Macroeconomic policies should minimize conflicts between economic, environmental, and health goals. With increased knowledge of the social and environmental effects of macroeconomic policies the effects can be limited, including those which arise from structural adjustment, and special pro-grammes can be established for those whose health might otherwise suffer from loss of income or cuts in services—for instance health care or nutrition programmes or employment projects.

Food and agriculture

Agriculture, forestry and fishing provide not only the food and natural resources on which human society depends but also the livelihood of about half of the world's population. Their output can only be sustained if the ecological systems on which they draw are not overexploited.

The output of the world's food-producing systems has greatly increased over the past few decades. As yet there is no global shortage of food or the capacity to produce it in the world, but for a large part of the world's population undernutrition and the infections associated with it will remain the main cause of ill health and premature death because they do not have enough land to grow the food they need or the income to purchase it. Foodborne diseases are among the most common diseases in every country, although they are far less often life-threatening in developed countries. Most disease agents that contaminate food and water are biological and come from human or animal excreta, although food contaminated by toxins produced by plants and moulds, and those present in fish and shellfish, can be a serious problem.

The ecological base for feeding the world's population is under stress owing to the rapid degradation of land and water resources. Production and distribution methods remain inefficient, as is shown by the size of the losses before and after harvesting. A continued rise in the population in a number of developing countries, greater substitution of meat, eggs and dairy products for grains and vegetables, and increased food and soil losses put great stress on farmers and on the ecological underpinnings of farming systems. Conversely, reduced population growth, better-balanced diets, changes in production techniques, and greater attention to reducing food losses would make it possible for farmers to sustain production and meet future demands.

Agriculture is not without occupational health risks, of which accidents, infection with diseases spread by animals, and exposure to agricultural chemicals are the most common. In tropical countries, water reservoirs and canals for irrigation have been constructed and new land opened up for agricultural use without proper control of disease vectors. The result is that they have often been followed by a great increase in many of the most lethal and debilitating diseases, including malaria and schistosomiasis.

Agricultural chemicals are widely misused, most seriously in developing countries where pesticide regulations and their enforcement are less strict and products that have been banned or restricted in developed countries are still widely available. Agricultural chemicals are damaging water resources. Drainage water often contains high levels of salts and nutrients, the latter causing blooms of algae in lakes, reservoirs, and shallow coastal waters.

Health and its environmental determinants are closely related to land tenure. Farmers with secure tenure of adequate amounts of fertile land usually avoid extreme poverty and the ill health that accompanies it. Those with little security and too little land or holdings of only marginal productivity are often poor; so is their health. Many small farmers have developed a sophisticated knowledge of how to sustain yields in difficult circumstances. However, environmental degradation is common where high concentrations of poor farmers have only land of poor quality to exploit.

Certain strategic principles can promote health and more sustainable patterns of food production. They include the promotion of good agricultural practice (for instance, crop rotation, avoidance of excessive fertilizer application, use of correct dosage of chemicals or pesticides, reduction of food losses before and after harvesting). They also include wider use of integrated pest control and better integration of farming, forestry, and water resource management. Several major innovations are likely to prove of particular importance for increased food production or better preservation; they include food irradiation and the use of modern biotechnology to improve productivity and processing.

The Commission recommended that:

- Countries should take steps to ensure that all households can afford and obtain an adequate diet, and in particular that income and employment programmes should play a role in ensuring that everyone has the means to acquire sufficient food.

- Efforts to increase food production should be accompanied by measures to protect and enhance land and water resources.
- Research and extension services should be more participatory, more responsive to the needs of small and poor farmers, including those dependent on poor-quality or fragile land, and give more attention to health and environmental issues.
- Governments should integrate health goals in their agricultural policies, including promotion of the health of farmers and agricultural workers.
- More research should be carried out on how to increase food production in the tropics while reducing tropical diseases and harmful effects on the environment.
- Governments should give high priority to reducing food losses before and after harvesting.

Water

Fresh water is considered a renewable source, but there are limits on the supplies available. In many countries or regions, shortages of fresh water are the main obstacle to agricultural and industrial production. Some of the shortages (or seasonal or annual variations in supplies) lead to poverty and soil degradation. Many cities and agricultural regions are now drawing supplies from underground aquifers at a rate far above their natural rate of recharge.

Fresh water is essential to health not only for its part in production but also for domestic consumption and use (drinking, cooking, washing, laundry). A high proportion of life-threatening and health-threatening infections are transmitted through contaminated water or food. Nearly half the world's population suffer from diseases associated with insufficient or contaminated water, mostly the poor and virtually all in developing countries. Two thousand million people are at risk from waterborne and foodborne diarrhoeal diseases, which are the main cause of nearly four million child deaths each year. Schistosomiasis (200 million people infected through contact with infested fresh water) and dracunculiasis (10 million infected through drinking water containing the disease vector) are two water-based diseases. Insect vectors breeding in water transmit malaria (267 million infected), filariasis (90 million infected), onchocerciasis (18 million infected), and dengue fever (30–60 million infected every year).

Water shortages usually lead to problems of water quality since sewage, industrial effluents, and agricultural and urban run-off overload the capacity of water-bodies to break down biodegradable wastes and dilute non-biodegradable ones. Water pollution problems are most serious in cities in developing countries where controls on industrial emissions are not enforced and sewers, drains, or sewage treatment plants are lacking. Sewage and industrial effluents can be treated before disposal if sewers exist and the regulatory authorities are effective. Agricultural and urban run-off cannot be treated and in many areas in both developed and developing countries it is a growing threat to the quality of lakes, rivers, and the groundwater. Fisheries have been damaged and drinking-water sources contaminated by pollution in many areas of the world.

The Commission stressed that:

- Fresh water should be considered as a scarce, valuable, and finite resource and water resource management should be promoted to reconcile competing demands from different sectors and consumers.
- Because of the immense effect of water-related diseases on human health, a greater priority should be given not only to ensuring safe and sufficient water supplies but also to sanitation and to increased education about personal hygiene. Improving the quantity and quality of water and providing safe excreta disposal services are usually possible at relatively low cost, especially if optimal use is made of local knowledge and resources and the users are fully involved in the design, implementation, and management of the services provided.
- Fresh water should be priced and protected in accordance with its value to health and to production. Innovative schemes can often reach poorer groups with major improvements at a cost they can afford. Preferential tariffs or subsidies should be avoided for most consumers, and used only to ensure that the poorest receive a level of service sufficient for health.
- The priority for water pollution control in the world is control of bacteriological and parasitic waterborne diseases, but contamination of water by heavy metals and other chemicals should also be prevented or minimized.
- More emphasis should be placed on making the best use of existing water supplies; shortages of drinking-water can often be remedied by greater attention to maintenance (since up to 60% of water supplies in a piped system may be lost in leaks) and by charging the users of the largest amounts of water a realistic price.

Energy

The main goals of energy development have been to reduce the cost of producing energy, to make systems more efficient, and to open up previously untapped energy sources. Reducing the adverse environmental and health effects has also become a goal. More recently, concern about climatic change has emerged, since the combustion of fossil fuels, which accounts for nearly 90% of the world's commercial energy production, is the largest source of the so-called greenhouse gases.

People in developed countries use roughly ten times more commercial energy than those in developing countries and burn 70% of all the fossil fuel used, most of it for electricity generation, industry, transport, and domestic heating. To strengthen their economies and so provide the economic basis for good health, most developing countries will need to increase their fossil fuel consumption.

One of the Commission's central concerns was whether the need for developing countries to increase their use of fossil fuel can be met at the same time as the adverse health effects are reduced, especially indoor air pollution from coal and urban air pollution from fossil fuel use, within a global agreement that limits greenhouse gas emission.

Fossil fuels are the single largest source of atmospheric pollution; when burnt, they release in the air particulate matter, carbon monoxide and dioxide, oxides of nitrogen and sulfur, and metal compounds. More than 1000 million city dwellers are now exposed to high levels of air pollution. High levels of sulfur dioxide and particulates in urban areas have been associated with respiratory disease and increased mortality. Vehicle exhausts pollute the air in large cities with carbon monoxide and with lead (except where lead additives to petrol are no longer used). Exposure to the latter may impair mental development in children. Vehicle emissions also contribute to the formation of ozone and photochemical smog, which may decrease lung performance. Several studies have shown an association between levels of air pollution and respiratory symptoms, but it is still uncertain whether protracted exposure to low levels of air pollutants, such as occur in many cities of the developed and developing world, has any long-term effects on health. However, policies, regulations, and incentives can greatly reduce air pollution and increase the efficiency with which fossil fuels are used. Their adoption in many developed countries has improved air quality in a number of cities in recent years.

Indoor air pollution from the combustion of coal or unprocessed biomass fuels (e.g., wood, crop wastes) represents perhaps the largest energy-related source of ill health. Biomass fuels are used to meet the energy needs of nearly half the world's population. They are often burnt in open fires or inefficient stoves in poorly ventilated houses, and give off smoke and chemicals that contribute to respiratory disease, with long-term cardiovascular effects. Because of the presence of known carcinogens in the indoor air, an increased risk of lung cancer must be assumed. Women are generally responsible for cooking and looking after children in the home and they and their children are at greatest risk.

There are a number of alternatives to fossil fuels and unprocessed biomass fuels, including hydropower, nuclear energy, and solar power. Hydropower can bring extra benefits such as flood control and an increased supply of water for drinking and irrigation. However, dams can cause environmental changes that affect health: people living in the flooded area must be resettled, the quality and reliability of the water supply downstream are often reduced and, in the absence of appropriate control measures, the large area of water behind the dam can become a breeding ground for disease vectors (including those of schistosomiasis and malaria). Smaller hydro systems that draw power direct from flowing rivers can avoid most of these health, social, and environmental costs.

Nuclear energy is another option. Under normal working conditions, discharges from power plants result in exposures to levels of radiation about 1000 times lower than natural background levels. However, the risk of accidents and the difficulty of safely disposing of high-level radioactive waste are major concerns of the public. Moreover, nuclear power is rarely an appropriate choice for developing countries. The use of direct solar and wind energy is likely to increase, although it will be limited by cost and space requirements.

Use of electricity is likely to continue growing rapidly, since it provides the energy for virtually all communications and most lighting and mechanical work apart from road transport, and is essential to development and to the operation of medical services. The expansion of electricity supplies has led to increased exposure of the population to electromagnetic fields. Only since 1979 has it been suggested that such exposure may increase the risk of some cancers. No clear evidence has been obtained that such exposure is harmful, but the possibility requires investigation.

The Commission stressed five priorities for a national strategy:

- The reduction of indoor air pollution from the domestic use of coal or unprocessed biomass fuels in developing countries (e.g., by the use of improved stoves and ventilation, the local adoption of biomass processing techniques to produce cleaner fuels, or a switch to cleaner fuels).
- The reduction of urban air pollution from the fossil fuels used for energy production and transport in both developed and developing countries by adoption of mitigating technologies at source (particularly in new thermal power plants and vehicles), improved public transport systems, and greater priority for practical alternatives to the use of petrol.
- The reduction of the potential risk of climatic change by achieving a balance between the need for increased use of fossil fuels in many developing countries and reduction in carbon dioxide emissions and

acidic aerosol production from the combustion of fossil fuels in developed countries. Achieving greater energy efficiency through such measures as the wider adoption of co-generation plants and more efficient end-use devices and the wider adoption of energy conservation measures should be the goal in both developed and developing countries.

- More resources for research and development and wider use of renewable energy sources, aimed at lowering the costs of waste incineration and at exploiting solar and wind power and the possibilities of small-scale hydro-electricity generation.
- Continuing research and development on major accident prevention, particularly the development of inherently safe nuclear reactors. Developing the capacity for the transport and storage of high-level nuclear waste is an important safety issue.

Industry

Industrialization has made many positive contributions to health, among them increased personal incomes, greater social wealth, and improved services, particularly transport and communications. But industrial activities carry the risk of adverse health consequences for the workforce and the general population, either directly, through exposure to harmful agents or practices, or indirectly, through environmental degradation. Industrial emissions and products also threaten the global environment.

Industrial practices in both developed and developing countries produce adverse environmental health consequences through the release of air and water pollutants and the generation of hazardous wastes. Occupational diseases include silicosis, pneumoconiosis, lead and mercury poisoning, hearing loss, and skin diseases. Serious health risks are also faced by workers in small-scale or cottage industries, where exposure to toxic chemicals and accident rates are often higher than in large industries.

Industrial emissions have polluted many rivers, lakes, and coastal environments, especially in developing countries where pollution control is rarely enforced. A number of major accidents in developing countries such as the release of chemicals or explosions have been dramatic reminders of the adverse health effects of inadequate attention to safety and prevention. Only in a minority of countries are potentially dangerous industries sited away from population concentrations. In most countries too little attention is given to controlling the disposal of hazardous industrial and commercial waste so as to prevent human exposure and leakage into the environment.

There is a serious lack of quantitative data on the links between environmental agents and health effects. It has been difficult to establish the relation between industrial emissions, and especially long-term low-dose exposure to them, and the health of the general population, because factors other than industrial pollution are implicated. More is known about health risks inside industry and this information has contributed to the identification of health risks for the general public. Health problems are most severe in developing countries, where fewer health standards are applied to limit workplace exposure. Even where standards exist, many countries have neither the funds nor the institutional structure to ensure that they are upheld. Partly for these reasons, there has been a transfer of some hazardous industries to developing countries.

The Commission stressed the need in each country for:

- A planning process where health and environmental considerations influence decisions about plant siting, design characteristics, the choice of process, and the incorporation of safety and pollution control devices.
- The adoption of the principle "the polluter pays" to control liquid and gaseous emissions and place the full responsibility on the producers of hazardous wastes, from production to final disposal.
- A higher priority for the control of air and water pollution, including fitting control technology on existing plants to protect the health of the workers and the public; the direct and indirect costs of health effects should be included in decisions about the economic feasibility of such controls.
- More attention to monitoring the release of industrial discharges and quantifying the health and environmental effects, concentrating on susceptible populations and on the long-term as well as the short-term consequences.
- Educational and training activities for six groups: health care professionals, particularly in developing countries; workers and managers in health and safety and in the prevention of environmental releases and the reduction of wastes; decision-makers, who need to incorporate health and environmental costs into decisions; journalists and other workers in the media; the public and especially schoolchildren, to increase their understanding of environmental problems; and experts to train and give advice to the other groups.
- Addressing the occupational and environmental health problems in small-scale industries.
- Adherence to global agreements on the management of wastes to prevent transport accidents and the export of hazardous industries or hazardous wastes.
- Increased understanding of the interaction between chemical or physical agents and biological systems so as to improve recognition

and prediction of the consequences of industrial releases. The use of area profiles within which exposure data and health manifestations are carefully monitored over many years will help such understanding.

Human settlements, urbanization, and basic services

Environmental management is needed in all settlements to provide water, protect public spaces, remove wastes, and protect air and water quality. Even in a small village, water sources must be protected, and all households must be ensured sufficient water. Human and animal excreta must be disposed of in ways that minimize the possibility of human infection and of food and water contamination. As a settlement's population size and density increase from village to market town to major city, so too do the scale and complexity of the environmental management needed to ensure a healthy environment.

Rapidly growing urban centres are a particular challenge for environmental health. Urbanization is usually associated with the development of a more productive economy, and it can bring major benefits to health and the environment; the concentration of population and business lowers the unit cost of piped water and health services, sanitation, and the collection and treatment of household and commercial wastes. But in the absence of government action to ensure that the infrastructure and services are in place and pollution controlled, environmental health problems are greatly exacerbated.

These problems are particularly apparent in developing countries. Despite some slowing of the growth rates in many major cities in recent years, population growth still outstrips the ability of local authorities to provide even minimal levels of service. Local governments are often hampered in their efforts by a weak revenue base, poor financial management, and few trained personnel, and by budget cutbacks that cause a further decline in the coverage and quality of the water, sanitation, refuse collection, and health care services.

Housing problems are widely different in developed and developing countries. In the former the major issues concern the design, the physical structure, and the living environments of poor quality that are associated with physical and psychosocial problems contributing significantly to ill health in the urban areas affected. Legislation exists to ensure adequate standards in many of the areas listed above, but improved building and safety standards are still needed.

Housing should contribute to a sense of well-being and security. Poor housing is associated with social and psychological problems, including alienation, isolation, drug abuse, family break-up, and urban violence. Strong community networks can act as a buffer against the psychosocial effects of poor physical environments. Action to improve psychosocial health often combines improved services and employment opportunities. A related issue is noise, at home and at work, which can result in hearing loss, sleep disturbance, impaired mental performance, increased anxiety, and aggression.

Much of the housing in both the rural and the urban areas of developing countries lacks the most basic requirements for health. More than 2000 million people live in life-threatening and health-threatening housing and living environments. Most of the housing is overcrowded; space is nearly always at a premium, and many families live in one-room shelters or single rooms in tenements. Such overcrowding encourages the spread of acute respiratory infections, tuberculosis, meningitis, and intestinal parasites. Four or more persons to a room make it almost impossible to protect infants and children from burns or scalds and to store safely hazardous household substances such as bleach or kerosene. In urban areas a high proportion of housing is in illegal settlements and built of flammable materials; many dwellings are built on land prone to flooding, on steep hillsides or otherwise dangerous sites. The low commercial value of such sites means that the inhabitants have a greater chance of not being evicted.

Most of the poor have incomes that are too low to enable them to afford better housing with adequate space, security and services. Fear of eviction is a constant worry for most tenants and inhabitants of illegal settlements. The risk of infection, particularly from pathogens associated with excreta, is high. Most illegal settlements have only rudimentary water supply systems and no sewers or drains. An estimated 30–50% of the solid wastes generated in urban areas in developing countries is left uncollected.

Most poor people in developing countries have no health service to turn to when they are sick or injured. Some 1600 million have no access to health care. In the least developed countries more than half the population may have no access to health services. Health services are particularly important for vulnerable groups, especially for prevention and rapid treatment of common illnesses. Although the proportion of pregnant women and children covered by immunization has grown considerably in recent years, hundreds of millions remain unprotected and millions die each year from diseases that could be prevented by immunization. Most spending on health is still for curative services, usually in major hospitals, although preventive and community primary health care services are far more effective in reducing morbidity and mortality.

Enough knowledge and resources exist in most developing countries to improve housing and basic services at a relatively low cost. New participatory partnerships between local authorities, nongovernmental organizations, and community organizations have shown this to be so and have proved cost-effective. Institutional frameworks at national and local level are needed to encourage and support these partnerships.

The Commission's recommendations included:

- High priority for the provisioning of all forms of housing with sufficient supplies of water and services for the hygienic disposal of wastes, and for the education of their inhabitants in personal and domestic hygiene.
- Greater priority to ensuring that all individuals or households can afford to purchase, rent, or build adequate housing on safe sites.
- The development of new urban and rural planning structures and processes that are more participatory, work with community organizations, and meet the identified health needs of the poorer groups.
- Higher priority for the provision of primary health care into which national population policies are fully integrated.
- A much more active role by health personnel in the planning and implementation of community development projects; health personnel should have the knowledge and skills to work with other social services, especially in the provision of child care for working or sick parents, shelter for the homeless, care for the disabled, and services to cope with violence and drug and alcohol abuse.
- The development of national strategies to reduce overconsumption and waste generation and encourage resource conservation and recycling.
- Increased research on the health status of urban populations, on the methodologies used in successful community health projects, on low-cost appropriate technologies related to housing and services, and on the development of models allowing choices to be made between alternative methods of waste disposal.

Transboundary and international issues

Certain environmental issues have health implications on a wider scale than the local or national level. They include the long-range transport of air pollutants, the transboundary movement of hazardous products and wastes, stratospheric ozone depletion, climatic change, ocean pollution and loss of biodiversity. Solutions are being sought mainly through intergovernmental agreements.

Acid precipitation

Sulfur and nitrogen oxides emitted from tall chimney stacks by fossil fuel-fired power stations are transported over long distances, often across national boundaries. In the atmosphere they are converted to acids and eventually fall to ground as acid rain or snow. This has acidified many poorly buffered lakes and soils and contributed to forest dieback and in many places (especially Central Europe) to the destruction of large forests. Health may be affected if acidified water is used untreated in water supplies, since it contains higher concentrations of metals, e.g., copper and lead from pipes, cadmium from plumbing solder, and mercury and aluminium from soils. Progress towards reduction in atmospheric pollution in Europe is being achieved through implementation of the 1979 Convention on Long-Range Transboundary Pollution and its protocols.

The ozone layer

The stratospheric ozone layer is being damaged by the release into the atmosphere of various chemicals, including chlorofluorocarbons used in refrigerants, aerosols, plastic foam blowers and other equipment, halons used by fire-fighting services, and various organic solvents. Depletion of the ozone layer is likely to lead to higher levels of biologically active ultraviolet radiation at the earth's surface. At certain wavelengths, UV radiation increases the incidence of skin cancer and cataract in humans and probably affects other organisms that have no protection against it. Small changes in recreational habits, such as the avoidance of sunbathing at midday and the use of protective clothes and creams, could do much to reduce the health risks. International efforts are being made to control the production and consumption of some of the chemicals responsible through the Montreal Protocol to the Vienna Convention on the Protection of the Ozone Layer. They should be strongly supported.

Greenhouse gases

A related issue concerns the build-up of greenhouse gases in the atmosphere, thought likely to lead to global warming and a rise in the sea level. During the 1980s, carbon dioxide emissions, mostly from fossil fuel combustion, were responsible for more than half of the total warming effect, and chlorofluorocarbons for a quarter. Uncertainties about the magnitude, rate, timing, and distribution of any future warming make it impossible to predict the health implications quantitatively.

Heat stress and heat stroke, which can be fatal, are a direct effect that may become more common, particularly among susceptible groups such as the old, the young, and those with cardiovascular disease. The indirect health effects, however, are likely to be much more significant. Agriculture may be affected, in some areas by increased precipitations, in others by drought and desertification. Changes in rainfall may diminish the variety of crops available and lead to or aggravate food shortages. The distribution of vectors that carry the agents of infectious diseases is likely to be affected; diseases such as malaria may spread to areas where they are currently unknown. The adverse effects would be especially serious in developing countries, where lack of human, financial, and technical resources would hinder an effective response.

The seriousness of the possible health and environmental consequences of global warming is such that every effort should be made to reduce greenhouse gas emissions now, through individual efforts and through such measures as are now being developed by the United Nations.

Hazardous wastes

Hazardous wastes are exported from developed to developing countries when the export cost is much lower than the cost of disposal in the country of origin. Disposal abroad is rarely accompanied by concern about the health of those involved or living near disposal sites. The growing concern about the health and environmental implications led to the Basel Convention on the Control of Transboundary Movements of Hazardous Wastes and their Disposal. Once in force, this should considerably reduce the risks arising from such movement.

Oceans

Large stretches of coastal waters, especially in semi-enclosed seas and where tidal flushing is limited, are heavily polluted by industrial and domestic wastes from rivers and outfalls, land run-off, and accidental spills. Biological and chemical pollution is high near river mouths and sewage outfalls. Fishing beds and beaches in their vicinity are at particular risk of contamination. Seafood poisoning and epidemics, such as the cholera epidemic in Latin America in 1991, may result from disposal of inadequately treated effluents into the sea.

Beyond the coastal waters the open sea is still relatively unpolluted. Although contamination by metals and organic compounds can be detected, the level is not yet significant for human health, and biological contamination from domestic effluents is virtually non-existent.

The need to improve the quality of coastal waters and to preserve that of the open ocean has led to the adoption of a number of international agreements. Their extension to the many ocean areas that are not yet covered

should be greatly accelerated and ways and means for their rigorous implementation should be provided.

Biodiversity

Biodiversity is acknowledged as a condition for the long-term sustainability
of the environment and its current destruction must be halted. Knowledge
about many species is still limited, and their destruction may deprive the
human population of future sources of food and medicine and of biological
means of controlling pests and pathogens. However, the protection of
biodiversity cannot be unconditional; there may be conflict between the need
to improve health or provide necessities and the need to preserve a species.
In such instances the health cost of ensuring the survival of species that are
pathogenic to humans or are pests of food crops will need to be carefully
taken into account. There seems for example to be little ground for preserving the human immunodeficiency, smallpox, or poliomyelitis viruses, malaria
parasites, or guinea worm. An international convention on biological diversity is being developed by the United Nations Environment Programme.

Strategy and recommendations

People need to have the means to acquire the resources on which health
depends: safe food and water, fuel, and a secure shelter. They need to be
protected not only from physical, chemical, and biological hazards, but also
from crime and violence, which are encouraged by poverty and the use of
drugs, and from injuries at their place of work. A healthy environment is not
only a need, it is also a right; the right to live and work in an environment
conducive to physical and mental health is enshrined in the Universal
Declaration of Human Rights. Everyone shares the responsibility for ensuring that this right is duly acknowledged.

Everyone also shares responsibility for health and for passing on to the
next generation a world whose resources are not depleted and whose natural
systems are not degraded. There is a powerful synergy between health,
environmental protection, and sustainable resource use. Individuals and
societies who share the responsibility for achieving a healthy environment
and managing their resources sustainably become partners in ensuring that
global cycles and systems remain unimpaired.

The responsibility for action lies with individuals and with business.
Governments have the responsibility of setting up the strategic and institutional framework within which action is taken. They should put in place the
services, financial and other incentives, and controls that encourage in-

dividuals, households, communities, businesses, and bureaucracies to promote health and sustainable resource use. They should take the lead in ensuring that the levels of consumption and waste generation within their boundaries do not damage global systems and deplete resources known to be finite.

There are three main global objectives:

- Achieving a sustainable basis for health for all. This demands a slowing down and eventual halt to population growth as soon as possible, and the promotion of lifestyles and patterns of consumption among affluent groups and developed countries that are consistent with ecological sustainability.
- Providing an environment that promotes health. This involves reducing the risk of physical, chemical, and biological hazards and ensuring that everyone has the means to acquire the resources on which health depends.
- Making all individuals and organizations aware of their responsibility for health and its environmental basis. Health professionals should take the lead in moves to improve the environment and to inform governments and the public about the health implications of development and the costs and benefits of different options to reduce health risks.

Two principles are central to a healthier and more sustainable planet: first, more equitable access to resources within and between countries; second, citizen participation. Participation can promote health and environmental quality because it provides a means of organizing action and motivating individuals and communities. It enables individuals and communities to shape policies and projects to meet their priorities. Involvement in planning gives people the possibility to influence choices about the use of limited resources. Primary environmental care is one way of helping communities to apply their skills and knowledge to satisfy their own needs, improve their own environment, and promote the sustainable use of resources. Participatory political structures are a check on abuse of the environment, since citizens with clear rights and knowledge and access to a legal system that allows speedy redress can exercise a powerful restraint on those contravening health and environmental regulations.

The Commission's main general recommendations were:

- All governments and international agencies should give higher priority to developing a sustainable basis for the health of their people and countries. Achieving such a sustainable basis for health requires high priority in development policy to reducing population growth, over-consumption and waste generation.

- A rapid and sustained fall in population growth rates is best achieved by providing people with the knowledge and means to control fertility and by dealing with the economic, social, and cultural reasons for large families. The knowledge, capacity, and health of people are the most valuable resource for development; higher priority must be given to primary health care, including family planning, and education for all groups, especially women.
- Responsible action should be taken at all levels, from the individual citizen to the government, to reduce overconsumption and the generation of wastes, especially wastes with serious adverse health and environmental effects. High priority should be given to creating awareness and to providing economic and other incentives to encourage conservation and efficient use of resources. The long-term goal is the promotion of lifestyles and patterns of consumption consistent with sustainability of development and with health for all.
- Government structures should be changed to give greater priority and support to participation and community-based initiatives. Official bodies and scientific advisers should devise and apply new, more participatory, ways of working with the poor so that perception of their needs and their knowledge can be used in designing, implementing, and monitoring action.
- Changes should be made in the planning process for social and economic development and in the institutional and regulatory structures of governments to give stronger emphasis to the prevention of environmental pollution, intersectoral decision-making, and participation.
- Governments and aid agencies should give high priority to providing the means and building up the capacity needed by each locality to make the best use of local knowledge, skills, and resources to promote health and environmental quality. This includes providing the education and training needed to enable individuals and organizations to protect the environmental foundation of their own health.
- Governments and international agencies should give higher priority to creating the basis of an international consensus on environmental, economic, and health issues with the aim of alleviating poverty and sustaining the quality of the environment.
- Governments, international agencies, and public and private institutions should develop the national capacity for the systematic collection, analysis, and monitoring of environmental effects on health in the context of development, so that government policies on health promotion and environmentally sound management of industrial development and of rural and urban settlements are based on reliable information.

1.

Health, environment, and development

Introduction

This report places health at the centre of the discussion about the environment and development. Every year biological and chemical agents in the human environment—in the air, soil, food, and water—cause or contribute to the premature death of millions of people, mostly infants and children, and the ill health or disablement of hundreds of millions. Little consideration is given to the improvement of environmental conditions that contribute to the ill health and premature deaths of many millions of people, including:

— the hundreds of millions of people who suffer from respiratory diseases caused or exacerbated by indoor or outdoor air pollution
— the hundreds of millions exposed to unnecessary physical and chemical hazards in the workplace or living environment (including 500 000 who will die as a result of road accidents)
— the four million infants and children who die every year from diarrhoeal diseases—largely as a result of contaminated food or water
— the hundreds of millions of people who suffer from debilitating intestinal parasite burdens
— the two million who die from malaria every year and the 267 million who are ill with the disease
— the three million people who die every year from tuberculosis and the other 20 million in whom the disease is active
— the hundreds of millions who suffer from undernutrition (including those who suffer seasonally or during times of drought).

Health has also so far been absent from the public discussion about the environment and development and is seldom given high priority in development plans. Yet, without health, development and a protected environment have little value, and development can only be achieved through the contributions of healthy people. As a result, the environmental basis of the health, and even the survival, of current and future generations is being undermined. Continued population growth, irrational use of resources, and increasing generation of wastes create unsustainable demands on the environment.

1

Their adverse health effects are now evident in many localities and regions and can only worsen and spread unless current trends are reversed.

Health and development are so intimately connected that the state of health within a country is one of the most revealing indicators of its development. Yet health is still seen as the responsibility of the health authorities alone, rather than as the shared responsibility of individuals, communities, employers, and all government agencies at all levels. Some of the limitations of the last four United Nations Development Decades may stem partly from that view and are reflected in the hundreds of millions of people still suffering from preventable diseases and working in environments that threaten life and health.

Sound management of the environment brings major health benefits while inadequate or no management results in large adverse effects on health. Sound management is essential to a sustainable interaction between people and their environment in a world where finite resources are being depleted and the capacity of natural cycles and systems to absorb wastes is being exceeded. There are limits to the extent to which the soil and freshwater resources can be exploited and ecosystems used as a receptacle for the wastes generated by human society. There are also global limits to the exploitation of non-renewable resources and to the capacity of the planetary system to absorb wastes. Only recently have these global limits become apparent, as in the depletion of the stratospheric ozone layer, which has implications for health and agricultural production, and in the possibility of climatic disruption as a result of the release of greenhouse gases. At local level the challenge is to meet human needs, including those essential to health, while also exploiting resources sustainably. At intercountry and global level, the challenge is to ensure that everyone can obtain the resources essential for health without imposing an environmental burden on natural cycles carrying health risks for present and future generations. Meeting this challenge will require intergovernmental agreements that limit each country's use of finite resources and its right to dispose of non-biodegradable wastes freely.

The need to act is as urgent in the developed as in the developing countries, although the priorities differ. In the developed world the priority is to arrive at more sustainable patterns of resource use and ecosystem exploitation. Developed countries have almost stable populations, most of which enjoy relatively good health and safe living and working environments. These countries enjoy increasing prosperity and a relatively equitable income distribution, and more effective preventive and curative government interventions have greatly reduced what are often termed the diseases of poverty (undernutrition and many communicable diseases), even if for some pockets or population groups they remain a serious problem. However, developed countries are increasingly exposed to many other health problems.

Besides those related to pollution there are those due to dietary and behavioural patterns, such as a large proportion of neoplastic, chronic respiratory, and cardiovascular diseases, as well as various psychosocial problems such as alcohol and drug abuse, against which even the wealthiest governments have found few effective actions.

In addition, developed countries contribute more to the burden of waste in the environment, despite the implementation of strict controls on some types of emission. They also make larger claims per person on the global stock of non-renewable resources. New technological advances have brought many benefits to society, but they have also brought risks to health in the form of exposure to chemicals and to physical hazards. While there have been remarkable efforts in the past 20 years to understand better the significance of such exposure and the health effects it may have, large gaps in knowledge remain. Thus too many chemicals are released into the environment without prior toxicological testing. Broadening and improving programmes aimed at promoting and protecting health deserve increased consideration. From a global point of view the development of a coherent programme to achieve more sustainable levels of resource use and waste generation should receive a higher priority. There are no signs of such a programme, though steps are being taken in this direction, such as the Montreal protocol to limit emissions of chlorofluorocarbons, the Basel convention regulating the transport of hazardous wastes, and the European Charter.

By contrast, developing countries are striving to reduce morbidity from long-established disease patterns. But their inhabitants are also increasingly exposed to the hazards that beset the inhabitants of developed countries, from industrial and traffic pollution and urban stress to diet-related and behaviour-related diseases.

In most developing countries the priority is development in the sense of stronger, more stable and prosperous economies, where health, environmental protection, and a more equitable distribution of the benefits of economic growth take a central place. Lack of development frequently results in poor living conditions and poor health and education standards for the majority of the population, while current practices and trends in the exploitation of their natural resources, both renewable and non-renewable, are unsustainable. In many instances growth in agricultural, industrial, or mining production and in urban population has been accompanied by an increased incidence of environment-related diseases and physical hazards. While many developing countries have made substantial gains in the scale of their economies, these are often at the cost of severe degradation of their stock of natural resources and of air and water pollution, especially in urban areas. Commonly, too many of the workforce suffer exposure to occupational hazards that have long been controlled in developed countries.

Global inequalities remain one of the most serious constraints on the improvement of health and environment, and over 40 years of international discussion about North–South relations, trade and aid have done little to alleviate them. The discussion has not produced tangible results helping poorer countries achieve the prosperity and economic stability they need to underpin sustained improvement in health and in the institutional capacity for sound environmental management. High standards of health could, however, be achieved in developing countries without a high per caput income and without heavily industrialized and urbanized economies. But governments cannot maintain a role as promoters and supporters of health and of a sustainable use of environmental resources with unstable economies and severely limited public funds. Everyone needs a certain income to gain access to the goods and services essential to health. Economic instability or decline, and large debt repayment burdens, are also incompatible with environmental management, especially for the many countries dependent on the export of natural resources for much of their foreign exchange.

Priority given to human health raises an ethical dilemma if "health for all" conflicts with protecting the environment. Two extreme positions may be envisaged. The first stresses individual rights, societal good being seen as the aggregate of everyone's personal preferences and any controls over the individual's use of resources as an infringement of the individual's freedom. The other extreme—a response to increasing environmental degradation— gives priority to the environment and to the maintenance of the ecosystem. All species are seen as having rights as people do, environmental welfare thus coming before human welfare. A middle ground between these extremes can be found by distinguishing between first-order and second-order ethical principles (1). Priority to ensuring human survival is taken as a first-order principle. Respect for nature and control of environmental degradation is a second-order principle, which must be observed unless it conflicts with the first-order principle of meeting survival needs.

The first order assigned to meeting human survival needs is consistent with the United Nations Universal Declaration of Human Rights (1948), which states that all people have the right to a standard of living adequate for the health and well-being of themselves and their family, including food, clothing, housing, health care, and the necessary social services. This implies the right of all individuals to have access to the resources needed to meet their needs. The second-order principle of respect for nature and control of environmental degradation should guide all human activities except where they conflict with the first-order principle, as recognized by the World Charter for Nature (1982) (2) and the WHO European Charter on Environment and Health (1989) (3).

The report of the World Commission on Environment and Development, *Our common future*, defined sustainable development as development meeting the needs of all the present population without compromising the ability of future generations to meet their own needs (4). This could prove contradictory if meeting present needs implies the irreversible depletion of natural resources and the degradation of ecosystems. But the intelligent application of what is known, combined with caution and a continuous commitment to improving understanding of links between the environment, development, and health can change these trends. Ensuring that everyone has access to the environmental resources needed to fulfil their rights under the Universal Declaration of Human Rights need not imply an unsustainable level of resource use. Nor need it overwhelm the finite absorptive capacities of natural ecosystems if development is guided by a commitment to ensuring that costs are not passed on to future generations. Development must also be pursued with caution in the face of uncertainty concerning its environmental and health implications, with action being taken early to address global threats to health and the environment, even if present knowledge is insufficient to evaluate the risks fully.

Focusing on health provides many insights into how a better balance can be achieved between the environment and development. This report draws on the knowledge and experience of the last few decades on how to reduce the prevalence of disease with levels of resource use that can be sustained. The existence of villages, cities, regions, and countries where good health has been achieved with much less use of resources and environmental degradation than elsewhere provides clues for the strategies and recommendations presented in subsequent chapters. It also helps to broaden the discussion of health and environment beyond concern with levels of income and consumption only, and permits consideration of non-consumption aspects of health and well-being. The extent to which sustainable development and health for all can be made compatible depends on a new understanding of what is meant by development in which health takes a more central role.

The meaning of health

Health means more than an absence of disease, as is recognized in the WHO definition of health (Box 1). Health is only possible where resources are available to meet human needs and where the living and working environment is protected from life-threatening and health-threatening pollutants, pathogens, and physical hazards. But health also includes a sense of well-being and security. Deficient living and working environments are associated with both physical and psychosocial health problems. Violence and alienation are associated not only with poor job prospects but also with overcrowded poor-quality housing, deficient services, and inadequate provision for leisure, recreation, and children's play and development. Growing understanding of this link has led to the concept of a health-promoting environment where not only are health risks minimized but personal and community fulfilment, self-esteem, and security are encouraged.

Box 1. WHO definition of health

"Health is a state of complete physical, mental and social well-being and not merely the absence of disease or infirmity."

Constitution of the World Health Organization

The complex relationship between health and the environment extends the responsibility for promoting health to all groups in society. Health is no longer the responsibility only of doctors, nurses, midwives, and other health professionals who seek to prevent or cure disease or of those who seek to remove pathogens from the human environment and reduce accidents. It is also the responsibility of planners, architects, teachers, employers, and all others who influence the physical or social environment. It is the responsibility of health professionals to work with all groups in society in promoting health.

This understanding of health also means, above all, that individuals, households, and communities have substantial responsibility for their own health. Personal and community responsibilities for health are essential adjuncts to individual and community rights. The right of individuals to adequate shelter, health care, and education (including health education) must have as a counterpart their commitment to the promotion and protection of their own and their neighbours' health and welfare. Indeed, each adult has the duty as a citizen to ensure that health risks within human environments are minimized and government resources wisely used. Citizens' rights and citizens' capacity to organize and act become crucial in health. Households and communities with the knowledge, confidence, and capacity to improve their own environment are likely to be more healthy, not only because of the physical improvements they can make but also because of the important links between mental health and self-esteem and capacity for action.

Health and the environment

Human health ultimately depends on society's capacity to manage the interaction between human activities and the physical and biological environment in ways that safeguard and promote health but do not threaten the integrity of the natural systems on which the physical and biological environment depends. This includes maintaining a stable climate and continued availability of environmental resources (soil, fresh water, clean air). It also includes continued functioning of the natural systems that receive the wastes produced by human societies—domestic, industrial and agricultural—without exposing people to pathogens and toxic substances.

The physical environment has a major influence on human health not only through temperature, precipitation and composition of air and water but also through its interaction with the type and distribution of the flora and fauna (the biological environment). The biological environment is a major influence on the food supply and on the reservoirs and transmission mechanisms of many diseases. Box 2 is a much simplified illustration of these interrelationships.

Environmental factors that impair health include:

(a) pathogenic agents and their vectors and reservoirs;

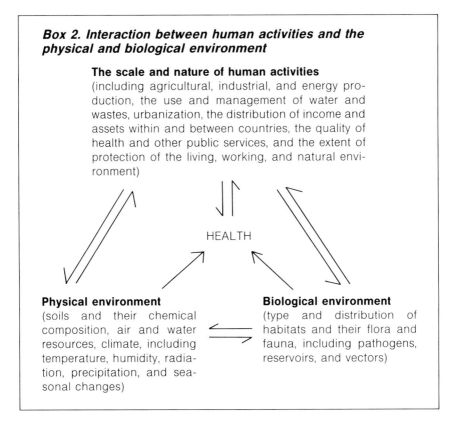

Box 2. Interaction between human activities and the physical and biological environment

The scale and nature of human activities
(including agricultural, industrial, and energy production, the use and management of water and wastes, urbanization, the distribution of income and assets within and between countries, the quality of health and other public services, and the extent of protection of the living, working, and natural environment)

HEALTH

Physical environment
(soils and their chemical composition, air and water resources, climate, including temperature, humidity, radiation, precipitation, and seasonal changes)

Biological environment
(type and distribution of habitats and their flora and fauna, including pathogens, reservoirs, and vectors)

(b) physical and chemical agents present in the environment that are in-dependent of human activities and can impair health either by their presence (e.g., naturally occurring radionuclides, ultraviolet light) or by their relative deficiency (e.g., iodine, selenium);

(c) noxious physical and chemical agents added to the environment by human activities (e.g., nitrogen oxides, polycyclic aromatic hydrocar-bons, particulates arising from fossil fuel combustion, gaseous, liquid, and solid wastes produced by industry, radioactive wastes).

The effects of these agents can be magnified or diminished by human intervention or activity. Draining marshlands within or close to settlements in malarious areas can greatly reduce the incidence of malaria by removing the mosquito's breeding sites. Buildings can modify the physical environ-ment, reducing some health risks (e.g., by providing protection against extreme heat or cold and precipitation) and increasing others (e.g., by causing the accumulation of natural radon indoors). Buildings can be designed specifically to protect occupants against certain diseases, for instance by excluding insect vectors. Buildings and settlements also modify the biological environment in ways that can increase or decrease health risks. Concentrated populations permit major cost savings in the provision of piped water, sewers, and storm drains, and in the collection of household wastes, greatly reducing the risk of foodborne and waterborne diseases and many other health problems.

Restricting discussion of the interactions of health and the environment to the three groups of factors described above excludes noxious agents to which humans are exposed largely as a result of their own chosen form of behaviour. The health problems resulting from the use of tobacco and the excess consumption of alcohol, saturated fat, and salt, which in many socie-ties have become the principal causes of avoidable disease, will therefore not be covered in detail in this report, although some will be referred to as affecting the way in which individuals react to agents in the environment.

Health and development

Development is generally understood as the process of improving the quality of human life. It has three equally important aspects: raising people's living standards (reflected in increasing income and consumption); creating con-ditions conducive to self-esteem; and increasing people's freedom to choose (5). Health and the means to maintain it are crucial for development, but good health is not easily measured. Income alone is an inadequate indicator of development, but it remains the most widely used because it is more easily measured than other aspects of development. There are clear links between health and income both when considering individuals and when considering averages for countries. A comparison of health indicators with economic indicators at country level shows that the countries whose inhabitants enjoy the highest life expectancy tend to be those with the highest income per person. The link can also be seen over time; the countries whose per caput income has increased most over the past 30 years tend to be those in which health indicators show the greatest improvements. There is also some evidence of a decline in health indicator levels in countries that experienced economic decline during the 1980s (6).

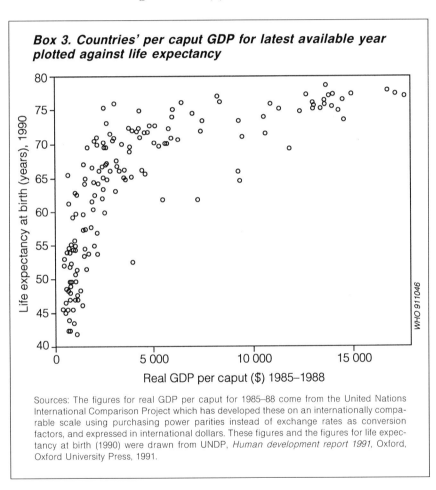

Box 3. Countries' per caput GDP for latest available year plotted against life expectancy

Sources: The figures for real GDP per caput for 1985–88 come from the United Nations International Comparison Project which has developed these on an internationally comparable scale using purchasing power parities instead of exchange rates as conversion factors, and expressed in international dollars. These figures and the figures for life expectancy at birth (1990) were drawn from UNDP, *Human development report 1991*, Oxford, Oxford University Press, 1991.

However, the average level of income per person in a country is only one among many social, economic, cultural, and political factors that influence people's health. These factors range from the wealth of a society (which in turn is influenced by its role within the world economic system) to the level of education of each individual, including knowledge of health-enhancing action and behaviour. Between these two extremes come a large range of variables: the distribution of incomes and capital assets within a society; the quality of the housing and living environment; and the quality of the infrastructure and services (of which the quality and availability of water supply, sanitation, and health care services are perhaps the most important). The health profile of any society is influenced not only by the scale of incomes and assets and their distribution but also by taxation structures and the macroeconomic policies of governments. This complicates the task of establishing the contribution of different factors to health, but it also provides policy-makers with a much greater range of possible interventions to promote it.

The limitations to equating the wealth of a society with its health can be seen in the many countries where health indicators such as infant mortality rates or average life expectancy at birth are well above or below the average for countries with the same level of income per person. These exceptions provide important clues as to how health improvement can be achieved without high levels of per caput income, resource use, and waste generation. Box 4 shows that countries such as China, Costa Rica, Cuba, and Sri Lanka and the Indian state of Kerala have life expectancies well above the norm for

---

Box 4. Some exceptions in regard to links between wealth and health

In Sri Lanka and China, two relatively poor countries if wealth is measured by per caput income, the governments' health policies have greatly improved the average level of health, well above the norm for countries with comparable income levels. The same is true for the State of Kerala in India. One reason is that at an early stage resources were directed to strengthening the community primary health care system and successfully integrating traditional indigenous health care systems with modern health services. Two countries with higher per caput incomes, Costa Rica and Cuba, also have higher life expectancies and lower infant mortality rates relative to their per caput incomes; here a long-term government priority for education and health is an important factor. In Cuba, China, and Kerala, an agrarian reform resulted in a more adequate livelihood for many rural dwellers. In all five areas there has also been a long-standing commitment to education, and in each literacy rates are well above the norm for countries with comparable income levels. In addition, there are long-standing policies to improve the dietary intake and the nutritional status of the population.

Source: Halstead, S.B. et al., eds. *Good health at low cost.* New York, Rockefeller Foundation, 1985.

their per caput income level. The appendix to this chapter (p. 17) ranks all developing countries according to life expectancy at birth and in regard to average per caput income and to an index of human development (a composite indicator incorporating life expectancy, educational attainment, and real per caput income, developed by UNDP). It also shows the many countries where high life expectancy at birth has been achieved without a high per caput income and also several countries with among the highest per caput income and a relatively low life expectancy.

While life expectancy at birth has been increasing in the great majority of countries, suggesting that global health is improving, national statistics conceal extreme variability within countries. Because income level and social status are important determinants of health, higher-income groups enjoy longer lives and better health than lower-income groups. The differentials tend to be greatest in Africa, Asia, and Latin America, where life expectancy among poorer groups is often 20–30 years less than for richer groups. The proportion of children born to poorer groups who die before the age of five is often 40 or more times that of richer groups (7). Disparities in health between rich and poor are also apparent within developed countries, although they are usually smaller; wealthy groups have the most concentrated medical attention, eat better, tend to smoke less, and have the opportunity to live away from industrial effluents and disaster-prone areas.

Although this report concentrates on the links between health and the environment, it should be stressed that growing prosperity in any society provides significant advantages for achieving health only if it also means that a growing proportion of the population enjoy adequate incomes, an improved housing and working environment, and access to preventive and curative health services. The rapid increase in life expectancy achieved in the developed world at the end of the nineteenth and the first half of the twentieth century was much influenced by the increased purchasing power of most people, combined with better public health. It is also notable that the countries with above-average health indicators relative to their per caput income level tend to be those with the most equitable distribution of income. Differences in average life expectancy between the richer developed countries may be more influenced by the degree of inequality in income distribution than by the average level of income (8). Box 5 shows one indicator of income distribution: the proportion of total GNP accruing to the poorest 40% of households for 46 countries or territories for which data were available. Many of the countries in which the poorest 40% of households had relatively high proportions of the total GNP are also countries with a high average life expectancy relative to average income level. UNICEF has argued that the per caput GNP of the poorest 40% of the population might be a more meaningful development indicator than the average per caput GNP (9).

11

Box 5. Proportion of GNP available to poorest 40% of households (1985)

Country or territory	% of total GNP accruing to poorest 40% of households (1985)	GNP per caput in 1985 US$		Life expectancy at birth (years)
		Total	Poorest 40%	
Netherlands	22.4	9 180	5 141	77.2
Japan	21.9	11 330	6 203	78.6
Belgium	21.6	8 450	4 563	75.2
Hungary	20.5	1 940	994	70.9
Sweden	20.5	11 890	6 094	77.4
Germany, Federal Republic of	20.4	10 940	5 579	75.2
Ireland	20.3	4 840	2 456	74.6
Switzerland	20.0	16 380	8 231	77.4
Spain	19.4	4 360	2 115	77.0
Norway	18.9	13 890	6 563	77.1
Yugoslavia	18.7	2 070	968	72.6
United Kingdom	18.5	8 390	3 880	75.7
Finland	18.4	10 870	5 000	75.5
Israel	18.0	4 920	2 214	75.9
Denmark	17.4	11 240	4 889	75.8
Italy	17.4	6 520	2 853	76.0
Bangladesh	17.3	150	64	51.8
USA	17.2	16 400	7 052	75.9
Canada	17.1	13 670	5 844	77.0
France	17.0	9 550	3 916	76.4
Republic of Korea	16.9	2 180	921	70.1
Egypt	16.5	680	281	60.3
Hong Kong	16.2	6 220	2 519	77.3
India	16.2	250	101	59.1
New Zealand	15.9	7 310	2 906	75.2
Sri Lanka	15.9	370	147	70.9
El Salvador	15.5	710	275	64.4
Australia	15.4	10 840	4 173	76.5
Portugal	15.2	1 970	749	74.0
Thailand	15.2	830	315	66.1
Indonesia	14.4	530	191	61.5
Argentina	14.1	2 130	751	71.0
Philippines	14.1	600	213	64.2
Trinidad and Tobago	13.3	6 010	1 998	71.6
Costa Rica	12.0	1 290	387	74.9
Mauritius	11.5	1 070	308	69.6
Turkey	11.5	1 130	325	65.1
Malaysia	11.2	2 050	574	70.1
Zambia	10.8	400	108	54.4
Venezuela	10.3	3 110	801	70.0
Mexico	9.9	2 080	515	69.7
Kenya	8.9	290	65	59.7

Box 5 *(continued)*

Country or territory	% of total GNP accruing to poorest 40% of households (1985)	GNP per caput in 1985 US$		Life expectancy at birth (years)
		Total	Poorest 40%	
Côte d'Ivoire	8.6	620	132	53.4
Panama	7.2	2 020	364	72.4
Brazil	7.0	1 640	287	65.6
Peru	7.0	960	168	63.0

Source: UNICEF, *The state of the world's children, 1989*, Oxford, Oxford University Press, 1989. Life expectancy figures drawn from UNDP, *Human development report, 1991*, Oxford, Oxford University Press, 1991.

Balancing rights and responsibilities

An ethical basis guided by the first-order and second-order principles outlined earlier requires that two conditions be met: sufficient resources are available to poorer groups to ensure that their needs are fulfilled; and careful limits are set on the capacity of individuals, companies, and countries to pollute and to draw on finite resources so they neither degrade the environment nor conflict with the second-order principle of respect for nature. Achieving this will depend as much on responsible behaviour by individuals, communities and businesses as on more effective recognition of the rights of citizens.

Everyone has responsibility in the achievement of health and a good environment. Successful solutions to most health and environmental problems depend on a great variety of actions by a considerable range of people working within different sectors and at different levels, united by the common goal of health and environmental quality. Government still retains its central responsibility for protecting individuals against threats to their health and environment and ensuring that all people have access to health care and other services and resources essential to health. But it also has an important strategic role in promoting and supporting the initiatives of individuals, community organizations, local governments, consumer associations, non-governmental organizations, and businesses in favour of improved health and environment through the "governance of diversity" (*10*), i.e., incentives and legislation encouraging and supporting the multiple interventions of citizens, businesses and municipal governments in promoting health at minimal environmental cost. Such governance must also ensure that short-term and long-term environmental health considerations are systematically taken into account in all new developments.

There can be conflicts in the short term and within specific localities between the cheapest means to improve health and the maintenance of a healthy functioning environment. In most instances this is because the action taken to improve health simply transfers risks to other locations or to the future. Tall chimneys for coal-fired or oil-fired power stations can greatly reduce air pollution within their immediate environment, but they contribute to acid deposition at a considerable distance. A country with the resources to import timber and minerals avoids the environmental degradation that often accompanies logging and mining, the environmental costs being transferred to the producing country. This transfer of costs can also be inter-generational: the use of fossil fuels or the cutting down of forests to meet present needs or desires contributes to global warming. The health impact will be felt in future years and, perhaps most acutely, by future generations.

There are also differences between richer and poorer groups in relation to the environmental damage arising from resource use. In the case of richer groups, the costs of this damage are rarely borne by those responsible for it. Their health is not immediately impaired by the diminution of resources and the waste generated. Poorer groups generally bear the immediate cost and suffer the direct consequences of the environmental degradation.

Case studies of particular cities or regions confirm that wealthy groups generally enjoy the least polluted environments and work in the safest occupations. The contrary is true for poorer groups. Richer and poorer groups also differ in the type and extent of environmental damage they produce. Most of the wealthiest societies have been more successful in removing pathogens and pollutants from the human environment (or treating the health problems they cause) and in maintaining the quality of key renewable resources such as soils and forests, but at the cost of high levels of non-renewable resource use and greenhouse gas emissions. Poorer societies draw much less on the planet's stock of non-renewable resources and contribute much less to greenhouse gas emissions, but it is more common for their soils to be overexploited and their living and working environments degraded.

Market forces have exerted a major influence on economic growth in many countries. While this growth has provided a small proportion of the world's population with the income to pay for goods and services essential for health, many countries have not able to develop the necessary economic basis. Furthermore, uncontrolled market forces can contribute to ill health and to the degradation of the environment. Where unregulated disposal of health-threatening products or wastes into the human environment is allowed, there may be serious adverse health effects for many people.

Countries—and the planet—need mechanisms to ensure that market forces do not result in the depletion of finite resources and the degradation of the environment. But no simple set of indicators exists for permitting measurement of the quality of each country's environment and the extent to which current patterns of resource use can be sustained. New techniques are being developed to incorporate environmental costs into national accounts, including estimates of the depletion of non-renewable resources and of the capacity of soils and forests to produce sustainable yields. If these were included as "capital depreciation" in national accounts, the economic growth rates achieved by many countries over the last few decades would be substantially lower (*11*). But these techniques have yet to gain widespread acceptance by governments.

There is also no agreement on appropriate indicators for measuring the extent to which any national economy draws on the world's resources or the environment is capable of absorbing pollutants. This makes it difficult to compare the performance of different nations in using resources sustainably. It will be even more difficult to reach international agreement on reducing the disparities. At present most of the focus is on domestic issues within each country's boundaries. There is a need for citizens with a commitment to the planet and the welfare of all its people. Only they can press their governments to reach the international agreement on which a healthy and sustainable planet depends.

References and notes

1. Shrader-Frechette, K. *Environmental ethics, human health and sustainable development: a background paper*. Paper prepared for the WHO Commission on Health and Environment, 1990 (WCHE/2/14; available on request from Division of Environmental Health, World Health Organization, 1211 Geneva 27, Switzerland).

2. *World Charter for Nature*. Nairobi, United Nations Environment Programme (Environmental Law Guidelines and Principles, No. 5).

3. *European Charter on Environment and Health*. Copenhagen, WHO Regional Office for Europe, 1990.

4. World Commission on Environment and Development. *Our common future*. Oxford, Oxford University Press, 1987.

5. Todaro, M.P. *Economics for a developing world*. Hong Kong, Longman, 1977.

6. UNICEF. *The state of the world's children, 1990*. Oxford, Oxford University Press, 1990.

7. *Urbanization and its implications for child health: potential for action*. Geneva, World Health Organization, 1989.

8. Donnison, D. Sinking with the tide. *The Guardian*, Wednesday 21 August 1991.

9. UNICEF. *The state of the world's children, 1989*. Oxford, Oxford University Press, 1989.

10. Duhl, L. J. *The social entrepreneurship of change*. New York, Pace University Press, 1990.

11. See, for instance, Repetto, R. et al. *Wasting assets: natural resources in national income accounts*. Washington, DC, World Resources Institute, 1989; and Pearce, D. et al. *Blueprint for a green economy*, London, Earthscan Publications, 1989.

Appendix
Developing countries ranked according to life expectancy at birth, with indicators for real GDP per caput and human development index

Country or territory	Life expectancy at birth (1990)		Real GDP per caput (1985–88)		Human development index (1991)	
	Years	Rank	$	Rank	HDI	Rank
Hong Kong	77.3	1	14 010	3	0.934	3
Dominica	76.0	2	3 020	41	0.800	21
Israel	75.9	3	10 860	5	0.950	1
Cuba	75.4	4	2 500	52	0.754	29
Barbados	75.1	5	6 020	13	0.945	2
Costa Rica	74.9	6	4 320	26	0.876	9
Singapore	74.0	7	10 540	7	0.879	7
Brunei Darussalam	73.5	8	14 590	2	0.861	11
Kuwait	73.4	9	9 310	10	0.827	17
Jamaica	73.1	10	2 630	46	0.761	26
Panama	72.4	11	3 790	32	0.796	22
Uruguay	72.2	12	5 790	14	0.905	5
Antigua and Barbuda	72.0	13	3 940	28	0.832	15
Chile	71.8	14	4 720	21	0.878	8
Trinidad and Tobago	71.6	15	4 580	23	0.876	9
Bahamas	71.5	16	10 590	6	0.920	4
Grenada	71.5	16	2 810	43	0.751	31
Argentina	71.0	18	4 360	25	0.854	12
Bahrain	71.0	18	9 490	8	0.810	19
Sri Lanka	70.9	20	2 120	60	0.665	41
United Arab Emirates	70.5	21	19 440	1	0.767	24
Saint Lucia	70.5	21	2 940	42	0.699	35
Democratic People's Republic of Korea	70.4	23	2 000	64	0.665	41
Republic of Korea	70.1	24	5 680	15	0.884	6
Malaysia	70.1	24	5 070	20	0.802	20
China	70.1	24	2 470	53	0.614	49
Venezuela	70.0	27	5 650	16	0.848	13
Seychelles	70.0	27	3 430	36	0.752	30
Saint Vincent and the Grenadines	70.0	27	2 100	63	0.636	46
Mexico	69.7	30	5 320	18	0.838	14
Mauritius	69.6	31	5 320	19	0.831	16
Suriname	69.5	32	3 830	30	0.792	23
Belize	69.5	32	2 600	47	0.700	34
Solomon Islands	69.5	32	2 540	50	0.521	63
Vanuatu	69.5	32	1 620	73	0.490	68
Qatar	69.2	36	11 800	4	0.812	18
Colombia	68.8	37	3 810	31	0.757	28
Brazil	68.6	38	4 620	22	0.759	27
Saint Kitts and Nevis	67.5	39	3 150	39	0.719	32
Paraguay	67.1	40	2 590	48	0.667	40
Cape Verde	67.0	41	1 410	80	0.428	76

Country or territory	Life expectancy at birth (1990)		Real GDP per caput (1985–88)		Human develop- ment index (1991)	
	Years	Rank	$	Rank	HDI	Rank
Jordan	66.9	42	2 570	49	0.614	49
Dominican Republic	66.7	43	2 420	56	0.622	47
Tunisia	66.7	43	3 170	38	0.588	57
Samoa	66.5	45	1 870	69	0.618	48
Islamic Republic of Iran	66.2	46	3 560	34	0.577	59
Thailand	66.1	47	3 280	37	0.713	33
Syrian Arab Republic	66.1	47	4 460	24	0.681	39
Lebanon	66.1	47	2 250	58	0.592	55
Ecuador	66.0	50	2 810	44	0.655	44
Oman	65.9	51	9 290	11	0.604	53
Sao Tome and Principe	65.5	52	620	118	0.399	79
Turkey	65.1	53	3 900	29	0.694	37
Algeria	65.1	53	2 470	54	0.490	68
Iraq	65.0	55	3 510	35	0.582	58
Honduras	64.9	56	1 490	76	0.492	67
Fiji	64.8	57	3 610	33	0.689	38
Nicaragua	64.8	57	2 660	45	0.612	52
Saudi Arabia	64.5	59	9 350	9	0.697	36
El Salvador	64.4	60	1 950	67	0.524	61
Philippines	64.2	61	2 170	59	0.613	51
Guyana	64.2	61	1 480	77	0.589	56
Guatemala	63.4	63	2 430	55	0.488	70
Peru	63.0	64	3 080	40	0.644	45
Viet Nam	62.7	65	1 000	91	0.498	66
Mongolia	62.5	66	2 000	65	0.596	54
Maldives	62.5	66	1 050	86	0.534	60
Morocco	62.0	68	2 380	57	0.431	75
Libyan Arab Jamahiriya	61.8	69	7 250	12	0.665	41
South Africa	61.7	70	5 480	17	0.766	25
Indonesia	61.5	71	1 820	70	0.499	65
Myanmar	61.3	72	660	115	0.437	73
Egypt	60.3	73	1 930	68	0.394	81
Botswana	59.8	74	2 510	51	0.524	61
Kenya	59.7	75	1 010	90	0.399	79
Zimbabwe	59.6	76	1 370	82	0.413	78
India	59.1	77	870	101	0.308	90
Pakistan	57.7	78	1 790	71	0.311	87
Namibia	57.5	79	1 500	75	0.440	72
Lesotho	57.3	80	1 390	81	0.432	74
Swaziland	56.8	81	2 110	62	0.462	71
Haiti	55.7	82	970	95	0.296	92
Ghana	55.0	83	970	94	0.311	87
Comoros	55.0	83	760	105	0.274	93
Papua New Guinea	54.9	85	1 960	66	0.353	84
Bolivia	54.5	86	1 480	78	0.416	77
Madagascar	54.5	86	670	113	0.371	83
Zambia	54.4	88	870	100	0.351	85

Country or territory	Life expectancy at birth (1990)		Real GDP per caput (1985–88)		Human development index (1991)	
	Years	Rank	$	Rank	HDI	Rank
Liberia	54.2	89	890	99	0.220	99
United Republic of Tanzania	54.0	90	570	121	0.266	94
Togo	54.0	90	700	111	0.225	98
Congo	53.7	92	2 120	61	0.374	82
Cameroon	53.7	92	1 670	72	0.328	86
Côte d'Ivoire	53.4	94	1 430	79	0.311	87
Zaire	53.0	95	430	125	0.299	91
Gabon	52.5	96	3 960	27	0.510	64
Nepal	52.2	97	770	104	0.158	112
Uganda	52.0	98	410	126	0.204	101
Bangladesh	51.8	99	720	109	0.186	103
Nigeria	51.5	100	1 030	88	0.242	96
Yemen	51.5	100	1 560	74	0.242	97
Sudan	50.8	102	970	96	0.164	110
Lao People's Democratic Republic	49.7	103	1 000	92	0.253	95
Cambodia	49.7	103	1 000	93	0.175	107
Rwanda	49.5	105	730	107	0.213	100
Central African Republic	49.5	105	780	103	0.166	108
Bhutan	48.9	107	750	106	0.159	111
Burundi	48.5	108	550	122	0.177	106
Senegal	48.3	109	1 250	84	0.189	102
Burkina Faso	48.2	110	650	116	0.081	121
Malawi	48.1	111	620	119	0.179	105
Djibouti	48.0	112	730	108	0.083	120
Mozambique	47.5	113	1 070	85	0.155	113
Equatorial Guinea	47.0	114	700	112	0.186	103
Mauritania	47.0	114	960	97	0.140	115
Benin	47.0	114	1 050	87	0.114	117
Chad	46.5	117	510	123	0.087	119
Somalia	46.1	118	1 330	83	0.118	116
Ethiopia	45.5	119	350	127	0.166	108
Angola	45.5	119	840	102	0.150	114
Niger	45.5	119	610	120	0.079	122
Mali	45.0	122	500	124	0.072	123
Gambia	44.0	123	650	117	0.064	126
Guinea	43.5	124	910	98	0.066	125
Guinea-Bissau	42.5	125	670	114	0.088	118
Afghanistan	42.5	125	710	110	0.069	124
Sierra Leone	42.0	127	1 030	89	0.048	127

Notes and sources: Statistics drawn from UNDP, *Human development report 1991*, Oxford, Oxford University Press, 1991. Figures for real GDP per caput are drawn from the United Nations International Comparisons Project, which has developed measures of real GDP on an internationally comparable scale using purchasing power parities instead of exchange rates as conversion factors, and expressed in international dollars. The human development index is a composite indicator incorporating life expectancy, educational attainment (adult literacy and mean years of schooling) and real GDP per caput.

2.

Global challenges to health and the environment

This chapter considers issues of a general nature that underlie most environmental problems. They are population size and growth with their determinants (fertility, mortality, and migration), poverty, and macroeconomic policies. Mention will be made later of other less general issues, such as the unprecedented mobility of people and goods, which also contribute to environmental change.

Demographic issues

The impact of people on the environment depends on their numbers and on their level of consumption (including the use of renewable and non-renewable resources). Both expand independently and both lead to increasing pressure on the environment as a supplier of resources and as a repository of wastes.

In the tropics and subtropics, in which are to be found most of the developing countries and all of the poorest, demands on resources are somewhat lower because requirements for clothing, heating, and housing are less exacting. These are also the countries where development has had a greater effect on lessening mortality than on increasing well-being and where fertility rates have also been declining more slowly. The population is therefore increasing. Limited resources have made development yet more difficult, with increasing demand for water, arable land, and energy for domestic use, in direct proportion to the number of users. Increasing numbers of people are at the same time moving to urban areas, where the infrastructure is rarely able to keep up with the influx of new entrants, while in cities and rural areas alike the amount of domestic waste to be disposed of also rises with the number of people.

In temperate and subarctic countries, most of them highly developed, energy needs may be somewhat higher than in other parts of the world because of the climate. However, they are magnified by affluence, which until recently was unaccompanied by any concern for the possible environmental consequences and the effect on the conservation of resources on which human survival depends. Problems in relation to the disposal of effluents and wastes have increased, even when the population has stopped growing.

The size and structure of the human population have been completely changed by a number of factors, including higher incomes, improved nutrition, safe and sufficient water and sanitation, wide availability of immunization, highly effective drugs against infectious diseases, increased education (especially of women), and technological developments. Rapid demographic change began first in Europe in the early nineteenth century and was marked by decreasing mortality accompanied by lowered fertility. It now affects the whole world population, but in most countries the dominant factor has been a fall in mortality that has been much more sudden and rapid than that in Europe. By contrast, fertility long remained, and still is, very high in many countries. As a result, the rate of growth of the world's population grew steadily through the nineteenth and twentieth centuries until the 1980s, when it began to slow down.

Population size

Estimated at 1000 million in 1800, 1500 million in 1900, and 2500 million in 1950, the world population in 1990 was 5300 million, and is expected to exceed 7000 million by the year 2010 and 8000 million by the year 2020 (1) (Box 6). Different areas of the world have experienced different rates of increase, but the rates have been falling everywhere except in Africa, where the decline is expected to start soon as a consequence of a fall in fertility rates during the 1980s. Because of these differences, the proportion of the world's population in Northern America and Europe has been shrinking while that in other parts of the world has been expanding or has remained stable.

Differences in rates of population growth will lead to striking results in some geographical areas. In the Mediterranean area, for instance, the population of the countries on the northern shore is expected to increase by 40% from 1950 to 2010, according to the United Nations medium variant projections, and to remain stable afterwards. That on the eastern and southern shores will have increased fourfold by 2010 and will grow by a further 20% over the following 15 years. This will result in a population density on productive land (crops, grasslands, forests) remaining under 100 per km^2 on the northern shore, whereas it will be well over 200 per km^2 on the eastern and southern shores by 2010 and continue to grow thereafter.

It must be stressed, however, that these projections are based on demographic considerations only, essentially expected trends in birth and death rates. Other factors will come into play and need to be taken into account in the future. Improvements in the provision of health care will alter the pattern of mortality. The current AIDS pandemic will have major significance,

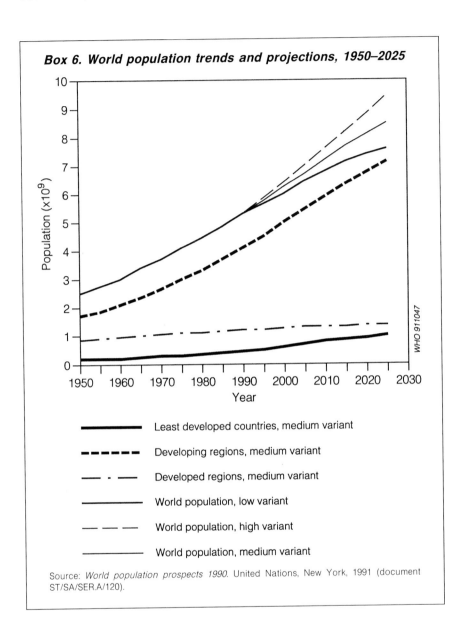

Box 6. World population trends and projections, 1950–2025

WHO 911047

Least developed countries, medium variant

Developing regions, medium variant

Developed regions, medium variant

World population, low variant

World population, high variant

World population, medium variant

Source: *World population prospects 1990.* United Nations, New York, 1991 (document ST/SA/SER.A/120).

especially in Africa south of the Sahara, where children and young adults are most affected. Changes in lifestyle (e.g., in reproductive and dietary habits or tobacco, alcohol, and drug consumption), though difficult to predict, may also contribute in the future to altered population size and age structure and so make adjustments of the projections necessary.

Mortality

Crude death rates are declining in developing countries while remaining steady in developed ones. However, comparing crude death rates may yield misleading results when, of two populations, one has a larger proportion of young people and the other of elderly people. The mortality experience of a population is better expressed in terms of life expectancy at birth, since this makes possible comparisons unbiased by age structure.

Life expectancy at birth has been increasing throughout the world, but the scale of the improvement is very different in developing and developed areas (*1*). While life expectancy in the developing world is much the lowest, there are exceptions. Thus, the temperate part of Latin America (Argentina, southern Brazil, Chile, Uruguay) has a mortality pattern close to that of developed countries, and Sri Lanka has achieved a life expectancy of close to 70 years in 1990, from nearer 60 years in 1950. On the other hand, all African countries had a very low life expectancy in the 1950s, and only a few, mostly in northern Africa, are expected to achieve an expectancy of 70 years by early next century.

Among developed countries the differences are wide, though less pronounced than between developed and developing countries. Within Europe there are significant differences between east and west, the life expectancy being consistently lower in east as compared with west Europe (71 compared with 76 years). The life expectancy for men has in fact been decreasing in Hungary, Romania, and the former USSR, while remaining steady in the other east European countries. Most of the recent gains in life expectancy in developed countries (up to 58% in Japan between 1980 and the mid 1980s) have been the result of reduction in mortality among elderly people (*2*). In developing countries the gains are due largely to reduction in the mortality of the young, but statistics are inadequate to quantify the effect.

Infant and child mortality

A major component of mortality is the death of infants in their first year of life. Infant mortality rates have been declining sharply in both developed and developing countries. While the rate of decline has recently been slowing down in a few countries, only in countries with a very high prevalence of AIDS or long exposure to war or internal strife has the decline been halted or reversed. National statistics, however, are likely to conceal local areas where the trends may be quite different.

Causes of mortality

The distribution of the causes of death helps explain differences in mortality experienced over time and from population to population. It also provides

23

an insight into the burden of disease by serving as a crude proxy for the morbidity experienced. But it only informs us of the loss of life experienced in a population and tells us little about the sufferings and loss of productivity among the victims of disease or the physically or mentally disabled. Direct information on the incidence and prevalence of diseases would be a better indicator but is available only from surveys of limited temporal and geographical scope. There are severe limitations to mortality analysis, particularly when it is carried out for comparative purposes.

Although causes of death are recorded systematically in all developed countries (3), differences in diagnostic, therapeutic, and reporting practices may affect comparisons between countries and between different times within most countries. In most developing countries causes of death are not recorded systematically. The pattern of mortality is therefore obtained indirectly, on the basis of limited studies in a few areas, extrapolated regionally and globally.

Age-standardized mortality figures are not generally available for developing countries. To make some comparison possible between developed and developing countries, the estimated number of deaths from various causes and their percentage contribution to the total number of deaths are given in Boxes 7a and 7b. There are dramatic differences between the two patterns. Even if they reflect in part a different age composition in the two groups of countries, no demographic consideration can bridge the tenfold disparity in mortality from infectious diseases in general or the twentyfold difference in mortality from tuberculosis. The current mortality rate from tuberculosis in developing countries equals the figures that used to be recorded in the United Kingdom (about 1000 per million per year in the 1920s, down from 3500 per million per year at the turn of the century (4)), while only 2 per 10 million occur now (5).

The excess mortality from gastrointestinal and respiratory diseases in developing countries is also of the same order as was recorded at the turn of the century in some of the European countries that now enjoy among the highest standards of health. Cholera, dysentery, and typhus claimed 3000 deaths per million in the United Kingdom in the 1850s, 100 times more than in 1971 (6), and mortality from respiratory diseases also experienced a sharp fall, undoubtedly as a result of improvements in the quality of the water supply, food safety and sanitation, as well as in the availability of adequate medical care and medicines.

In contrast, neoplasms and cardiovascular diseases account respectively for 21% and 54% of all deaths in developed countries and for 7% and 17% in developing countries. Mortality from these causes is likely to rise in the future in developing countries, as the life span increases and lifestyle habits, especially smoking and diet, approach those of developed countries.

Box 7a. Causes of death in industrialized countries, 1985

Cause of death	Number of deaths (in thousands)	Percentage of deaths from all causes
Infectious and parasitic diseases	506	4.6
Acute respiratory infection	[368]	[3.3]
Tuberculosis	[40]	[0.4]
Neoplasms	2 293	20.8
Circulatory and certain degenerative diseases	5 930	53.7
ischaemic heart disease	[2 392]	[21.7]
cerebrovascular disease	[1 504]	[13.6]
diabetes	[153]	[1.4]
Complications of pregnancy	4	0.0
Perinatal conditions	100	0.9
Chronic obstructive lung disease	385	3.5
Injury and poisoning	772	7.0
Ill-defined causes	247	2.2
All other causes	807	7.3
All causes	11 045	100.0

Source: See Box 7b.

The extent to which the health situation in a country can be improved by modifying its environment is difficult to quantify. Supplying water and food in adequate amounts and of acceptable quality, and breaking the faecal–oral chain, are essential to reduce gastrointestinal diseases. These had already declined significantly in most of Europe and North America well before the introduction of therapeutic drugs and oral rehydration therapy. The high mortality of infectious respiratory diseases is probably the combined result of overcrowding (which facilitates infection) and poor nutrition, but much could be prevented or alleviated by immunization and the use of modern drugs. The environment has an indirect role in mortality from circulatory and many other chronic diseases (e.g., cirrhosis of the liver, stomach ulcers, diabetes) and is likely to have some in the causation of chronic obstructive lung disease. Its role in the etiology of neoplasms is briefly reviewed in Box 8.

Box 7b. Causes of death in developing countries around 1985

Cause of death	Number of deaths (thousands)			Percentage of deaths from all causes		
	<5 years	5+ years	All ages	<5 years	5+ years	All ages
Infectious and parasitic diseases	10 500	6 500	17 000	72	28	45
diarrhoeal diseases	[4 000]	[1 000]	[5 000]	[27]	[4]	[13]
tuberculosis	[300]	[2 700]	[3 000]	[2]	[12]	[8]
acute respiratory diseases	[4 300]	[2 000]	[6 300]	[29]	[9]	[17]
measles, pertussis, diphtheria	[1 500]	–	[1 500]	[10]	–	[4]
other acute respiratory diseases	[2 800]	[2 000]	[4 800]	[19]	[9]	[13]
other measles and pertussis (without acute respiratory involvement)	[700]	–	[700]	[5]	–	[2]
malaria	[750]	[250]	[1 000]	[5]	[2]	[3]
schistosomiasis	–	[200]	[200]	–	[<1]	[<1]
other infectious and parasitic diseases	[450]	[350]	[800]	[3]	[2]	[2]
Maternal causes	–	500	500	–	2	1
Perinatal causes	3 200	–	3 200	22	–	8
Neoplasms	–	2 500	2 500	–	11	7
Chronic obstructive lung disease	–	2 300	2 300	–	10	7
Circulatory and certain degenerative diseases	–	6 500	6 500	–	28	17
External causes	200	2 200	2 400	1	9	6
Other and unknown causes	700	2 800	3 500	5	12	9
All causes	14 600	23 300	37 900	100	100	100

Source: Lopez, A.D. Causes of death: an assessment of global patterns of mortality around 1985. World health statistics quarterly, 43 (2): 91–104 (1990).

Box 8. Cancer mortality

After cardiovascular disease, cancer is the second most frequent cause of death in developed countries; accounting for 21% of all deaths. In developing countries, where it ranks well below infectious and parasitic diseases, it accounts for 7% of all deaths. As the incidence of cancer is strongly dependent on age, the different age structure of the population in the two groups of countries may be largely responsible for the difference in mortality between the two. The disparity may also be due to the different lifestyles and environmental exposure in the two groups, giving rise to different types of health risks. In addition, the vulnerability of cancer patients to infectious diseases may conceal cancer mortality in developing countries by masking the attribution of the ultimate cause of death.

In both groups of countries, cancers of different sites make different contributions to total cancer mortality. Here again differences in health care standards and dietary and other lifestyle habits are likely to play a major role. Thus, screening and therapy contribute to the lower mortality from cervical cancer in developed countries, and high exposure to hepatitis B and to aflatoxins to increased liver cancer in developing countries. A substantial fraction of excess mortality from cancer of the colon and rectum and of the breast in developed countries is probably related to dietary factors (such as high fat and low fibre content), while the very high mortality from lung cancer, which is now declining in some of these countries, at least among middle-aged men, reflects the high frequency of smoking a few decades ago. If spread of the use of cigarettes continues at the present rate in developing countries, mortality from lung cancer may be expected to reach epidemic proportions in the future, as development brings about a lengthening of the life span and a reduction in deaths from infectious diseases.

Time trends in cancer mortality based on historical data from the United States have been studied in detail. The figure overleaf shows the changes in mortality from cancers of various sites over a 55-year period. The sharp increase of lung cancer and the steady decrease of stomach cancer stand out as the most significant, the former mostly due to past trends in tobacco smoking, the other possibly to changes in food preservation and the amount of fruit and vegetables in the diet. These two cancers show broadly similar trends in all countries for which data are available. The other cancers recorded in the figure have undergone little variation since the 1950s, after rising until that time.

The list of exposures that have proved or are likely to be carcinogenic in humans is very long. It is not possible, however, to assess the burden of cancer attributable to most of them in either developed or developing countries, except in such cases as occupational exposure (e.g. to asbestos, vinyl chloride, benzene), urinary schistosomiasis which carries a high risk of cancer of the bladder, or hepatitis B virus, associated with a high incidence of liver cancer. Indeed, the most significant factors for the general population, beside tobacco smoking

Box 8 (continued)

Age-standardized death rates from cancer at selected sites in men, USA, 1930–85

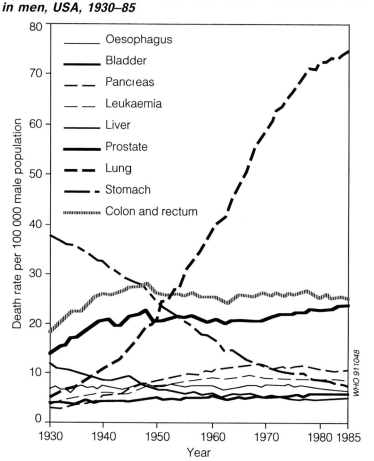

and alcohol consumption, appear to be dietary composition, probably responsible for a large fraction of some of the most common cancers (stomach, colon, breast, endometrium), and reproductive and associated behaviour (breast, ovary, cervix). The role of ionizing radiation in inducing cancers of various types is also well established but forms only a small percentage of the total. Exposure to the ultraviolet component of sunlight is responsible for a significant number of skin cancers.

Chemicals in the environment make a contribution to the ocurrence of cancers in the general population, but the extent cannot be assessed with any certainty. If the factors mentioned above play the major role they are assumed to in the causation of cancer, a fraction of the order of 5% of all cancers in the general population is likely to be due to environmental chemicals. This gives no cause for compla-

---

Box 8 (continued)

cency. The variety of chemicals produced, used in everyday life, and released to the environment is increasing even in developing countries, and exposure to them often involves more than the possible occurrence of cancer. Efforts should therefore be made to limit exposure so that the benefits deriving from their use are not offset by the damage they may cause to health. But this should not divert attention from the other factors, avoidance of which will achieve a significantly greater measure of prevention of cancers and other diseases.

Sources: Doll, R. & Peto, R. *The causes of cancer: quantitative estimates of avoidable risks of cancer in the United States today.* Oxford, Oxford University Press, 1981; Kurihara, M. et al. *Cancer mortality statistics in the world, 1950–1985.* Nagoya, University of Nagoya Press, 1989; Silverberg, E. & Lubera, J.A. Cancer statistics, 1988. *CA–A cancer journal for clinicians,* **38**: 5–22 (1988) (cited in Tomatis, L., ed. *Cancer: causes, occurrence and control.* Lyon, IARC, 1990).

The conditions in which environmental factors are most prominent are tropical diseases, which to a large extent are caused by infection by parasites requiring one or more intermediate hosts and vectors for their development. The best known example is malaria, the vectors of which are a number of mosquito species. Malaria exacts a toll of more than one million deaths a year, mostly among children, and seriously reduces the productivity of those affected. In general, intermediate hosts and vectors need precise conditions of temperature and moisture for their survival and for the development of the parasite inside them. They are often dependent on the presence of animal reservoirs with very specific habitats. The fight against vector-borne diseases may therefore involve many fronts—the reduction of sites that favour breeding, the rational use of insecticides, the maintenance of passive immune protection of children through protracted breast-feeding, better sanitation and personal hygiene, even in some cases simply the wearing of boots. While environmental measures can be effective when coupled with other appropriate action, mismanagement of the environment in the tropics may result in the further spread of disease by rendering the environment more favourable to a vector or widening its habitat.

Mortality statistics can provide only a broad picture of the disease burden to which people are exposed, especially when considered at the necessarily very high level of aggregation presented in Boxes 7a and 7b. A more detailed assessment of the burden will emerge when the main human activities impinging on the environment have been reviewed.

Fertility

Fertility is usually measured by the total fertility rate (TFR). For a generation to be fully replaced, the TFR must be at least 2.5 in countries where the average life expectancy at birth is 55 years, as it is in many developing countries. It must be at least 2.1 in developed countries, where the average life expectancy at birth is 73 years. TFR is a better measure of fertility than crude birth rate, which depends strongly on the age structure of the population.

Developed regions achieved TFRs below replacement rates by the late 1950s, whereas, on conservative assumptions, developing ones are considered unlikely to do so until early next century. China, the Democratic People's Republic of Korea, and the Republic of Korea have shown the sharpest drop. China's TFR fell by 50% between the early 1960s and the early 1970s, and by almost two-thirds between 1950 and 1990; it is now down to renewal rate, a stage that most developed countries took more than a century to reach. Other Asian countries that stand out because of their fast-declining TFRs are Indonesia, Malaysia, the Philippines, Sri Lanka, and Thailand.

In contrast, rates in central, east, and west Africa were rising until the late 1970s, but now appear to be falling and are projected to continue to do so in the next few decades. In all other areas, except in several countries south of the Sahara, the rates have continued to fall since 1950. At that time rates were much higher in Latin America (with the exception of Argentina, southern Brazil, Chile, and Uruguay) than in developed countries, where the process had started much earlier (*1*).

The extent to which family planning is applied and the methods used are largely responsible for the differences in fertility between countries. The diffusion of methods varies widely from one part of the world to another but has been increasing throughout the developing world, although much more slowly in Africa than elsewhere. There is a strong negative correlation between TFR and the prevalence of contraceptive methods (*9*), and the continued decline in TFRs will depend on the increasing use of such methods. The growth in the use of contraceptive methods presupposes that they are accessible, known, needed by those concerned, and culturally accepted.

Reductions in TFR also depend on reductions in the number of children desired. Improved education, health, and living conditions are necessary for that purpose. They make possible the operation of three essential factors—less need among poor households for large families, support for strong family planning programmes, and increased child survival. A recent study by the United Nations Population Division showed the extent to which increased child survival rates accounted for the decline in fertility in a number of developing countries, after a lag of some years (*10*). Achievement of the fertility rates projected under the United Nations medium variant will clearly require major joint efforts by those responsible for health, education, and family planning, as well as a more secure livelihood for poorer groups.

Migration and urbanization

Rural-to-urban migration—in demographic terms the dominant cause of urbanization (*11*)—is the form of migration that receives most attention. In some countries (e.g., Brazil) massive population movements have been facilitated by improvement of the road network, encouraging the unplanned shift from traditionally poor and inaccessible areas to industrial districts. However, in recent decades rural-to-rural migration has also taken place in certain countries on a scale comparable to or greater than from rural to urban areas.

In many countries there has been a large-scale movement from poor rural areas to the agricultural frontier, which has meant colonization and population concentration in areas that were virtually uninhabited or only sparsely populated in 1950. Examples are the transmigration programme in Indonesia and the expansion of the agricultural frontier and rapid growth of the migrant population in the Amazonian regions of several Latin American countries. These population movements have important implications for health and the environment. In Latin America, the colonization and exploitation of formerly unexploited lands have brought a rapid growth in the population and in agricultural development of areas with more fragile soils and ecosystems less able to support sustainable exploitation than other areas (*12*). Changes in the spatial distribution of national populations reflect underlying economic, social, and political changes that are themselves specific to each country and subject to rapid variation from decade to decade.

However, a general trend evident in most countries over the past 40 years has been rapid growth in the urban population. The fact that an increasing proportion of the world's population live in urban areas has important implications for health and the environment. A nation's level of urbanization and the spatial distribution of its urban populations have major consequences for the scale and nature of resource use. Urban growth can bring substantial health and environmental benefits. The concentration of production in urban areas brings many cost advantages in waste management, while the per caput cost of piped water, many kinds of sanitation, education, health care, and other services is also less in concentrated populations. The process of urbanization generally accompanies, and contributes to, the development of a more prosperous and productive economy. Growing urban populations can also stimulate and support agricultural development and reduce the rural population pressure. However, without effective policies, these potential

31

advantages are not put to profit. The result is that urban growth usually brings substantial health and environmental problems, especially for poorer groups.

No overall picture of the scale and spatial distribution of urban growth for the 1980s will become apparent until the data from censuses taken in 1990 and 1991 become available; the most recent data for urban populations in most countries are from censuses taken between 1978 and 1982. Statistics on urbanization are difficult to interpret, regardless of the level of urbanization or extent of industrialization in the countries from which they are drawn. The differences in the criteria used by each nation to define an urban centre limit the validity of international comparisons. Analysis of intercensal urban trends within a country may also be complicated by changes in definitions between censuses.

These uncertainties cannot conceal the main trends. In virtually all the world's countries the last 40 years have brought rapid urbanization and increase in the proportion of the economically active population working outside agriculture and forestry. A hundred years ago the world's urban population was less than 200 million; by 1990 it exceeded 2000 million. By 1990 more than half the population in over 70 countries were in urban centres. Only a few countries had this level of urbanization 100 years ago.

The distribution of the urban population between developed and developing countries has also changed in recent decades. Thirty per cent of the world's population lived in urban areas in 1950—three-fifths in developed and two-fifths in developing countries. By 1970, 37% were in urban areas, the urban populations of developed and developing countries being roughly the same size. Estimates for 1990 suggest that more than half of the world's population live in urban areas, almost three-quarters of the urban population in developing countries (see Box 9).

The rural population has been growing at a slower pace than the urban population in developing countries and is beginning to level off. In developed countries the rural component has remained stable since the 1950s.

Urbanization levels differ from region to region; they are highest in developed countries and in Latin America, reflecting more industrialized and urban-based economies. Most developed countries and several of the more prosperous Latin American countries began urbanizing rapidly in the nineteenth century, but in recent decades both the rates of population growth and the increase in levels of urbanization have slowed or stopped. By contrast, rapid urbanization only began in most African countries in recent decades and, while current urbanization levels are among the lowest of any region, many African countries rank among those showing the most rapid growth rates for urban population—reflecting both high rates of natural increase and heavy rural-to-urban migration.

Box 9. Urbanization trends and projections

	1950	1970	1990	2010
Proportion of population living in urban centres (%)				
World	30	37	45	56
Developing countries	17	25	37	52
Developed countries	54	67	73	78
Urban population (millions)				
World	730	1350	2380	4070
Developing countries	280	650	1510	3050
Developed countries	450	700	870	1020

The projections for 2010 assume a continuation of trends deduced from analyses of intercensal data for the 1960s and 1970s up to 2010. Recently detected changes in urban trends in more urbanized countries (for instance counter-urbanization) and lower-than-expected increases in urban populations in a few countries revealed in preliminary results from a few censuses taken in 1990 and 1991 may imply a slower increase in the level of urbanization and the scale of the urban population (*13*).

Source: United Nations. *World population prospects: 1990.* New York, 1991.

The limited data available on urban change during the 1980s suggest that the rate of urbanization has slowed in many countries. In much of Europe and North America, counter-urbanization has been evident in the past 10–20 years as small towns and rural areas have attracted new enterprises and populations. Many major cities in the developed world had a population decline, and many major cities in developing countries had much slower growth rates during the 1980s than during the 1960s and 1970s. In most countries a large part of the urban population live in relatively small urban centres; estimates for the mid-1980s suggested that more than half the world's urban population lived in centres with fewer than 500 000 inhabitants (*14*). Analyses of long-range trends in the spatial distribution of urban populations (*13*) point to a lower population concentration in the largest cities than that suggested by United Nations projections (*1*).

Many developing countries are no longer undergoing rapid urbanization, especially the more urban countries whose economies have stagnated. There is a strong association between growth in the level of urbanization of countries between 1960 and 1980 and economic growth (*13*). Slower economic growth or economic stagnation during the 1980s will have slowed much urban growth. Many of the economic, social, and political factors that underpinned rapid urban growth in earlier decades were no longer present during the 1980s.

There are complex population movements into and out of most urban centres, some temporary, some permanent, some seasonal. Migrants from rural areas to major cities account for most of the urban population growth. In developing countries migrants are mostly (over 70%) under 25 years of age, with a high proportion of children (over 40%). In developed countries children (0–14 years) and youth (15–24 years) account in general for a smaller but still very high proportion (over 50%) of the migrants to urban areas. However, natural increase on aggregate contributes more to urban population growth than net rural-to-urban migration, although a high rate of natural increase in a city's population may owe much to the in-migration of young fertile people in previous years (15).

The influx of new people into a city (whether as migrants, refugees, or victims of natural disasters) exerts environmental pressure and heightens the risk of outbreaks of disease in different ways. A rapid influx usually overwhelms the capacity of the authorities to ensure adequate housing, water, sanitation, and health care. The susceptibility of the host population to imported disease or that of incomers to endemic disease may set off an epidemic (16).

In any urban centre to which there has been sustained migration, the age structure of the migrants will influence that of the urban population (17). As and when natural increase becomes the dominant source of population growth, it becomes an increasingly important factor in determining the age distribution. Data on the structure of the urban and rural populations, though available for a number of countries, have not yet been analysed.

International migration

Movements of population across borders are, in certain countries, a major component of their demographic pattern. Migrants are traditionally driven by economic need towards countries where there is a demand for labour or the possibility of opening up new land. Increasingly too, political refugees have been contributing to migratory movements as well as people fleeing drought or other environmental hazards or internal or international upheavals. The total number of migrants represents only a small fraction of the world's population, but they may have a major influence on the resources and structure of the host population, especially when unpredicted environmental or political events cause a large number of people to move to a neighbouring country. Migrants involved in unplanned or unstructured international migrations are often confronted with severe health and environmental problems. They seldom benefit from basic health services and health insurance coverage. Their living conditions are usually of a lower environmental quality than those of the population, resulting in a negative effect on their health.

Labour migrants[a]

The development of North America and of many South American countries as well as of Australia and New Zealand has depended on immigration, mostly from a few European countries. In the early 1980s immigration was still making a significant contribution to the population of Australia (0.4 million in the period 1981–1985), Canada (0.4 million), and the USA (2.9 million), although the European component of the immigrant population in 1981–1985 was less than a half in Australia, a quarter in the USA, of what it had been 20 years earlier. It is now being replaced by a sixfold to tenfold increase in the proportion of migrants from other parts of the world, mostly Asia and Latin America.

Europe, once a source of emigrants, is now a major immigration area. In the 12 Member States of the European Community alone, with a total population of 325 million, there are at present 13.3 million migrants. Of these, 5 million are people migrating between Community members; the remaining 8.3 million are from outside the Community, 57% from Mediterranean countries. Other European countries also have major immigrant populations—Switzerland, for instance, had a foreign population of about a million in 1989, or 15.6% of its total population (18).

Western Asia has seen major changes in immigration patterns in response to the development of the oil industry and to changes in oil prices, but there are few reliable figures. Altogether Kuwait, Saudi Arabia, and the United Arab Emirates counted 2.5 million foreigners in 1970. No figures are available for Iraq. While it is believed that the foreign population has increased substantially since 1970, only in Kuwait is it known that the numbers of foreigners rose from 0.5 million in 1975 to 1 million in 1985—this in a country that had a total population of 1.7 million in 1985. All these figures are now in need of drastic revision after recent events in the area.

In Latin America emigration is dominated by a very strong and increasing flow towards the USA, where Mexicans, for instance, who accounted for 0.78 million in 1970, now number 2.2 million. Other countries attracting immigrants are Argentina, Brazil, and Venezuela. Altogether 4.8 million

---

[a] Except where indicated otherwise, the statistics in this section are drawn from data available to the United Nations (17).

immigrants were present in Latin America in 1980, 59% originating from outside the region, mostly Europe.

The region with the largest proportion of immigrants in its population may be in Africa, but the figures are neither complete nor recent. They are available for only 12 countries of West Africa, representing 16% of the continent's population. They indicate that the foreign population in those countries in the 1970s numbered over 2.7 million, compared with a total population of 58 million.

Refugees[a] and displaced persons

These form a fast-growing population. Statistics provided by the United Nations High Commissioner for Refugees (UNHCR) show the trends in the number of people involved in the various continents (Box 10).

Box 10. Number of refugees worldwide

	1970	1980	1985	1990
Africa	999 083	3 660 800	3 477 300	5 972 392
N. America	635 000*	1 187 000	1 353 000	1 508 593
S. America		177 600	332 700	1 198 880
Asia	137 700	2 314 400	5 666 700	7 495 693
Europe	644 424	575 500	690 000	931 783
Oceania	44 000	314 000	93 600	102 581
Total	2 460 207	8 229 300	11 613 300	17 209 722

* Includes South America.

Source: United Nations High Commissioner for Refugees, unpublished data, 1991.

To these must be added the 2.42 million people registered in 1991 by the United Nations Relief and Works Agency for Palestinian Refugees (UNRWA). At the latest count there were therefore close to 20 million refugees throughout the world, mostly in tropical and subtropical countries. While their needs are simpler than if they had taken refuge in temperate or subarctic areas, they are exposed to the same environmental risks as the inhabitants of the host areas, but are often housed in substandard accom-

---

[a] According to United Nations instruments (the 1951 Convention relating to the Status of Refugees and the 1967 Protocol relating to the Status of Refugees), a refugee is a person who "owing to well-founded fear of being persecuted for reasons of race, religion, nationality, membership of a particular social group or political opinion, is outside the country of his nationality and is unable or, owing to such fear, is unwilling to avail himself of the protection of that country; or who, not having a nationality and being outside the country of his former habitual residence, is unable or, owing to such fear, is unwilling to return to it" (United Nations, Treaty Series, vol. 189, No. 2545, p. 150; and vol. 606, No. 8791, p. 267).

modation, depend on precarious supplies of water and food, and suffer from poor sanitation and limited medical assistance. When their number is large compared with the population of the host country, or when they are highly concentrated in a small part of the country, their survival may have negative effects on the environment and therefore on their own health and that of their hosts.

Similar subjects of concern are those people who, without falling under the official designation of refugees (and therefore under the responsibility of either UNHCR or UNRWA), have been forced to leave the country where they usually live or work for economic or ecological reasons or because of war. They are estimated to number at least as many as the refugees (*19*). Because they have less legal protection, their environmental and health circumstances are even more precarious.

Migratory movements seem to be on the increase. They are likely to grow in the near future as a result of international conflict, demographic pressure on scarce land, or socioeconomic transformation.

Conclusions

Population is an issue that affects the environment of developing countries in a direct way. It does so differently from country to country, but it also affects the whole world indirectly because of the increasing exploitation of the earth's resources and pollution by agents with global distribution and global effects such as chlorofluorocarbons and carbon dioxide, although the main contributors to these so far are the developed countries (*20*).

From the purely environmental point of view, the direct and immediate concern of developing countries is population size. From the health point of view, mortality and morbidity, especially in children, whether from water-, food-, air- or vector-borne diseases, have in each case a strong environmental component. Protecting both the environment and the children may therefore seem to involve a contradiction. However, the increased survival of children as a result of better health and education of mothers and improved sanitation, nutrition, and primary health care, along with effective family planning programmes, can lead to a reduction in fertility rates.

Only strong, large-scale, sustained, accepted efforts to improve the education and health conditions of the people, especially mothers and children, and simultaneous provision of family planning services will significantly reduce fertility rates and thus population size, for the immediate benefit of the countries concerned but ultimately of the world as a whole.

No amount of primary health care and family planning, however, will prevent the population of some countries with scarce arable land from almost doubling within the next 20 years. Not only will this lead to dramatic degradation of the local environment but also, unless secure livelihoods are available to the new generation, such demographic pressure will lead to attempts to migrate towards new labour markets, with the disruption, upheaval, and possible conflicts that any such movement will tend to bring about if carried out on a massive scale.

Poverty

Poverty is generally defined as the inability of an individual or household to attain a minimal standard of living (21). The level of prosperity in a country and the distribution of assets and income within it are the major factors determining the scale and nature of poverty.

There are strong and obvious associations between poverty and health. The poor usually have a much lower life expectancy, a high infant mortality, and a higher incidence of disablement. They suffer more from communicable diseases and a higher proportion of their lives is spent in poor health.

Since poverty is largely due to lack of income and/or assets, the number of poor people in a given country or in the world is usually estimated from the number of people with incomes below a certain defined level (the poverty line). The World Bank estimates that in 1985 there were 1115 million people living below a poverty line defined as US$370 per person per year (at 1985 prices) (21). If the poverty line is set at US$275 per person per year (which might correspond to extreme poverty), there were 630 million poor people (Box 11).

However, poverty defined solely by level of personal income cannot cover health, life expectancy, literacy, or access to public goods or common property resources. Clean drinking-water, for example, is essential for a reasonable standard of living but is not reflected in consumption or income as usually measured. Many poor rural households have lost access to common property resources or to fuel, fodder, food, and building materials, but this is not reflected in income statistics. Likewise, such aspects of a minimum quality of life as security against crime and physical violence and participation in the economic, cultural, and political activities of the community are also not revealed in income-based poverty definitions. If they were, the number of poor people would be even higher and a significant number would be found in developed countries.

Setting a single international poverty line based on income per caput may be misleading since it cannot take sufficient account of differences between countries in the income needed to attain an adequate living standard. Furthermore, variations in living costs between different areas within countries are such that some people with incomes well above the poverty line may have

Box 11. World Bank estimates of the scale of poverty in developing countries in 1985

Region	Extremely poor			Poor (including extremely poor)			Social indicators		
	Number (millions)	Headcount index (%)	Poverty gap	Number (millions)	Headcount index (%)	Poverty gap	Under-5 mortality (per thousand)	Life expectancy (years)	Net primary enrolment rate (%)
Sub-Saharan Africa	120	30	4	180	47	11	196	50	56
East Asia	120	9	0.4	280	20	1	96	67	96
China	80	8	1	210	20	3	58	69	93
South Asia	300	29	3	520	51	10	172	56	74
India	250	33	4	420	55	12	199	57	81
Eastern Europe	3	4	0.2	6	8	0.5	23	71	90
Eastern Mediterranean and North Africa	40	21	1	60	31	2	148	61	75
Latin America and the Caribbean	50	12	1	70	19	1	75	66	92
All developing countries	633	18	1	1 116	33	3	121	62	83

Note: The poverty line in international dollars (using purchasing power parities) is $275 per caput a year for the extremely poor and $370 per caput a year for the poor.
The headcount index is defined as the percentage of the population below the poverty line.
The poverty gap is defined as the aggregate income shortfall of the poor as a percentage of aggregate consumption. Under-5 mortality rates are for 1980–85, except for China and South Asia, where the period is 1975–80.

Source: World Bank. World development report. Oxford, Oxford University Press, 1990.

very inadequate living standards while some with incomes below the poverty line have adequate standards.

Estimates of poverty based on the local cost of a minimum "basket of goods" allowing for differences in living costs between locations within countries are usually much higher than those based on income alone, supporting the suggestion that the poverty line should be set within each national context. For instance, a study in ten Latin American countries made allowances for differences in living costs between countries and, within countries, between large cities, smaller urban centres, and rural areas; it estimated that 137.5 million people were living in poverty in 1986. If this is extrapolated to the whole region, it suggests that 170 million people were living in poverty in Latin America (22). This is more than twice the number suggested by the World Bank report. Case studies also suggest that the nature of poverty and the relative importance of the factors contributing to it within a country vary between individuals and social groups, in some cases influenced by seasonal and meteorological circumstances, in others by reduction of purchasing power due to economic contingencies, in others still by war and civil strife.

Deficiencies in the physical environment

An alternative way of calculating the number of people living in poverty is to count how many lack a minimum standard of living. Such a standard would include adequate food, safe and sufficient supplies of water, secure shelter, access to education and health care and, in high-density settlements, provision for the removal of domestic wastes. One recent estimate suggests that some 2200 million people live in poverty in the developing world, the criteria being related to lack of access to health-promoting services. Nine out of ten have no access to safe drinking-water and most have no primary health care service (23). Most of these poor people in rural areas live in one-room or two-room houses and lack the means to ensure that the houses provide protection from disease vectors. Most of the urban poor live in overcrowded conditions in tenements, cheap boarding-houses, squatter settlements, or settlements developed on illegal sites (13). In most cities in developing countries, between one-third and two-thirds of all inhabitants live in illegal settlements with inadequate or no infrastructure or services (24).

In virtually all countries the needs of a large proportion of the poor population for health-promoting housing and basic services are not met. Even in the richest countries a proportion of the population suffer the adverse health effects of physical deprivation. Many people are trapped in declining industrial cities or decaying city districts as the young, well educated, and rich move out. These people are less able to adapt to a decline in employment by moving to where jobs are available. As urban shops and services close down, most new shops and services develop in the suburbs, small towns, and rural areas to which the richer, younger, better educated people move. This process of entrapment usually affects the less educated, the poor, and the elderly. In many cities ethnic minorities suffer disproportionately from these changes. Particular cities or districts within cities that suffer most from such changes not only have high levels of unemployment, particularly among young people, but also often high levels of poor-quality housing and social problems. They may have significantly higher-than-average infant mortality rates or a lower life expectancy. For instance, the life expectancy in certain of the poorest parts of New York City is reported to be some 20 years less than the national average. Particular psychosocial problems tend to be concentrated in such areas. Local governments often find themselves trying to cope with increasing demands for social and welfare services and a declining tax base. Comparable entrapment processes are also evident within particular rural areas, usually linked to poorer-quality land and on occasion to inequitable land-owning structures.

Countries of Eastern Europe also have problems. In rural and agricultural regions, many of the population have inadequate incomes and basic services, and major industrial centres are in decline. In addition, serious housing problems affect a high proportion of the population, and the recent rapid political changes will have short-term and long-term effects on health and the environment that are likely to be significant.

In the developing world a far higher proportion of the population lack a minimum standard of living, and their unmet needs are much greater. Box 12 illustrates the scale of the health indicator disparities between rich and poor groups within particular countries, regions, cities and settlements.

Women and children are often more vulnerable to the health risks associated with poverty and inadequate standards of living. That children in poor households are especially vulnerable to disease is evident from the high rates of infant and child mortality associated with poor housing and living conditions. Women's vulnerability during pregnancy and childbirth is also evident from the very high levels of maternal mortality in most developing countries (Box 13). In many low-income settlements there is a significantly higher incidence of certain diseases among women, linked to the fact that they spend more time within the settlement and its contaminated environment (for instance in managing the house and looking after the children). Women suffer more from the diseases associated with inadequate water and sanitation and from the respiratory problems associated with smoky living environments because they spend more time inside the house, where cooking or heating is on open fires or cheap stoves using coal or wood. In rural areas, where commercial pressures and environmental degradation are depriving

Box 12. Comparisons of health indicators between high-income and low-income groups

India

A study of infant mortality rates in a village in India found a tenfold difference between the poorest families (typically landless labourers) where 180 infants died per 1000 live births and the richest families (virtually all of whom were large landowners).

Bombay and Delhi. In some low-income settlements (bustees) in Delhi the child mortality rate was 221 per 1000 but nearly twice this rate among poorer castes within these settlements. In Bombay the crude death rate of Bombay island (the central city area) was twice as high as that of the suburbs and three times that of the extended suburbs.

Pakistan

Karachi. In three low-income areas, between 95 and 152 infants per 1000 live births died before the age of 1 year; in a middle-class area only 32 per 1000 died.

Philippines

Manila. A series of surveys in the mid-1970s revealed the disparities between health problems in a large squatter settlement (Tondo) and other non-squatter areas of the city. In Tondo the level of severe malnutrition among infants and young children was three times the level for non-squatter areas. Tondo's infant mortality rate was 210 per 1000 live births, compared with 76 for non-squatter areas in Manila. The proportion of people with tuberculosis in Tondo was nine times the average for non-squatter areas, while diarrhoea was twice as common. In Tondo anaemia was twice as common and typhoid four times as common.

Haiti

Port-au-Prince. In the slums one in five infants dies before its first birthday, while another one in ten dies between its first and second birthdays. This is almost three times the mortality rate in rural areas and many times the rate in the richer areas of Port-au-Prince, where infant and child mortality rates are similar to those in urban areas of the United States.

Brazil

Porto Alegre. In 1980 a study examined differentials in health between those living in shanty towns (one-fifth of Porto Alegre's population) and those living elsewhere. Infant mortality rates among residents of shanty towns were three times as high as among the non-shanty-town residents. Neonatal mortality rates were twice as high, postneonatal mortality more than five times as high. Mortality from pneumonia and influenza was six times higher in shanty towns and from septicaemia eight times higher.

São Paulo. Infant mortality rates vary by a factor of four depending on the district. In the central area 42 infants died for every 1000 born alive, while in one of the predominantly poor periurban municipalities the rate was 175 per 1000 live births. Infant death rates from enteritis, diarrhoea, and pneumonia on the city's periphery were twice as high as in the centre.

Sources: Most of these examples are quoted in Stephens, C. et al. *A review of the health impacts of environmental problems in urban areas of developing countries*; paper prepared for the Panel on Urbanization of the WHO Commission on Health and Environment; see note 25 for a complete list of sources.

Box 13. Maternal health

In many developing countries pregnancy and childbirth account for more than a quarter of all deaths of women of childbearing age. About half a million women, 99% of them in the developing world, die in childbirth each year. Of every 100 000 women who give birth in Africa, from 200 to 1500 may die, compared with fewer than 10 in most developed countries. About three-quarters of maternal deaths are from one of five causes: haemorrhage, infection, toxaemia, obstructed labour, and abortion (especially unsafe abortion performed by untrained personnel in unhygienic conditions). Because women in many developing countries especially the poorest countries, tend to have many pregnancies, the cumulative lifetime risk of dying in pregnancy may reach 1 in 20. Most of these maternal deaths could be prevented by relatively cheap and simple measures.

A woman's health and nutritional status substantially affect her capacity to cope with difficulties during pregnancy, childbirth, and the postpartum period, produce a strong, healthy baby, and nurse and care for it. Most pregnant women in developing countries are anaemic and many teenage mothers are not fully grown. Women could help themselves if they had basic information about nutrition and health. Improving women's income, education, health, and nutrition could greatly reduce maternal mortality and morbidity.

Family planning information and services can also improve maternal health by enabling women to time and space pregnancies. In many countries, 20–40% of maternal deaths could be averted by avoiding unwanted pregnancies. The three essential elements are prevention of complications, routine care, and back-up for high-risk emergency cases. Existing programmes could be modified to stress:

— Stronger community-based health care, with non-physician health workers to screen pregnant women, identify those at high risk, and refer them for help; to provide good prenatal care and ensure safe delivery for women at less risk; to provide family life education and family planning services; and in general to promote better family health and nutrition.

— Stronger referral facilities—hospitals and health centres with beds to act as a back-up network, to take care of complicated deliveries and obstetrical emergencies, and to provide clinical and surgical methods of family planning.

— An alarm and transport system to transfer women with high-risk pregnancies and emergencies from the home to the referral facilities.

Source: World Bank. *World development report 1990*. Oxford, Oxford University Press, 1990.

poorer groups of access to common property resources, it is generally women whose workload is increased—for instance in gathering fuel, collecting water, and foraging (26, 27). Within many low-income urban settlements there is a higher-than-average number of women at the head of households (28) and they often face discrimination in the job market (in both the formal and the informal sector) and in obtaining access to public services, housing, and credit (29, 30).

Rural and urban poverty

Most poor people live in rural areas, the majority in the largest, most populous Asian countries such as Bangladesh, China, India, Indonesia and Pakistan although the proportion of poor people within national populations is often higher in sub-Saharan Africa. Estimates for the number of poor people living in rural areas vary from around 800 million to more than 1500 million, depending on the criteria used. The World Bank's study of poverty notes that many of the poor live in areas where arable land is scarce, agricultural productivity low, and drought, floods, and environmental degradation common.

Several recent studies suggest that the scale and nature of urban poverty tend to be underestimated in terms both of the proportion of urban dwellers who are poor and the extent of physical deprivation and health effects (31, 32). The World Bank's report on poverty (21) noted that "although urban incomes are generally higher and urban services and facilities more accessible, poor town-dwellers may suffer more than rural households from certain aspects of poverty. The urban poor, typically housed in slums or squatter settlements, often have to contend with appalling overcrowding, bad sanitation and contaminated water. The sites are often illegal and dangerous. Forcible eviction, floods and landslides, and chemical pollution are constant threats." The CEPAL study of poverty (22) suggests that, by 1986, the number of urban poor in Latin America was greater than the number of rural poor and that with the trend towards a more and more urbanized world, an increasing proportion of the world's poor are likely to be in urban areas.

While the average levels of disease, malnutrition, and premature death in many cities are lower than in the surrounding rural areas, the averages are kept down by the presence in such cities of a high proportion of the nation's middle-income and upper-income groups, who generally enjoy a relatively good standard of health. Data on average urban incomes are often inaccurate because they underrepresent poorer groups who live in illegal settlements or are based on surveys taken only in the capital city, where the income levels are unrepresentative of all the urban centres (33). A review of case studies of

44

poverty suggests that poorer groups in the larger cities generally have rates of disease and death comparable with or even higher than their rural counterparts (*31*). The close proximity of large numbers of people in environments that provide no protection from the pollution caused by city wastes creates favourable conditions for the rapid spread of a variety of infectious diseases, often in disastrous epidemics.

An estimated 600 million urban dwellers in developing countries live in life-threatening and health-threatening circumstances because of inadequate housing, a bad infrastructure and services, and house sites prone to flooding or some other natural disaster (*33*). Perhaps as many (if not more) have insufficient or no access to effective health care, although this is not evident from official statistics, which generally overestimate the coverage, sometimes even claiming as much as 99–100% coverage in poor countries where few facilities are known to exist (*33*).

Although it is common to contrast health problems in urban and rural areas, ill health, disablement, and premature death are likely to be more closely associated with age, gender, and household income (or assets) than with living in large cities, smaller urban centres, or rural areas (*33*). This is supported by the studies whose findings are summarized in Box 12. An increasing number of detailed studies of strategies for survival in poorer households also show that these cross the rural–urban divide—for instance, farmers or agricultural workers may work part of the year in urban areas or households and rely on both urban and rural incomes. This weakens the view that rural and urban poverty must necessarily be discussed as separate phenomena. The fact that rural poverty has contributed much to rapid urbanization through the movement of poor rural people to urban centres suggests the need for a more integrated understanding of poverty.

Resource use

The impact of any population on the environment depends on the type and level of its resource use and waste generation. To take an extreme case, there are hunter-gatherers, pastoralists, and farmers who make virtually no use of non-renewable resources, generate negligible amounts of waste, and draw hardly at all on the carrying capacity of the ecosystem in which they live and work. Some of these farmers also obtain high crop yields on limited land areas (*34, 35*) and their per caput contribution to environmental degradation worldwide is negligible. At the other extreme, the high-consumption lifestyle enjoyed by many of the world's richer households may imply levels of per caput environmental degradation many times that of any global average for the use of non-renewable resources, degradation of soils, and generation of wastes.

This can be illustrated by some comparisons between average per caput figures for developed and developing countries. On average, each person in the developed world consumes natural resources at a rate at least 10–20 times as high as the corresponding average in the developing world (*36*). The average per caput consumption of paper is around 120 kg a year in developed countries, compared with 8 kg in developing countries; of steel, 450 kg compared with 43 kg; and of the purchased energy-equivalent of coal almost 6 tonnes compared with 0.5 tonnes.

These averages hide large differences in per caput consumption levels within the developed and the developing world, and large differences between income groups within countries. For instance, the per caput energy consumption in low-income economies other than China and India in 1985 was around 1% of that in Canada, Norway, and the United States (*21*). Within cities where a significant proportion of the population do not have water piped to their homes, the differences in per caput water consumption can vary by a factor of 10 or more when consumption levels in richer and poorer households are compared.

A consideration of the different levels of resource use by different population groups requires a separation of the environmental effects of such groups into:

— use of non-renewable resources such as fossil fuels and other mineral resources
— exploitation of renewable resources such as soils and groundwater beyond the ecosystem's maximum sustainable yield
— use of the environment to absorb production and consumption wastes.

Most of the world's non-renewable resource consumption is concentrated in Europe and North America, with very low levels of consumption among the poorest countries. Box 14 lists the countries with the highest levels of consumption for a selection of non-renewable resources in terms of the percentage of world consumption for 1988, and compares this percentage with the percentage of world population in that nation. Thus, Japan, with 2.4% of the world's population in 1988, accounted for more than 10% of the world's consumption of aluminium, copper, iron ore, nickel, crude steel, tin, and zinc and more than 20% of the cadmium. The United States, with less than 5% of the world's population, accounted for more than 15% of the world's consumption of cadmium, nickel, and zinc and more than 20% of aluminium, copper, lead, and mercury. Other OECD countries figure prominently in terms of high proportions of world consumption relative to population. The USSR also, relative to its share of world population, has a particularly high level of consumption for many natural resources.

Box 14. The major consuming countries for selected non-renewable resources, 1988

Country	% of world popula-tion	% of world consumption									
		Alumi-nium	Cadmium	Copper	Iron ore	Lead	Mercury	Nickel	Steel	Tin	Zinc
Belgium	0.2		9.9	3.0							2.5
Brazil	2.8		1.9		3.9					2.8	
Canada	0.5	2.4									
China	21.7	3.4	1.9	4.4	17.8	4.4	6.5	3.2	10.5	5.9	5.4
Czechoslovakia	0.3				1.9						
France	1.1	3.7	5.2	3.8	2.4	3.8	5.2	4.6	3.9	3.3	4.1
Germany	1.2	7.0	4.7	7.5	4.6	6.6	5.2	10.5	2.1	8.2	6.3
India	16.1	1.9									
Italy	1.1	3.3	1.9	4.2	2.1	4.3		3.4	3.2	2.5	3.5
Japan	2.4	12.0	22.6	12.5	12.4	7.2	2.6	19.0	10.2	13.7	10.9
Poland	0.7				1.9				2.1		
Republic of Korea	0.8			2.5		2.6			2.0	3.1	2.4
Romania	0.5						3.9	2.0			
South Africa	0.7						1.3	2.0			
Spain	0.8										
Sweden	0.2										
United Kingdom	1.1	2.4	7.1	3.1		5.3	5.2	3.1	2.0	4.3	2.7
USA	4.8	26.1	19.8	21.3	6.4	21.2	26.0	16.6	13.7	16.0	15.6
USSR	5.6	10.2	12.3	11.7	21.4	13.9	23.4	15.3	22.0	12.7	15.2
Yugoslavia	0.5					2.3					
Rest of World	37.5	27.7	12.7	26.1	25.2	28.3	15.6	20.3	28.1	27.2	31.5

Source: World Resources Institute. *World resources, 1990–91.* Oxford, Oxford University Press, 1990.

Box 14 also shows China and India to be among the world's largest consumers of certain non-renewable resources, but their per caput consumption is much less than that of most other countries. It is perhaps worth noting that the 2000 million or so poorest people make a very small contribution to the depletion of non-renewable resources. However, figures for some of the largest resource-using countries overstate the levels of national consumption, since they take no account of the non-renewable resources within exported products.

There are too few data on the relationship between populations and the exploitation of renewable resources such as soils and groundwater (and whether these are kept within sustainable levels). The dietary preferences of middle-income and upper-income groups tend to encourage more land-intensive and more energy-intensive exploitation (often with a higher input of agricultural chemicals). It is also clear that in many countries there is a strong association between rural poverty and soil degradation in particular regions, districts, or settlements, although this is often the result not of poor-quality land management or lack of land but of poorer groups being forced on to marginal land. The fact that most of the world's poorest nations have among the largest per caput endowments of arable and cultivable land also precludes simple generalizations about population and overuse of soils and groundwater. Box 15 discusses the relationship between population pressure and the degradation of renewable resources.

Regarding the environment's capacity to absorb wastes, there is a clear association between high-consumption lifestyles and the production of all types of wastes, and between household income and the volume of household waste. By the late 1980s annual per caput municipal waste generation was 826 kg in North America, 394 kg in Japan, and 336 kg in the European countries of the OECD (36). In many developing countries the per caput average is below 50 kg. In addition, perhaps not surprisingly, it is in the developed world that most industrial and hazardous wastes are generated. The OECD estimates that industries in the OECD countries are responsible for 77% of all hazardous industrial wastes, though having only some 15% of the world's population (36).

There is also a strong association between income and the use of fossil fuels, and thus between income and contributions to carbon dioxide emission into the atmosphere. It is clear that, if current population levels are already overtaxing finite resources and carrying capacity within specific regions and also increasingly globally, meeting the health needs of current and future populations by available techniques may be impossible to achieve without causing even more serious environmental degradation. If this is to be avoided, it will require a more rapid reversal of population growth and a new approach to the solution of social and environmental problems.

Box 15. Population pressure and resource degradation

To see the problems of environmental degradation as a consequence of increasing population and subsistence requirements alone is to oversimplify or diagnose the situation incorrectly. In some cases environmental problems are worse than would be expected from the increase in population alone; in others a growing population may be in balance with its environment. It is population growth working in conjunction with other factors that is bringing about widespread environmental deterioration. The most important of these factors are:

— The widespread breakdown of traditional systems of resource management under pressure from population growth and external commercial forces. Traditional communal forms of resource management commonly achieved sustainable exploitation of the resource. Efficient and ecologically sound production systems with extensive fallow periods evolved to manage a variety of fragile or difficult environments. Such systems were often kept in demographic balance by social regulation of fertility, mortality, migration, and marriage. In most cases such systems have been unbalanced or destroyed by human and livestock population pressure in the absence of appropriate technological responses and, to a lesser degree, commercial and political domination.

— Commercialization. The impact of commercial demands on the traditional cultural attitudes of indigenous populations—towards wildlife, for example, during the colonization of America—has been well documented. Other examples of the commercial exploitation of resources, often leading to their degradation, are logging in tropical forests in Asia, the clearing of forests in Latin America, and the expansion of groundnut and tobacco cultivation in sub-Saharan Africa.

— Inequality of access to land and other natural resources and fragmentation of holdings. Land distribution is worsening in many developing countries and holding sizes are declining. Compared with smallholdings, land in larger farms tends to be used less intensively and to employ less labour per unit area.

Source: Repetto, R. & Holmes, T. The role of population in resource depletion. *Population and development review*, **9** (4): 609–632 (1983).

Macroeconomic policies

While the main focus of this report is on the need for a greater share for health and the environment in the sectoral policies and actions of governments and international agencies, it cannot ignore the macroeconomic, pricing and fiscal policies under which all sectoral activities are conducted.

Macroeconomic policies have important direct and indirect effects on health and on the environment. Their effect on health is mediated both through the funds allocated to health care, basic services, and other sectors with an immediate influence on health and through the economic and social factors that affect health status (for instance household incomes, unemployment levels, and price and wage levels). Macroeconomic policies together with trade and sectoral policies also influence the use and degradation of natural resources by altering aggregate demand and changing the prices of natural resources relative to other goods in the economy.

These policies need to ensure that no conflicts arise between economic, environment, and health goals. Increased knowledge of the social and environmental effects of macroeconomic policies and pricing structures permits action to be taken to limit negative effects or intervene in favour of particular population groups (21).

In most instances the major health consequences of macroeconomic policies derive from their impact on the level and purchasing power of individual and household incomes. Macroeconomic policies may change the income level of households (either through changing the price of labour, or the hours worked, or both) and/or the prices paid for goods (including services) purchased by the household. The net effect is changes in the consumption of goods, which in turn affect health. For example, they may bring about changes in the quality and quantity of food purchased (and thus in nutritional status and susceptibility to disease) or in the type of accommodation that can be afforded. There is also the more direct link between income level and ability to afford medical services.

Macroeconomic policies also change the distribution of national income and government expenditure between various groups. For instance, policies that raise the price of basic foodstuffs will disproportionately affect poorer groups, except those which grow a significant proportion of their own food. Low-income households generally spend a higher proportion of their income on food (60–80%) (37) and are particularly vulnerable to increases in food prices.

Macroeconomic policies also affect health through the level of government expenditure on health services and on other services with an influence on health status, such as water supply, sanitation, education, and poverty relief. While the level of overall government expenditure is generally considered to be a matter of macroeconomic policy, the distribution of such expenditure between different categories is not, although there may be exceptions to this, for example in retraining to make the labour market function more efficiently. However, the amount spent on health and related services is determined both by the overall level of expenditure and by the priority given to such expenditure.

Structural adjustment and health

The last two decades have proved extremely difficult for the economies of many developing countries. Global economic changes, primarily the downturn in the growth of the world economy, adverse changes in the terms of trade for countries dependent on primary commodity production, and rises in real interest rates increasing the debt burden have greatly reduced national growth. Many national economies have had negative growth rates. Many governments have recognized the need to restructure their economies both to take account of changes in the world economy and to maximize their growth potential. For many developing countries the pace and form of such restructuring have been determined by conditions set by the International Monetary Fund (IMF) for debt rescheduling. An increasing number of developing countries have introduced structural adjustment programmes to secure the foreign currency that they need but are unable to purchase without IMF support.

One of the problems in assessing the health impact of such policies is determining what would have happened without their introduction. The severe economic crisis from which many countries were suffering prior to structural adjustment reduced the capacity of governments to provide health care and basic services and that of the population to obtain the goods and services they need to secure good health. Inflation, for example, often penalizes the poor in particular as they have less opportunity to maintain the value of their income and savings. The combined effect of the economic crisis and the subsequent recovery policies has been to increase the health risks for large sectors of the population. Box 16 presents the findings from a case study in the Philippines on the effects of structural adjustment on income levels.

Cuts in public expenditure are a main feature of most structural adjustment policies. Cuts in social expenditure are often demanded by outside agencies before aid or balance-of-payments support is given. This has often meant cuts in health services and other services important for health. Public works such as piped water supplies, sewers, and drains, which require large capital investment, often receive the largest cuts. In sub-Saharan Africa the social services budget fell by 26% between 1980 and 1985, and in Latin America by 18%. Health spending per person has declined in most countries since 1980. The 1990 edition of *The state of the world's children* (*38*) reported that a decline in health spending per person has been documented in more than three-quarters of the countries of Africa and Latin America in recent years and that the decline is almost certainly more widespread than the statistics suggest. "Hundreds of health clinics have been closed down, and many which remain open are understaffed and lacking essential supplies." This report also stated that infant mortality had risen in parts of Latin

---

Box 16. Structural adjustment and income levels in the Philippines

The main economic problems in the Philippines in the mid-1980s were diagnosed as excessive borrowing and structural weaknesses in the economy. Stabilization measures were nominal devaluation, strict import controls, cuts in public expenditure, and tight monetary policies. The initial effects were falling output, faster inflation, and an appreciating real exchange rate.

A study of the share of the poor in the national income between 1980 and 1986 found that an increase in the inflation rate of 10% reduced the share of the poorest fifth of the population by 10%, other things being equal. This is because nominal wages failed to keep pace with inflation, and because the poor were not successful in safeguarding their assets. Depreciation in the real exchange rate by 10% was found to increase the share of the poor by 20%. Depreciation encourages export of unskilled labour, and while the price of imports rises such goods are only a small part of those consumed by the poor. The same study found that cuts in public expenditure affected the poor less than the rich because such spending mainly benefited the middle and upper classes.

Source: World Bank. *World development report 1990.* Washington, DC, 1990.

America and sub-Saharan Africa and that the incidence of low birth weight (a sensitive indicator of women's well-being) had increased in seven of the 15 countries for which recent information was available.

In sub-Saharan Africa there was a redistribution of government expenditure in favour of the social services, with a small increase in the percentage allocation of government funds. In Latin America other sectors were protected and the percentage of the total budget allocated to social services fell (*21*). In Indonesia real public expenditure fell by 17% between the fiscal years 1982/3 and 1987/8, but attempts were made to maintain expenditure on the economic and social infrastructure and to increase the employment content.

In respect of the health sector specifically, a joint WHO/World Food Programme study on the health impact of adjustment programmes in Africa (*39*) found that in more than half the cases studied, the health sector had been the first to suffer a cutback when there were budgetary constraints. In Ecuador, Panama, Paraguay, and Peru, the consequences of cuts in government spending meant that, in the first quarter of 1989, the health services were unable even to afford vaccines (*38*). Some authors have drawn direct parallels between the decline in the availability of health services and increased infant mortality and low birth weight (*38*).

Although evidence is mixed as to the relationship between cuts in social service expenditure and structural adjustment policies, there is evidence to show that cuts in such expenditure are directly related to a decline in the health status of poorer groups. For example, a study of the consequences of a decline in government expenditure on social services on health status in ten countries (Botswana, Brazil, Chile, Ghana, Jamaica, Peru, Philippines, the Republic of Korea, Sri Lanka, and Zimbabwe) found that the nutritional status of children had declined in all but two, the Republic of Korea and Zimbabwe (40). In Zimbabwe another study showed that, while only marginal increases in health expenditure occurred between 1980 and 1985, there was a reallocation in favour of preventive services. As a result health improved, especially among children (41).

A review of the literature on macroeconomic policies and health concluded that, while it is commonly recognized that there might be adverse effects from adjustment policies on nutrition and health, there is much uncertainty as to the actual impact (41). Although there has been some research into feedback mechanisms at the level of the national economy, such research does not attempt to isolate the distributional effects, which might be expected to be most evident among groups with a low income. The review cites studies on the effects of unemployment in developed countries, noting that prolonged periods without work have had a number of different health effects including "higher infant mortality rates, and increases in mental illness, cardiovascular disease, suicide, alcohol dependence and drug abuse". However, the precise relationship between macroeconomic policies, unemployment, and health has not been studied.

Structural adjustment and the environment

There are a number of ways in which the macroeconomic policies adopted in structural adjustment may affect the environment. Cuts in government expenditure may alter the consumption and investment patterns within countries, with consequences in the environment difficult to predict. For example, a delay in investment in roads and related infrastructure in areas not yet settled may prevent deforestation. Alternatively, reduction in the real income of households dependent on agriculture may induce them to increase their exploitation of common (and possibly vulnerable) land resources, resulting in increased soil erosion and degradation. Price restructuring in favour of domestic agricultural suppliers will obviously favour domestic production, but the net effect on the environment is again uncertain, depending on the type of crops and on agricultural practices.

Energy prices may increase as price subsidies are removed. Reduced demand for energy will have a positive environmental effect, but if it also promotes a switch towards biomass fuels it may be detrimental. Exchange rate devaluation generally makes the export sector more competitive, but the net effect on the environment will depend on the nature of the exports. Box 17 outlines some typical linkages between economic policies and the environment.

In the second half of the 1980s World Bank lending in Côte d'Ivoire, Jamaica, Kenya, Malawi, Morocco, Nepal, Pakistan, the Philippines, Tunisia, and Turkey included environmental considerations and measures (42). It has been argued that the evidence from the World Bank and the Asian Development ment Bank suggests that adjustment programmes have had a net favourable impact on the environment and that it is relatively easy to ensure that the environment is protected under those policies (42). But several other factors also need to be taken into account. For example, the speed with which adjustment measures are imposed on the economy may be important; a demand for rapid results is likely to encourage rapid exploitation of natural resources rather than promote sustainable use. Also a reduction in the role of government in favour of market forces may increase the difficulty of ensuring effective control over polluting industries (43).

Box 17. Economic policy and potential environmental effects

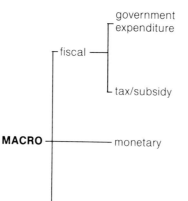

MACRO — fiscal	government expenditure	Publicly funded agencies may protect biologically unique areas; public works (roads and dams) may encourage land uses that degrade fragile areas
	tax/subsidy	Multisectoral action may alter general demand conditions and thus the total consumption of resources
monetary		Credit restrictions similar to tax/subsidy; credit rationing and interest rate increases may reduce demand but also make investment in conservation more expensive
international	exchange rate	Devaluation will increase prices of imports and raise the profitability of exports; the environmental effect will depend on the resources and products affected
	trade	Import/export taxes and quotas will alter prices of particular commodities; the environmental effect will depend on the resources and products affected
	capital controls	If used to maintain overvalued currency, they will reduce the prices of imports and the profitability of exports will fall; the environmental effect will depend on the resources and products affected
SECTORAL	price controls	They may be used to stimulate or retard environmentally damaging production; the environmental effect will depend on the nature of the resources and products affected
	tax/subsidy	They will have indirect effects through changes in aggregate demand; they may also be used to alter the choice of inputs and outputs through changes in relative prices (e.g., fertilizer subsidies).

Source: Adapted from Bishop, J. et al., *Guidelines for applying environmental economics in developing countries.* London, London Environmental Economics Centre, 1991 (Gatekeeper Series No. LEEC 91–02).

References and notes

1. United Nations. *World population prospects: 1990*. New York, 1991 (Document ST/SA/SER.A/120).

2. *World health statistics annual*, 1977–89.

3. Lopez, A. Causes of death: an assessment of global patterns of mortality around 1985. *World health statistics quarterly*, **43**: 91–104 (1990).

4. Lancaster, H.O. *Expectations of life*. New York, Springer-Verlag, 1990.

5. *World health statistics annual*. Geneva, World Health Organization, 1989.

6. McKeown, T. *The role of medicine*. Oxford, Blackwell, 1979.

7. Tomatis, L., ed. *Cancer: causes, occurrence and control*. Lyon, International Agency for Research on Cancer, 1990.

8. Kurihara, M. et al. *Cancer mortality statistics in the world, 1950–1985*. Nagoya, University of Nagoya Press, 1989.

9. United Nations. *Levels and trends of contraceptive use as assessed in 1988*. New York, 1989 (No. E.89.XIII.4).

10. United Nations. Correlates of fertility in selected developing countries. *Population bulletin of the United Nations*, **28**: 95–106 (1989).

11. Care should be taken not to confuse "growth in urban population" and "growth in a nation's (or region's) level of urbanization". Vitually all changes in the level of urbanization (i.e., in the proportion of population living in urban centres) are a result of population movements in or out of urban centres. Natural increase in population (i.e., the excess of births over deaths) does not contribute to increases in urbanization levels except where the rate of natural increase in urban centres is higher than that in rural areas. If this is the case, it may be the result of high proportions of migrants from rural to urban areas being of childbearing age and their movement to urban centres changing those centres' rate of natural increase. A small part of the change in a nation's level of urbanization is often due to rural settlements growing to the point where they are reclassified as urban (and thus are added to the urban population) and rapid rates of natural increase can increase this contribution. But in general, a nation's level of urbanization is not much influenced by population increases for it is essentially the result of changes in economic structure; increased proportions of national populations in urban centres reflect an increase in the proportion of employment opportunities (or possibilities for survival) concentrated in urban centres.

12. di Pace, M. J. et al. *Human settlements and sustainable development: the Latin American case*. Paper presented at an International Colloquium on Urbanization and the Environment, University of Toronto, June 1990. (A condensed version is to be published in: Stren, R. & White, R., eds., *Sustainable cities*, Boulder, CO, Westview Press (forthcoming).)

13. Hardoy, J.E. & Satterthwaite, D. *Squatter citizen: life in the urban Third World*. London, Earthscan Publications, 1989.

14. United Nations. *Estimates and projections of urban, rural and city populations 1950–2025; the 1982 assessment*. New York, 1985 (ST/ESA/SER.R/58).

15. United Nations. *Migration, population growth and employment in metropolitan areas of selected developing countries*. New York, 1985 (ST/ESA/SER.R/57).

16. WHO Commission on Health and Environment. *Report of the Panel on Urbanization*. Geneva, World Health Organization, 1992 (unpublished document WHO/EHE/92.5).

17. United Nations. *World population monitoring: 1989*. New York, 1990 (No. E.89. XIII.12).

18. *Continuous reporting system on migration 1990*. Paris, Organisation for Economic Co-operation and Development, 1991.

19. United Nations. *The coordination of activities related to early warning of possible refugee flows*. Geneva, United Nations Joint Inspection Unit, 1990.

20. United Nations Population Fund. *The state of the world population 1990*. New York, 1990.

21. World Bank. *World development report – 1990; poverty*. Oxford, Oxford University Press, 1990.

22. Feres, J.C. & Leon, A. The magnitude of poverty in Latin America. *CEPAL review*, **41**: 133–151 (August 1990).

23. Jancloes, M. More than a billion... *World health*, March 1990.

24. For city examples, see: Soliman, M. Informal land acquisition and the urban poor in Alexandria. *Third World planning review*, **9** (1): 21–40 (1987); Moser, C.O.N. A home of one's own: squatter housing strategies in Guayaquil, Ecuador. In: Gilbert, A. et al., eds., *Urbanization in contemporary Latin America*, Chichester, Wiley and Sons, 1982; van der Linden, J. Squatting by organized invasion—a new reply to a failing housing policy? *Third World planning review*, **4** (4): 400–412 (1982); El Agraa, O.M.A. et al. *Popular settlements in Greater Khartoum*. Khartoum, Sudanese Group for Assessment of Human Settlements, 1985; Peattie, L. Participation: a case study of how invaders organize, negotiate and interact with government in Lima, Peru. *Environment and urbanization*, **2** (1): 19–30 (April 1990); Schlyter, A. & Schlyter, T. *George—the development of a squatter settlement in Lusaka, Zambia*. Stockholm, Swedish Council for Building Research, 1980; Connolly, P. Uncontrolled settlements and selfbuild: what kind of solution? The Mexico City case. In: Ward, P., ed. *Self help housing: a critique*. London, Mansell, 1982; Amis, P. Squatters or tenants: the commercialization of unauthorized housing in Nairobi. *World development*, **12** (4): 87–96 (1984); Sobreira de Moura, A. Brasilia Teimosa—the organization of a low income settlement in Recife, Brazil. *Development dialogue*, **1**: 152–169 (1987).

25. **India**: Ghosh, S. et al. Mortality patterns in an urban birth cohort. *Indian journal of medical research*, **69**: 616–623 (1979); Basta, S.S. Nutrition and health in low income urban areas of the Third World. *Ecology of food and nutrition*, **6**: 113–124 (1977). **Karachi**: Harpham, T. et al., eds. *In the shadow of the city: community health and the urban poor*. Oxford, Oxford University Press, 1988. **Manila**: Basta, S.S. Nutrition and health in low income urban areas of the Third World. *Ecology of food and nutrition*, **6**: 113–124 (1977). **Port-au-Prince**: Rohde, J.E. Why the other half dies: the science and politics of child mortality in the Third World. *Assignment children*, **61/62**: 36–67 (1983). **Porto Alegre**: Guimaraes, J.J. & Fischmann, A. Inequalities in 1980 infant mortality among shanty town residents and non-shanty town residents in the municipality of Porto Alegre, Rio Grande do Sul, Brazil. *Bulletin of the Pan American Health Organization*, **19**: 235–251 (1985). **São Paulo**: World Bank. *Staff appraisal report: Brazil second health project*. Washington, DC, 1984.

26. Lee-Smith, D. & Schlyter, A. Women, environment and urbanization. *Environment and urbanization*, **3**(2): 3–5 (1991).

27. Sarin, M. Improved stoves, women and domestic energy. *Environment and urbanization*, **3**(2): 51–56 (1991).

28. Moser, C.O.N. & Peake, L., eds. *Women, housing and human settlements*. London and New York, Tavistock Publications, 1987.

29. Moser, C.O.N. *Housing policy and women: towards a gender aware approach*. London, University College, 1985 (DPU Gender and Planning Working Paper No. 7).

30. Falu, A. & Curutchet, M. Rehousing the urban poor: looking at women first. *Environment and urbanization*, **3** (2): 23–38 (1991).

31. Stephens, C. et al. *A review of the health impacts of environmental problems in urban areas of developing countries*. Paper prepared for the Panel on Urbanization of the WHO Commission on Health and Environment, 1991 (available on request from Division of Environmental Health, World Health Organization, 1211 Geneva 27, Switzerland).

32. Hardoy, J.E. et al., eds. *The poor die young: housing and health in Third World cities*. London, Earthscan Publications, 1990.

33. Cairncross, S. et al. The urban context. In: Hardoy, J.E. et al., eds. *The poor die young: housing and health in Third World cities*. London, Earthscan Publications, 1990, pp. 1–24.

34. Reij, C. *Indigenous soil and water conservation in Africa*. London, IIED, 1991 (Gatekeeper Series, No. 27).

35. Bunch. R. *Low input soil restoration in Honduras: the Cantarranas farmer-to-farmer extension programme*. London, IIED, 1990 (Gatekeeper Series No. 23).

36. *The state of the environment*. Paris, Organisation for Economic Co-operation and Development, 1991.

37. Pinstrup-Andersen, P. Macroeconomic adjustment policies and human nutrition: available evidence and research needs. *Food and nutrition bulletin*, **9** (1): 68–86 (1987).

38. UNICEF. *The state of the world's children 1990.* Oxford, Oxford University Press, 1990.

39. WHO/World Food Programme. *Structural adjustment: health, nutrition and food aid in the African Region.* 1988.

40. Cornia, G. A. et al. *Adjustment with a human face. Vol. 1: Protecting the vulnerable and promoting growth. Vol. 2: Ten country case studies.* Oxford, Oxford University Press, 1988.

41. Cooper Weil, D. et al. *The impact of development policies on health. A review of the literature.* Geneva, World Health Organization, 1990.

42. Hansen, S. Macroeconomic policies: incidence on the environment. In: Winpenny, J., ed. *Development research: the environmental challenge.* London, Overseas Development Institute, 1991.

43. Killick, T. Notes on macroeconomic adjustment and the environment. In: Winpenny, J., ed. *Development research: the environmental challenge.* London, Overseas Development Institute, 1991.

3.
Food and agriculture

Introduction

More than half the world's population derive their living from farming, fishing, or hunting. The environmental resources to which they have access and the capital and skills they bring to the exploitation of these resources are major determinants of their state of health, and of the extent to which such exploitation can be sustained. The production and distribution of food affect health not only through their central role in influencing people's nutritional status and resistance to disease but also through injuries or diseases associated with working in this sector and with the contamination of food and water arising from food production, distribution, handling, and preparation.

Current and emerging food production and preservation capabilities are sufficient to ensure an adequate global supply of safe nutritious food. The food trade has increased markedly, resulting in an international market and creating a growing demand for the safe preservation of food during prolonged shipment. Improved food storage and processing considerably increase the availability of food for human consumption by limiting food spoilage and reducing food and crop wastes. Chronic hunger is due less to food shortage than to lack of purchasing power or of land on which food can be produced, or disruption of food distribution systems by civil unrest or violence. However, drastic changes in the agriculture, food, and fishery sectors will be required to achieve an adequate food supply for the 7000 million or more people who will inhabit the world in the year 2010, if damage to the environment and risk of spreading infectious diseases are to be avoided. In particular, the problems of pre-harvest and post-harvest losses will need to receive special attention.

In general, trends in food production have shown impressive advances in recent decades and there has been a significant increase in the supply of calories per person. However, a considerable proportion of the world's population are malnourished as a result of too little food or specific nutrient deficiencies (for instance energy or protein deficiencies or specific vitamin or mineral deficiencies). Greater global efforts are required to ensure that those who are malnourished have access to the food they need or the means to produce it. Achieving this will involve significant changes in agricultural, economic and social policies and practices in many of the poorer countries. Such changes include giving greater priority to supporting small farmers and providing them with credit, advice, and market outlets. The objective is to guarantee food or income to poorer households and to provide them with insurance in times of stress due, for instance, to drought, seasonal hunger, or downturns in the economy.

Human society remains dependent on the natural productivity of both land and water ecosystems for most basic needs, including most staple foods and many other products such as biomass fuels, timber, fibres, resins, spices, and medicinal products. The ways in which soil and water resources are used in farming, forestry, and fishing within any country or region have important implications for its economy, the distribution of income, and the extent of poverty and malnutrition. They also have important implications for the environment and for the possibility of sustaining production in the future.

Other land ecosystems have profound though less direct importance since they protect catchments or river basins from floods and erosion, regulate microclimates, provide biodiversity or habitats for natural enemies of pests, or perform other functions of immediate importance to agriculture.

Food production

Trends in dietary energy supplies between the early 1960s and early 1980s showed substantial progress; worldwide, the supply of calories per person per day increased by 14%, the increase averaging 21% for developing countries. In Africa the improvement was less than 5% over this period, and there was a deterioration in the 1980s (1). Moreover, a large number of countries in sub-Saharan Africa showed a decline in the supply of calories per person per day for the period 1972–74 to 1984–86 compared with other regions; 18 countries out of a total of 45 in sub-Saharan Africa experienced such a decline.

So far agricultural development has permitted world food production to grow faster than population. The land and water ecosystems on which human food supplies depend have the potential to produce an adequate supply of safe, nutritious food for the world's population now and up to the year 2010 at projected rates of population growth, and even beyond. Much of this potential lies in developing countries, where food production increases could be achieved through increases in the yield, in arable land, and in cropping intensity. Box 18 summarizes the possibilities of increased food production for different regions between the early 1980s and the year 2000.

With appropriate cultivation or management practices, most land and water ecosystems can sustain production and be considered as a renewable

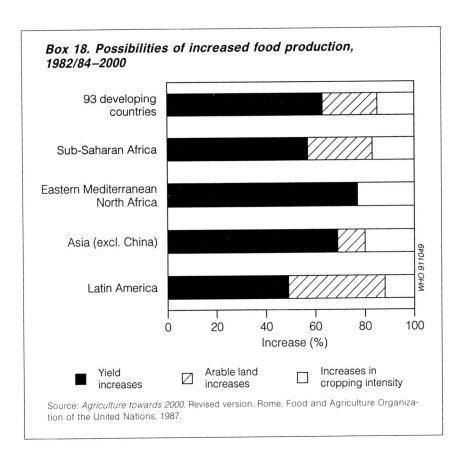

Box 18. Possibilities of increased food production, 1982/84–2000

Legend:
- ■ Yield increases
- ▨ Arable land increases
- □ Increases in cropping intensity

Source: *Agriculture towards 2000.* Revised version. Rome, Food and Agriculture Organization of the United Nations, 1987.

resource. However, a growing proportion of land-based productive and protective ecosystems are being irreversibly degraded and lost as a result of human activities. Many countries are facing an expanding demand for food, fuel, and other primary commodities and at the same time a growing loss of farmland and diminishing water resources and biological diversity. For example, fertile soils developed by natural processes over millennia are being subjected to destruction or degradation by overuse or misuse in a few decades or, on occasion, a few years. Soil degradation from erosion, salinization, waterlogging, and pollution are among the menaces that undermine soil fertility and the agricultural productivity of farmlands and rangelands. Land conversion to non-agricultural use has reduced the food-producing potential in many parts of the world. These problems are worldwide and may have been offset by agricultural intensification (the green revolution), but in countries with limited farmland they pose a very serious threat to agriculture.

The problem of land degradation in developing countries is particularly acute in arid and semi-arid regions, where pressure on land because of overgrazing, overcultivation, and overcutting taxes the natural resilience of the inherently fragile ecosystem. This process, desertification, is compounded by drought and has been the greatest environmental menace in the continent of Africa in recent decades. Food for famine relief was needed by 20 African countries in the 1980s.

Three constraints on sustaining production exist:

— The constraint on expansion of the area under cultivation. During the last three decades growth in food production was much helped by increases in the area under cultivation. In recent years the rate of increase in the area of arable land and permanent crops has declined and certain countries, such as Bangladesh and India, have exploited virtually all the available land resources.

— The special difficulty of sustaining and increasing production in environments with poor resources or great climatic variability. The green revolution technologies that contributed greatly to increased grain production in the 1960s and 1970s are less appropriate for these environments and for farmers with small and marginal holdings (2).

— The limits to increasing yields further. "Intensive mono-cropping has also made production more susceptible to environmental stresses and shocks . . . and there is growing evidence of diminishing returns from intensive production with high-yielding varieties . . . Moreover, it has become clear that these are not simple second- or third-generation problems capable of being solved by further technological adjustments" (2). There is the problem of the degradation of existing land, for instance through soil erosion, desertification, or salinization, and the conversion of fertile farmland to nonagricultural uses, for instance roads, hydroelectric reservoirs, building land.

Another factor placing additional pressure on production capacity is the growth in demand for livestock feed, owing to the increasing demand by higher-income groups for meat products. Meat consumption per person in developing countries with annual per caput incomes above US$ 1250 is almost ten times that in countries with incomes below US$ 250. If incomes rise, so too will the demand for feed grain; the projection is that it will account for about 25% of all cereals consumed in the developing world by the year 2000 as compared with 16% in 1980 (3). As demand for livestock products expands, the production will become more intensive and more concentrated in specialized production units, and the demand for feed will increasingly be based on cereals and concentrates. This may mean diversion of production capacity from producing food to meet the needs of poorer groups, to producing grain for livestock feed to meet the demand for meat of the higher-income groups. The conversion of cereals and concentrates to animal products involves large losses of food energy and a corresponding increase in the demand for resources.

People in higher-income countries or higher-income groups within many poorer countries obtain a smaller and decreasing proportion of their calories from cereals and an increasing proportion from sugar and animal products. In low-income developing countries people still largely rely on cereals, roots, and tubers.

Pre-harvest and post-harvest losses remain an enormous problem in developing countries. According to the National Academy of Sciences in the United States, more than 100 million tonnes of cereals and legumes are lost annually in the developing countries (4), sufficient to provide the minimum energy requirements of about 300 million people (5). The magnitude of the losses varies among products and places and over time. It is estimated that the average losses in cereals and legumes are above 10% while in starchy staples, vegetables, and other perishables they exceed 20%. Losses are particularly high in fish and may be of the order of 25% on average. The losses are caused by biological, microbiological, chemical, biochemical, mechanical, physical, and physiological factors (6). Improvements in food processing, storage, transport, and other marketing activities provide the most promising opportunities for reducing these losses. Altering the characteristics of the products, including their resistance to pests, through the application of biotechnology offers considerable promise for reducing post-harvest as well as pre-harvest losses.

The rapid increase in the world's urban population has consequences for patterns of food consumption. Urban consumers generally purchase rather than produce food and eat less root crops, maize, millet, and sorghum and more wheat, rice, and animal products. These changes often mean replacement of locally grown crops with imported crops. Such developments lead to rising import bills and sometimes to surpluses of traditional foodstuffs. One example is the surpluses of maize in Kenya, Malawi, and Zimbabwe, which are sold below world market prices to pay for imported wheat and rice. The conflict between food production and urbanization is much less where a proportion of the low-income urban population still grow substantial amounts of food through intensive cultivation of small plots and achieve much higher yields per hectare than on high-quality farmland (7, 8).

In summary, the central issue is not the world's capacity to produce food but rather its ability to ensure a more equitable distribution of it so that everyone can obtain the food needed for a healthy life without detriment to the integrity of the ecosystems. This is something that the food and agriculture sector must achieve and sustain in the face of the competition of economic activities for finite land and water resources and against the trend towards increased consumption of animal products by wealthier groups.

Food, diet, and health

The existence of hunger and malnutrition and the persistence of diseases for which medical science has found the cure reveal the inequalities in the modern world. While food supplies are sufficient to meet the world's aggregate minimum requirements, they are so inequitably distributed among the different countries and among the people of each country because of income disparities that the lives of hundreds of millions are affected. Although agricultural supplies in most parts of the world appear to have kept up with the demand for food and, on the whole, per caput food supplies have shown some improvement over the last two decades except in some parts of Africa, FAO has estimated that by the end of the century the number of seriously malnourished people will reach 590 million. Underdevelopment and malnutrition will remain the greatest problems posed by the relationship of population, food, and health. For a large part of the world's population, malnutrition remains the major cause of mortality and morbidity. In addition to hunger and malnourishment, more specific forms of nutritional deficiency affect millions of people, in particular children and pregnant women (Box 19).

There is no single formula for dealing with malnutrition. In terms of numbers it affects mainly the rural poor but is also an increasingly serious problem among low-income urban groups, especially among infants, preschool children, and women. In some areas malnutrition reaches a seasonal peak during the period before harvest. The major dietary deficiency is that of protein, but often more specific forms of nutritional deficiency such as of iodine, iron, and vitamin A remain widespread. Many dietary deficiencies are related to environmental factors, in the sense either of limited access to foods that enable the deficiency to be remedied or of pollutants or pathogens in the environment exacerbating their effects. Communicable diseases remain principal causes of sickness and death, but it is not sufficiently recognized that the resistance of children and adults to infectious diseases often depends on their nutritional state since this may have a profound effect on the development of immunity. The prevalence of acute childhood malnutrition is generally falling in Asia and Latin America, although the absolute number of cases is still rising in Asia, reflecting population growth. In Africa south of the Sahara, both the prevalence and the numbers are still on the rise. Throughout the world, large populations of children and adults remain chronically undernourished, and particularly vulnerable to any further deterioration in their access to food.

Interactions between nutrition and infection to produce the "malnutrition/infection complex" create the greatest public health problem in the world. Infection influences nutritional status through its effects on the intake, absorption, and utilization of nutrients and in some cases on the body's

Box 19. Nutrient deficiency diseases

Iodine

Goitre and cretinism are clinically obvious and easily recognizable forms of this deficiency. But the more pervasive effects of milder deficiency on the survival and physical and mental development of children and the intellectual ability and work capacity of adults are now being recognized. About 1000 million people are affected in more than 80 countries; the Andes, Alps, Great Lakes basin of North America, and Himalayas are particularly iodine-deficient areas, but coastal areas and plains may also be deficient. Excessive intake of goitrogens (for example through eating cassava) interferes with the normal intake and metabolism of iodine and may amplify the effects of iodine deficiency.

Vitamin A

Vitamin A deficiency, leading to xerophthalmia and sometimes blindness, continues to be a widespread problem among children. This deficiency also decreases resistance to infections and thus increases mortality. Analyses of food supplies from different regions show that the availability of vitamin A is limited and the problem exacerbated by any tendency to withhold vegetables from children for cultural or other reasons. The problem is most pronounced in Asia because the overall availability of vitamin A is less than that required and any maldistribution of foods high in vitamin A within a population worsens the problem. Xerophthalmia continues to be a major problem in about 40 countries.

Iron

Anaemia, whose dominant cause is iron deficiency, remains a major problem. Estimates made in 1980 suggest that it affects close to 200 million children between 0 and 4 years of age, 217 million between 5 and 12 years, 174 million men, and 288 million women (including 54 million pregnant women). Most are in Southern Asia, although the proportion of those affected is high in Africa; in both these regions half or more of all children in both age groups and close to half of all women are affected. More than three-fifths of all pregnant women are affected in these two regions. Anaemia also affects significant proportions in each of the above groups in other developing countries. In many areas of the tropics or subtropics, dietary iron deficiency due to low intake and/or poor absorption may be complicated by hookworm infection, which causes intestinal blood loss and may lead to profound iron deficiency anaemia.

Others

Fluoride deficiency increases the incidence of dental caries. (On the other hand, excess of fluoride leads to mottling of teeth and in severe cases to bone damage.) Rickets, which is still widespread in parts of Northern Africa and the Eastern Mediterranean and is reported to be increasing in Mexico, is attributable to insufficient exposure to sunlight and lack of vitamin D in the diet. Ascorbic acid deficiency is a problem in some drought-affected populations, especially in Africa. Vitamin B_{12} deficiency, which causes anaemia and, if severe, neurological disorders, may occur in those consuming exclusively vegetarian diets.

requirement for them. A child's rate of growth may be retarded by too little food and/or too many infections or parasites. Malnutrition may result in lowered immunity. Infection can lead to loss of appetite, decreased efficiency of food and nutrient utilization, increased energy requirements, and decreased growth. The relationship between diarrhoeal diseases and physical growth has been clearly shown. These interrelationships produce the malnutrition and infection cycle so prevalent in many developing countries. The vulnerability of malnourished people to environmental health risks has been widely documented. Hence the importance of improved water supplies, sanitation, and safe food to reduce water-related and foodborne diseases and of programmes to control disease vectors supported by education and health care.

It is now widely accepted that chronic hunger is due more to lack of purchasing power or of land on which to produce food than to the non-availability of food. Alleviation of poverty is at the forefront of the development agenda, but waiting for its decline to alleviate malnutrition may take decades. The results of poverty—hunger, sickness, debility, early death—are centred on nutrition. Malnutrition results, and preventing malnutrition is an aim that can be monitored.

The best approach to malnutrition varies according to local and national circumstances. Special food and nutrition programmes—such as school feeding, nutrition education, food fortification, improved food handling at community and household levels, and the development and promotion of safe weaning foods at village level—have an important role to play but are not the answer to all the problems. The pivotal role of women in the successful implementation of many policies of nutrition improvement is increasingly recognized. In a given situation, for instance seasonal malnutrition, the problem may be tackled more effectively through improved home storage of the previous year's crop than through specific nutritional measures. Elsewhere, improvements may depend in the first instance on health programmes to deal with infectious diseases. A number of policies, including price policies, that stimulate the production and consumption of cereals, pulses, or other nutritionally valuable crops may have a significant effect in some circumstances. The development of policies for food and nutrition is thus in large part a question of orienting sectoral activities to achieve an effect on nutrition and thereby on health. The food industry could also play a useful role in the planning of food and nutrition policies and in the provision of foods that contribute to an adequate, safe, nutritionally balanced diet.

Box 20. Unlinking drought and malnutrition: the example of Botswana

Botswana suffered from six consecutive years of severe drought between 1982 and 1988 and yet managed to contain hunger and malnutrition in many of the rural areas.

The figures below show the food production index, the kilocalories available per day, and the prevalence of underweight children aged under five years for the period 1980–87. (The discontinuity in the third graph from 1984 to 1985 is the result of a redefinition of cut-off values for underweight.)

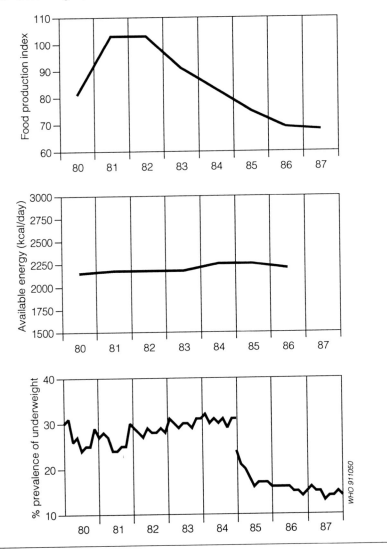

WHO 911050

Box 20 (continued)

The drought began in 1982. Cereal production declined from nearly 50 000 tonnes in 1982 to only 6000 tonnes in 1984. The number of head of cattle was reported to have fallen by about a quarter between 1982 and 1987. Cereal imports and food aid increased in the early years of the drought so that, by 1984, total cereal availability and calorie availability were higher than before the drought. The relative cost of food increased from 1980 but was largely stabilized by 1984.

Restoring the overall availability of food was only part of the strategy; access to food in rural areas was also tackled through compensating for income loss by labour-based relief programmes and food distribution. An estimate in 1985–86 suggested that nearly 700 000 people out of a national population of 1.2 million benefited from the drought food programme and some 74 000 workers participated in labour-based relief. The cost of the 1985–86 drought relief programmes was the equivalent of around US$ 40 per beneficiary—the amount split between governments and donors. Botswana is unusual in that, with normal rainfall, only about a quarter of the staple food needs can be met by domestic production. In addition, economic growth was particularly rapid until the 1980s and foreign exchange from diamond production and, to a lesser extent, beef exports made substantial cereal imports possible. However, the experience does demonstrate that well organized rural programmes to provide income and food linked to a widespread system of nutritional surveillance can minimize the hunger and malnutrition that usually accompany drought.

Sources: United Nations. *Update on the nutrition situation: recent trends in nutrition in 33 countries*; a report compiled from information available to the Administrative Committee on Coordination, Subcommittee on Nutrition, Jan/Feb 1989; and Quinn, V. et al. Crisis proofing the economy: the response of Botswana to economic recession and drought. In: Cornia, G.A. et al., eds. *Adjustment with a human face. Volume 2: Ten country case studies,* Oxford, Oxford University Press, 1988.

Food contamination

Despite substantial progress in knowledge and application in regard to food safety, contaminated food and water remain a major public health problem. They provide the medium through which a high proportion of disease is transmitted. Most of the disease agents that contaminate food and water are biological and come from human or animal faeces. This section concentrates on biological and chemical agents as they relate to food.

Foodborne diseases are caused by a wide range of agents; and can result in mild indispositions or life-threatening illnesses. The true scale of their impact on health remains unknown since only a small proportion of cases come to the notice of health services and even fewer are investigated. It is believed that in developed countries only about 5–10% of cases are reported. In many developing countries reliable quantitative data are by and large lacking.

A range of biological contaminants (bacteria, viruses, moulds, parasites) and chemical contaminants (including chemicals used in food processing and packaging and in pest control) have a significant impact on health.

Biological agents

Biological contaminants are the main causes of foodborne diseases and are responsible for a wide range of such diseases (e.g., salmonellosis, shigellosis, brucellosis, amoebiasis, campylobacteriosis, poisoning by toxin-producing microorganisms such as staphylococci and *Clostridium botulinum*). Parasitic diseases such as toxoplasmosis and trichinosis are a problem throughout the world, while in developing countries taeniasis and cysticercosis are also of importance. Box 21 lists a number of agents of important foodborne diseases and some of their epidemiological features.

Most foodborne or waterborne diseases can cause diarrhoea, and food as a vehicle may contribute to the transmission of up to 70% of all episodes of diarrhoea (*9*). In addition, "within the home there are likely to be numerous interconnections and interactions among water, sanitation, flies, animals, personal hygiene and food that are responsible for diarrhoea transmission" (*9*). To these must be added the temperature and time of cooking and the storage of food.

Some biological contaminants of food can be eliminated or considerably reduced by improvement in personal hygiene, safe piped water, good-quality sanitation, effective animal health programmes, the application of technologies such as pasteurization and irradiation, and effective control of the health and safety aspects of food production. These have helped in the elimination or reduction of several foodborne diseases such as typhoid fever, cholera, and shigellosis in the developed and in many developing countries.

Foodborne diseases nevertheless remain a serious problem in all countries. Box 22 illustrates the rise in reported cases in the Federal Republic of Germany in recent decades—with a rapid growth in infectious enteritis and a rapid fall in typhoid and paratyphoid fevers. In the United States one estimate is of 6.5 million cases of foodborne diseases a year, with 9000 fatalities (*10*); another is of up to 80 million cases (*11*). The growing demand for processed foods and the increasing scale and concentration of plants to achieve economies of scale can make a breakdown in the system more serious. For instance, in the United States a breakdown in the controls of a modern milk-processing plant that had replaced smaller older plants resulted in widespread salmonella infection, ultimately involving more than 200 000 people and a substantial number of deaths.

One reason why many bacterial foodborne diseases have become an increasing public health and clinical problem in recent years is linked to

Box 21. Some agents of foodborne diseases and salient epidemiological features

Agent	Important reservoir/carrier	Transmission[a] by			Multiplication in food	Examples of some incriminated foods
		water	food	person to person		
BACTERIA						
Bacillus cereus	Soil	−	+	−	+	Cooked rice, cooked meats, vegetables, starchy puddings
Brucella spp	Cattle, goats, sheep	−	+	−	+	Raw milk, dairy products
Campylobacter jejuni	Chickens, dogs, cats, cattle, pigs, wild birds	+	+	+	−[b]	Raw milk, poultry
Clostridium botulinum	Soil, mammals, birds, fish	−	+	−	+	Fish, meat, vegetables (home-preserved), honey
Clostridium perfringens	Soil, animals, man	−	+	−	+	Cooked meat and poultry, gravy, beans
Escherichia coli						
Enterotoxigenic	Man	+	+	+	+	Salad, raw vegetables
Enteropathogenic	Man	+	+	+	+	Milk
Enteroinvasive	Man	+	+	0	+	Cheese
Enterohaemorrhagic	Cattle, poultry, sheep	+	+	+	+	Undercooked meat, raw milk, cheese
Listeria monocytogenes	Environment	+	+	−[c]	+	Cheese, raw milk, coleslaw
Mycobacterium bovis	Cattle	−	+	−	−	Raw milk
Salmonella typhi and *paratyphi*	Man	+	+	±	+	Dairy products, meat products, shellfish, vegetable salads

Box 21 (continued)

Agent	Important reservoir/carrier	Transmission[a] by			Multiplication in food	Examples of some incriminated foods
		water	food	person to person		
Salmonella (non-typhi)	Man and animals	±	+	±	+	Meat, poultry, eggs, dairy products, chocolate
Shigella spp	Man	+	+	+	+	Potato/egg salads
Staphylococcus aureus (enterotoxins)	Man	–	+	–	+	Ham, poultry and egg salads, cream-filled bakery produce, ice-cream, cheese
Vibrio cholerae 01	Man, marine life	+	+	±	+	Salad, shellfish
Vibrio cholerae non-01	Man, marine life	+	+	±	+	Shellfish
Vibrio parahaemolyticus	Seawater, marine life	–	+	–	+	Raw fish, crabs, and other shellfish
Vibrio vulnificus	Seawater, marine life	+	+	–	+	Shellfish
Yersinia enterocolitica	Water, wild animals, pigs, dogs, poultry	+	+	–	+	Milk, pork, and poultry
VIRUSES						
Hepatitis A virus	Man	+	+	+	–	Shellfish, raw fruit and vegetables
Norwalk agents	Man	++	++	++	–	Shellfish, salad
Rotavirus	Man	++	++	++	–	0

Box 21 (continued)

Agent	Important reservoir/ carrier	Transmission[a] by			Multiplication in food	Examples of some incriminated foods
		water	food	person to person		
PROTOZOA						
Cryptosporidium parvum	Man, animals	+	+	+	–	Raw milk, raw (non-fermented) sausage
Entamoeba histolytica	Man	+	+	+	–	Vegetables and fruits
Giardia lamblia	Man, animals	+	±	+	–	Vegetables and fruits
Toxoplasma gondii	Cats, pigs	0	+	–	–	Undercooked meat, raw vegetables
HELMINTHS						
Ascaris lumbricoides	Man	+	+	–	–	Soil-contaminated food
Taenia saginata and *T. solium*	Cattle, swine	–	+	–	–	Undercooked meat
Trichinella spiralis	Swine, carnivora	–	+	–	–	Undercooked meat
Trichuris trichiura	Man	0	+	–	–	Soil-contaminated food

+ = Yes; ± = Rare; – = No; 0 = No information

[a] Almost all acute enteric infections show increased transmission during the summer and/or wet months, except infections due to rotavirus and *Yersinia enterocolitica* which show increased transmission in cooler months.
[b] Under certain circumstances some multiplication has been observed. The epidemiological significance of this observation is not clear.
[c] Transmission from pregnant woman to fetus occurs frequently.

Source: Adapted from WHO Technical Report Series, No. 705, 1984 (*The role of food safety in health and development*: report of a Joint FAO/WHO Expert Committee on Food Safety).

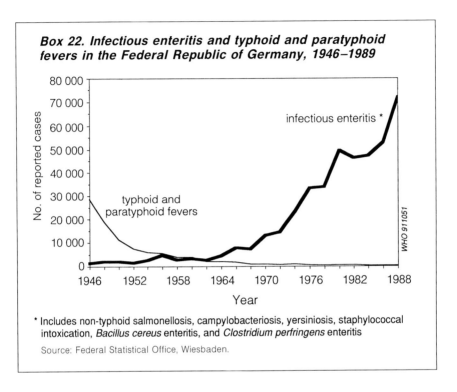

Box 22. Infectious enteritis and typhoid and paratyphoid fevers in the Federal Republic of Germany, 1946–1989

* Includes non-typhoid salmonellosis, campylobacteriosis, yersiniosis, staphylococcal intoxication, *Bacillus cereus* enteritis, and *Clostridium perfringens* enteritis

Source: Federal Statistical Office, Wiesbaden.

agricultural practice. Intensive methods of livestock production have enabled salmonella organisms to spread and become ubiquitous in poultry-raising and pig-raising. This has led to a large number of animals becoming subclinically infected carriers, either from feed contaminated with pathogens (especially salmonella) or from intensive breeding and fattening procedures. Millions of carrier animals all over the world have contributed to the contamination of surface water and soil and of wet surfaces during slaughtering, meat processing, and distribution, thus giving rise to infection cycles that at present play an important role in the epidemiology of the salmonelloses. Animal feed, the original cause, may no longer be the main source of infection; the contaminated environment—surface water, the soil, birds, rodents, and insects—now seem to be the main source of infection of clinically healthy animals.

In various countries hens' eggs have been identified as the main source of *S. enteritidis*, often causing severe gastrointestinal disorders. Outbreaks due to food containing raw or insufficiently cooked eggs have been described in the literature. In certain countries, 60–100% of poultry are contaminated with various salmonella strains; many other foods are also known to be contaminated. In addition, many countries are experiencing outbreaks of diseases due to relatively new types of foodborne pathogens. One is *Campy-*

lobacter jejuni, for which poultry meat and unpasteurized milk are the main vehicles of transmission. Another is *Listeria monocytogenes*, which has been implicated in several important outbreaks involving different types of food such as milk, cheese, and vegetables. It can cause severe foodborne infections with a high mortality rate in susceptible individuals (especially fetuses and immunocompromised adults) (*12, 13*). At present there is no clear understanding of its biology, but it is able to grow at refrigeration temperatures and within a wide range of pH.

A second reason for the increase in certain foodborne diseases is the rapid growth in consumption of ready-to-eat food products; in the absence of intrinsic safety factors (such as a low pH or low moisture content), any bacterial spores present can germinate and growth may occur. Both *C. botulinum* type E and certain *Bacillus* species are able to develop and produce toxin at temperatures below 5 °C. These products have therefore to be stored at low temperatures and only for a limited period. There is a trend towards food produced without intrinsic safety factors, much of it linked to a changing consumer taste for food that is not acidified and does not contain salt; in that case one of the main safety factors is storage at low temperature ($< 7\,°C$). However, there are a number of pathogenic psychrophilic organisms, such as *Listeria* and *Yersinia*, that are able to multiply at low temperatures. Although at present diseases induced by these microorganisms are infrequent, they pose a potential health danger and call for careful attention by food producers and food handlers.

Hepatitis A is common throughout the world. Some 6000 cases are reported annually in the western provinces of Germany, and the number of cases in the United States increased from 9.2 to 14.5 per 100 000 population between 1983 and 1989. Shellfish grown in contaminated water have often been recognized as a source of this disease; an epidemic of shellfish-borne hepatitis A in China in 1988 affected some 292 000 persons (with at least 32 fatalities) and was linked to the consumption of contaminated clams (*14*). Food contaminated by foodhandlers may also transmit the disease; many cases of hepatitis A are known to be so associated (*15*).

Other toxic agents in food

In the developed world an extensive food safety infrastructure (legislation, enforcement mechanisms, surveillance and monitoring systems, and responsible industries) ensures that the food supply is largely safe from the health viewpoint. Food processing becomes of increasing importance as the distance between producer and consumer increases and renders the consumer more dependent on the food-processing industry. There is increasing public concern about the safety of chemical additives in food, but little evidence that in general they represent a significant risk to human health. The public often forgets that traditional food preservation usually involves the use of chemicals. Many colours and flavours as well as antioxidants and antimicrobials are synthetic duplicates of natural substances. Accidental contamination or adulteration does occur and occasionally the health consequences are grave.

A number of chemical substances may occur in the food supply owing to contamination, environmental or otherwise, and their effects on health may be serious. For instance, lead-soldered food cans may contain food with higher amounts of lead than in raw commodities and unsoldered cans; in recent years, many countries have changed to unsoldered cans with as a result a significant decrease in the lead content of canned foods (*16*). There is also concern about the health effects of polychlorinated biphenyls (PCBs), which are used in various industrial applications. Major restrictions on the production and use of PCBs have been introduced in many countries since the 1970s (*16*).

The continued release of persistent toxic elements such as cadmium and mercury into the environment will inevitably lead to rising levels of these substances in various foodstuffs and eventually to levels that may be harmful to human health. Methylmercury is a major environmental contaminant in many areas of the world; it is neurotoxic and the fetal brain is specially sensitive to it. High concentrations of methylmercury are found in long-lived predatory fish in areas with natural or anthropogenic sources of mercury. Workers in the fishing industry, ethnic groups fishing for subsistence, and people on special diets have been shown to have methylmercury intakes exceeding the FAO/WHO Provisional Tolerable Weekly Intake (PTWI). Since impairment of fetal development may occur at intakes lower than the PTWI, very large groups of people may be at risk. Recent studies indicate that cadmium may induce functional impairment of the kidney at levels to which certain segments of the urban population in some industrialized countries are currently exposed. Food is a major source of cadmium for the general population.

Mycotoxins, the toxic products of microscopic fungi (moulds), may also cause serious adverse health effects in humans and animals. Animal studies show that, besides acute intoxication, mycotoxins may have carcinogenic, mutagenic, and teratogenic effects. Among the several hundred mycotoxins that have been identified aflatoxin is the most important from the point of view of public health. Aflatoxins are found mostly in groundnuts, oilseeds, cereals, treenuts, and some fruits. As fungi producing aflatoxin are prevalent in areas with a high humidity and temperature, crops in tropical and subtropical regions are especially subject to contamination. Epidemiological studies show a strong correlation between the high incidence of liver cancer in some African and south-east Asian countries (12–13 per 100 000 annually) and the exposure of the population to aflatoxin. Certain studies suggest that aflatoxins and hepatitis B virus are co-carcinogens and that the probability of liver cancer is higher in areas where both are prevalent (*17*). Besides environmental conditions and type of food, post-harvest handling of food is an important influence on the growth of moulds.

Intoxication from marine biotoxins is another concern. Ciguatera poisoning due to the ingestion of fish feeding on toxic dinoflagellates in the tropics is increasingly common and widespread. The occurrence of this poisoning in temperate areas is due to seafood imported from the tropics. More directly tied to environmental problems is poisoning (e.g., paralytic shellfish poisoning) caused by seafood harvested during certain algal blooms, usually resulting from a combination of enhanced nutrient levels from land-based sources and transient anomalies of climate and ocean circulation. In many parts of the world, plant toxicants also present a troublesome problem for food safety; poorer groups in some places eat pulses known to be toxic (producing lathyrism) to still their hunger (*18*).

Occupational hazards and accidents

People working in the agricultural sector represent the world's largest single occupational group. In most developing countries more than half the economically active population works in this sector; in eleven countries (ten of which are in Africa) the proportion exceeds 80%. The proportions are much lower in developed countries; in the United Kingdom and United States less than 3% of the labour-force work in agriculture. However, this understates the proportion working in the food sector, since most of those involved in food preparation, packaging, processing, storing, transport, and sale do not work on the farm and are thus classified within industrial or service employment (*19*).

Those at risk from occupational hazards can be divided into three groups: farmers, pastoralists and foresters; those making a living from hunting or fishing; and those working in related industries such as abattoir workers, butchers, tanners, and furriers. Each group has its own particular occupational hazards, but the first and second groups have most of the hazards specifically determined by environmental factors such as climate, close contact with animals, and disease vectors, and work with a variety of agrochemicals.

The boundaries are often unclear between occupational diseases and diseases endemic in rural communities that are aggravated by occupational factors. The distinction between workers and dependants is also often unclear, since most adults and many children within rural households contribute to some extent to agricultural activities. Conditions such as chemical exposure may be considered occupational, but uncertainties arise in classifying them because of the variety of different natural and synthetic chemicals to which a worker can be exposed and the simultaneous use or misuse of the same chemicals in households.

Those working in close association with animals generally face an increased risk of infection by zoonoses, infectious diseases transmissible between animals and humans. Over 120 pathogens/diseases have been identified and their incidence in humans is much influenced by the prevalence of the disease in animals in a particular area and the mode of contact. Certain vector-borne diseases are also associated with agriculture, for instance filariasis, malaria, schistosomiasis, and onchocerciasis, which figure prominently in the morbidity pattern of most rural areas in the tropics. Farmers and other workers in irrigated or naturally wet areas are at high risk of infection.

Accidents include physical accidents and poisoning from chemical exposure. While farmers have a higher accident rate than the general population, those working in fishing, forestry, and hunting have higher rates still, the differences clearly being environmentally determined. Most major accidents among farmers are caused by farm vehicles or unguarded machinery. Injury may also occur both in the handling of domesticated animals and from snake and poisonous spider bites. Data from developed countries suggest that accidents due to machinery or falls in slurry pits are much more common than accidental deaths from pesticide poisoning (20). Non-fatal poisoning occurring on or close to the farm also seems relatively rare, especially when compared with the much higher incidence of poisoning from pesticides in the general public; for instance, in California most pesticide poisoning incidents are non-occupational and occur in the home and garden, and at least half of those poisoned are children under six years of age (20). Hunters are at risk from wild animals and from their own firearms and knives. Forestry workers are liable to injury from saws, ropes, cables, and falling objects. At sea, falls and machinery are the most common causes of injury. In most developing countries, little is known about the number and nature of accidents in these sectors.

Exposure to chemicals is most common among those working in farming and there are a large number of potential exposures arising from fertilizers, pesticides (insecticides, herbicides, rodenticides, fumigants, soil and seed treatment agents), dipping and drenching of animals in disinfectants, plant growth regulators, and administration of antibiotics to animals. The level of risk is usually higher in intensive farming or horticulture. The factors that have increased output per unit of land (increased use of fertilizers, high plant population, increased intensity of cultivation, new varieties of crops) have also increased disease and pest problems.

Agricultural chemicals

The most common response to the growing problem of pests is the use of pesticides. The result has been disruption of ecosystems because of the death of non-target species, accumulation of pesticide residues in the environment and in food, and the build-up of pesticide resistance in the target species (21). Since the 1940s over 1600 insect species have developed significant resistance to major pesticides because of long-term and non-selective use. As another major consequence of widespread contamination of aquatic resources, several pesticides—particularly herbicides—have been detected in drinking-water. Most of the problems of pesticides in drinking-water have been found in developed countries, although high levels of chlorinated hydrocarbon pesticides have been reported in water in Colombia, Malaysia, Thailand and the United Republic of Tanzania (22). Besides having the potential to cause chronic adverse effects on human health, the presence of pesticides in water resources may lead to the emergence of resistance in vectors of water-related diseases, making the application of routine vector control techniques ineffective.

The largest users of pesticides are the United States and, formerly, the USSR, although on a per hectare basis European countries use higher levels (Box 23).

Insecticides are the agricultural chemicals that cause most health concern; Box 24 illustrates the population groups at risk and the estimated overall annual public health effect of pesticide use. Estimates suggest that, in developing countries, some 3 million people suffer from single short-term exposure (including that resulting from suicide or attempted suicide), with 220 000 deaths (23). Fatality rates vary from 1% to 9% in cases presenting for treatment (24, 25), depending on the availability of antidotes and the quality of the medical services. Over 700 000 people a year are thought to suffer from the chronic effects of long-term exposure (23), the scale and nature of such effects being likely to be underestimated because the symptoms of pesticide poisoning may be incorrectly ascribed to other causes. It is also difficult to assess the main factors contributing to mortality from pesticide poisoning—environmental contamination, accidental exposure during work, errors in preparation (for instance in mixing), failure to use protective clothing, and suicide are all concerned (26).

There is a growing feeling, however, that the health impact of agricultural chemicals in developing countries may have been underestimated. Lack of legislation, non-enforcement, widespread ignorance of the hazards involved, poor labelling, inadequate supervision, and not wearing full protective clothing in hot climates greatly increase the hazard both to agricultural workers and the general public (20). In many countries severe poisoning

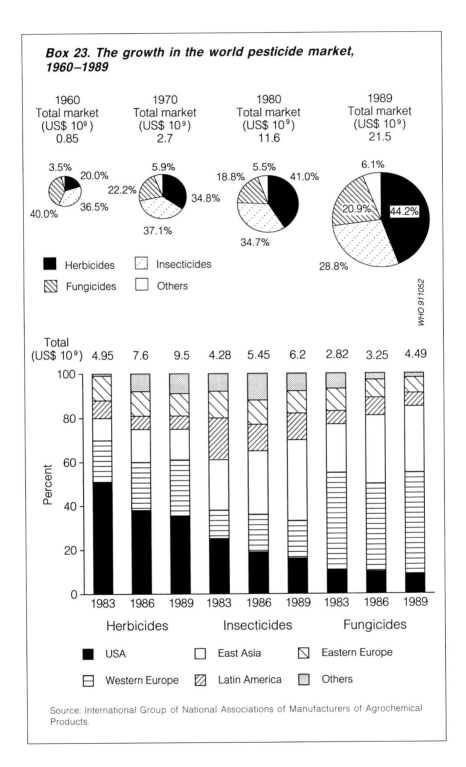

Box 23. The growth in the world pesticide market, 1960–1989

| 1960 Total market (US$ 10^9) 0.85 | 1970 Total market (US$ 10^9) 2.7 | 1980 Total market (US$ 10^9) 11.6 | 1989 Total market (US$ 10^9) 21.5 |

Source: International Group of National Associations of Manufacturers of Agrochemical Products.

WHO 911052

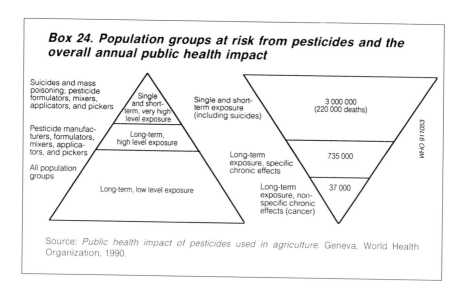

Box 24. Population groups at risk from pesticides and the overall annual public health impact

Suicides and mass poisoning; pesticide formulators, mixers, applicators, and pickers — Single and short-term, very high level exposure

Single and short-term exposure (including suicides) — 3 000 000 (220 000 deaths)

Pesticide manufacturers, formulators, mixers, applicators, and pickers — Long-term, high level exposure

Long-term exposure, specific chronic effects — 735 000

All population groups — Long-term, low level exposure

Long-term exposure, non-specific chronic effects (cancer) — 37 000

WHO 911053

Source: *Public health impact of pesticides used in agriculture.* Geneva, World Health Organization, 1990.

arises from misuse. In some, highly toxic pesticides are commonly used for treating certain health problems. For instance, in rural Guatemala, populations seek to treat botfly maggot infestation by applying a pesticide containing the organophosphorus compound, dichlorvos, to the infected area (27). In many countries it has become common to control lice by applying the herbicide paraquat to the skin or hair; paraquat is extremely toxic to humans and one mouthful may be fatal. Fatal paraquat poisoning has become a significant problem in many countries, associated with attempted suicide or accidental ingestion. Many low-income households do not have lockable cupboards or other devices to keep highly toxic chemicals out of the reach of children (20). Moreover, many pesticides known to be highly hazardous and either banned or severely restricted in industrialized countries, such as parathion, mevinphos, and endrin, are widely available in developing countries and often used without precautions.

In developed countries, while accidental poisoning still occurs, especially among children, there is little evidence of any long-term effects of occupational exposure. Health risks are likely to be low when pesticides are used according to good agricultural practice and when food safety systems ensure that residue limits meet current standards such as these adopted by the Codex Alimentarius Commission. A major contribution to good practices in the use and distribution of pesticides is the International Code of Conduct on the Distribution and Use of Pesticides.

There is no indication to date of any harm to human health arising from the residues of agricultural chemicals in food, when the limits established by the Codex Alimentarius Commission have been complied with. In most recorded cases where food has been implicated in pesticide poisoning, the chemical was found in the food following accidental contamination, through either negligence or ignorance. For example, in a number of cases food has been contaminated because of unsafe packing and leakage of pesticides during storage and transport. In other cases, chemically treated seeds intended for planting were eaten.

Box 25 outlines some of the worst cases of consumption of contaminated foodstuffs. In Iraq imported wheat and barley seed intended for sowing had been treated with methylmercury fungicide but much of the seed arrived too late for sowing; the warning labels on some sacks were in English or Spanish and rural families ate the seed and fed it to their livestock. Officially over 6000 people were poisoned and nearly 500 killed, but an unofficial estimate put the

---

Box 25. Pesticide poisoning episodes in developing countries

Country	Year	Cases	Deaths	Comments
Guyana	1966	88	10	Flour contaminated with parathion during international transport
Qatar and Saudi Arabia	1967	874	26	Flour contaminated with endrin during international transport
Jamaica	1968	NR	18	Flour contaminated with parathion during international transport
Iraq	1971–2	6000	500	Treated seed corn consumed as food
Jamaica	1976	79	17	Flour contaminated with parathion during international transport
Pakistan	1976	2810	5	Poor safety practice for new pesticide (malathion) in malaria control programme
Indonesia	1983	168	96	Eight episodes of poisonings from consumption of food (various pesticides)
Pakistan	1984	194	19	Sugar contaminated with endrin during in-country transport
Sierra Leone	1986	49	14	Flour contaminated with parathion during in-country transport

Sources: Conway, G.R. & Pretty, J.N. *Unwelcome harvest: agriculture and pollution*, London, Earthscan Publications, 1991. Data for Qatar and Saudi Arabia from: Weeks, D.E. Endrin food-poisoning, *Bulletin of the World Health Organization*, **37**: 499–512 (1967).

figures at over ten times these levels (*28, 29*). There have also been several cases of poisoning from eating pesticide-contaminated wheat in India, most recently at a wedding party where about 150 people died (*30, 31*).

Agricultural development

Many agricultural developments have a major health impact. Box 26 describes the exacerbation of schistosomiasis in the Upper Region of Ghana, linked to the construction of a large number of agricultural dams. No preventive measures were taken when the dams were built and the prevalence of schistosomiasis tripled as a consequence (*32*).

Box 26. Agricultural development projects and the exacerbation of schistosomiasis and other water-related diseases in Ghana

The construction of water impoundments for agriculture has long been known to accelerate the transmission of schistosomiasis in endemic areas. But the impact of the impoundments has been difficult to gauge, since rarely are there details of the prevalence of the disease prior to their construction. A historical reconstruction for the Upper Region in Ghana suggests that the hyperendemicity of disease caused by *Schistosoma haematobium* is related to the construction of a large number of agricultural dams in an endemic area. Onchocerciasis and probably other water-related diseases were also involved.

The figure on p. 84 shows the prevalence of *S. haematobium* infection in the Upper Region of Ghana, based on data from 38 survey districts in 1960–61. In the worst-affected areas more than 50% of the population were infected, while in certain hot spots the prevalence was over 70%. In many districts the levels were below 30% and for some even below 10%.

The figure also shows the distribution of small agricultural dams in the area, corresponding to the very high prevalence of schistosomiasis. In the late 1950s the United States Agency for International Development supported the construction of a large number of small clay-core dams to provide a community water supply, especially in the dry season, to water livestock, to encourage soil conservation, and to irrigate dry-season vegetable gardens both for cash crops and to help overcome seasonal hunger and dietary deficiencies. A total of 185 dams were constructed between 1951 and 1965, most between 1958 and 1960. From the hydrological and agronomic points of view the dams were found to be successful—holding water late in the dry season and being utilized for dry season vegetable gardening, domestic consumption, and commercial production. Fish harvesting came to be practised at a minor level.

Box 26 (continued)

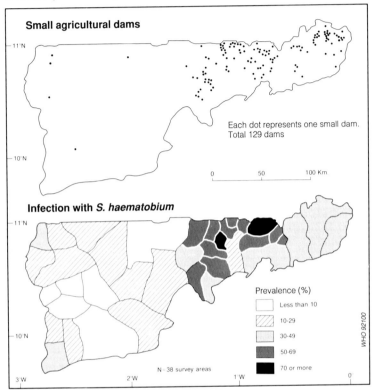

Small agricultural dams

Each dot represents one small dam.
Total 129 dams

0   50   100 Km

Infection with *S. haematobium*

Prevalence (%)

	Less than 10
	10-29
	30-49
	50-69
	70 or more

N = 38 survey areas

WHO 92100

   The strong spatial association between dams and disease is easily seen. In the western areas, which are without dams, the levels of schistosomiasis are below 30% and in some places below 10%. These perhaps would be the traditional, pre-intervention levels. In contrast, the areas that received the new dams show a greatly elevated prevalence. When the survey districts are ranked by prevalence and by inclusion of a dam (or not), for the 15 districts without dams the median prevalence of schistosomiasis is 17% compared with 50% in the districts where the new dams were built. It is also known that a minimal time-lag between dam construction and the appearance of disease effects would be expected where there is (a) substantial and widespread endemicity in the construction zone, (b) a heavy introduction of infected snails or (c) a heavy influx of human carriers.
   From this and other evidence drawn from the region, it may be suggested that there was an explosive increase of *S. haematobium* infection, virtually tripling the prevalence rates, due to the construction of a large number of small agricultural dams. The levels of infection have probably dropped somewhat owing to community adjustment following the initial ecological disruptions but will remain permanently elevated during the lifetime of the dams if there is no disease control.

Box 26 (continued)

The incidence of other diseases including filarial diseases, malaria, and dracunculiasis may have been affected by the water impoundments. The dams are known to have created spillway breeding sites for *Simulium damnosum*, the blackfly vector of onchocerciasis (river blindness). A direct relationship was found between two irrigated rice projects and intense hyperendemic transmission of bancroftian filariasis. Each project is a focal point for disease transmission, and human pathology and disfigurement are widespread. No health protection measures were introduced with the initial economic investment or in subsequent operations.

Unless control measures are taken, the construction of surface water impoundments creating favourable habitats on a larger scale for intermediate snail and mosquito hosts as well as increased population–water contact in an endemic area will undoubtedly lead to increased transmission of parasitic and infectious diseases. During the late 1950s and early 1960s no disease control measures were undertaken in tandem with the construction of the dams. The fact that north-east Ghana is a major source of seasonal and longer-term migration is likely to mean that many migrants are disease carriers. Migrant labourers from the Upper Region, an area endemic for urinary schistosomiasis, contaminated streams, pools, and ponds at intermediate stopping-points on the southern migration route and in southern workplaces. Where appropriate snail hosts are found, transmission ensues. The flare-up of *S. haematobium* infection (and probably other diseases) in the Upper Region, coupled with seasonal labour migration, therefore inadvertently disseminates disease southwards in part at least as a result of agricultural development in the north.

Despite such experiences, both governments and development agencies still fail to undertake disease prevention measures as a central part of any project to construct or restore agricultural dams. Acute and chronic morbidity and death should not be accepted as an inevitable cost of agricultural investment. Much of the disease can be prevented or controlled through appropriate integrated planning. There is a need to include measures for disease control and the maintenance of good health within the primary agricultural installations and their daily management. This entails a policy ensuring that the costs of health care are identified and included in both the infrastructural investment costs and the long-term operational costs of the development project.

Source: Hunter, J.M. Past explosion and future threat—exacerbation of Red Water Disease (schistosomiasis haematobium) in the Upper Region of Ghana. *GeoJournal*, 5 (4): 305–313 (1981); and unpublished material from J.M. Hunter.

Other examples include the extension of land use into forested ecosystems, which has increased leishmaniasis in Brazil and the southern parts of the former USSR (*26*). The opening-up of the Amazon region in Brazil to farming and ranching has been accompanied by a resurgence in malaria, concentrated in settlements, mining areas, and periurban areas throughout the region (*33–35*). Health problems have also been linked with the transmigration scheme in Indonesia and the resettlement of rural populations as a result of agricultural development schemes. However, the most serious health effects linked to new agricultural developments are associated with irrigation schemes (Box 27).

Box 27. The impact of irrigation on health

Well designed and well implemented irrigation systems raise incomes and improve food security, increasing the potential for better nutrition and health. But irrigation development has often been associated with an increased incidence of disease. Irrigation schemes, especially in the tropics, carry a high risk of introducing or increasing the transmission of vector-borne and water-related diseases. More than 30 diseases have been linked to irrigation, the major vector-borne diseases being schistosomiasis, malaria, onchocerciasis, and Japanese encephalitis. Vector-borne disease transmission is aggravated by man-made environmental changes that favour the proliferation of the vector, by human behaviour that increases contact with the vector (for instance occupation, location of dwelling) and by economic expansion and migration. Surtees (*36*) suggested six general environmental changes brought about by irrigation practices that may have effects on health:
— simplification of the habitat
— increase in the area of surface water
— a rise in the water table
— changes in the rate of water flow
— a modification of the microclimate
— urban development.

The health problems associated with irrigation developments and the environmental changes they produce have been extensively studied over the past 15 years, although lack of baseline data prior to the construction of the irrigation system precludes better knowledge of the negative health and social aspects. Some examples follow.

- Hunter et al. reviewed the negative effects on health of water resource development in 13 countries (including some from Africa, Asia, and Latin America) and in all there were indications that projects to develop water resources had resulted in a higher incidence of vector-borne diseases (*32*).
- The implementation of a large irrigation scheme on the Cukurova plain of Turkey in the 1970s resulted in a resurgence of endemic malaria, due to increased breeding of the vector species in poorly drained ditches receiving the run-off of surplus irrigation water. The absence of proper drainage systems in irrigation schemes is one of the most important factors contributing to the spread of vector-borne disease in irrigation developments. Gratz attributed the rise in malaria to "the sequence of construction … with very inadequate or … no provision for drainage, the increased agricultural activities requiring more and more irrigation, and the vast increases in popu-

---

> ### Box 27 (continued)
>
> lation densities of the main vector in the area, *A. sacharovi*, combined with an influx of migrants, inadequate surveillance activities, and the failure to institute satisfactory control measures in good time" (*37*).
>
> Different types of irrigation systems (surface, subsurface, oversurface, continuous flow, demand flow, and intermittent flow) and different water distribution cycles have different effects on the transmission of vector-borne diseases (*38*). The irrigation schemes that appear to present the greatest risk of increased transmission of vector-borne diseases are those located where:
> — soils present drainage problems
> — rice is cultivated
> — reservoirs are constructed
> — canals are unlined
> — there is compacted settlement or resettlement.
>
> Source: Cooper Weil, D.E. et al. *The impact of development policies on health: a review of the literature.* Geneva, World Health Organization, 1990, Chapter 3.

Land ownership or tenure

The close association between poverty and lack of or insufficient land has been noted earlier. Lack of or insufficient land is also a major negative influence on health and on nutritional status. The nature of land tenure may also influence the level of production, income, and investment (*26*); a study of land rights in Thailand concluded that registered, more secure tenure of the land resulted in improved access to credit and working capital (*39*). Box 28 draws on a World Bank study of north-east Brazil, a region long associated with high levels of poverty and emigration. Immigration has been an important factor in the rapid growth of many Brazilian cities and also in the colonization and deforestation of the Amazon basin. A reallocation of land currently unused or underused by large landowners to small farms would mean a million additional households with adequate incomes and a large increase in food supplies.

An earlier section discussed the impact on health of the size of rural landholdings or the terms under which they are farmed. The question whether those with smallholdings can sustain production at a level that ensures sufficient income and food is also important for health. Studies in many parts of the world have demonstrated the ability of smallholders to obtain high yields; some have also demonstrated the strong commitment of small farmers to sustainability (*20*). But, as the recent FAO study on *The state of food and agriculture* states (*21*):

> Understanding what sustainability means to the rural poor in developing
> countries requires a close examination of the choices they face in their

---

Box 28. The links between poverty and land ownership

A World Bank study shows that the main cause of poverty and emigration from north-east Brazil is not lack of land but a land-owning structure that keeps large amounts of high-quality land unused or underused. The study states that nearly one million farms or share-cropped plots in the north-east provide an acceptable standard of living for farmers. There are also "nearly 30 million hectares of under-utilized land of similar if not superior quality on the estates" on which "nearly another million families could achieve comparable living standards". Most of this land is unused or underused and is the property of large landowners; just 4% of landowners own more than half the agricultural land and only one in four households dependent on agriculture owns the land it works.

Transfer of this land to those with no land or too little land could provide adequate incomes for perhaps another million families. The smallest farmers in the region "employ 25 times more labour per hectare on their land than do the largest farms and obtain vastly higher productivity levels. The smaller farms (less than 50 hectares) cover only 10% of the agricultural land, produce over 25% of the region's sugar, cotton, and rice and 40% of the beans, corn, and manioc. Yet two million agriculturally dependent families own no land at all, while an area of land the size of France is unutilized or underutilized."

Such a land transfer would bring a major stimulus to agricultural production (which would help feed city populations) and also to small urban centres.

Source: Kutcher G.P. & Scandizzo, P.L. *The agricultural economy of north-east Brazil.* Baltimore, MD, Johns Hopkins University Press, 1981.

---

daily struggle to survive. An understanding of household decision-making is an essential pre-condition for strategy and policy formulation because in many instances it is the rural poor who determine the outcome of government actions to promote sustainable development through their decisions on resource allocation, production practices and consumption. The survival strategies they adopt involve many decisions about environmental goods: soil, woody biomass, pastureland and water. Some choices result in sustainable actions; others do not.

Frequently, poor people have no option but to overexploit natural resources in order to survive. Everyday security takes precedence over concern to any great extent with the future. Even meeting immediate food security needs is beyond the reach of many rural poor. Consequently, much natural resource degradation arises because the rural poor are forced to employ cultivation and pastoral practices that degrade the environment . . . Sheer necessity forces them into mining soil nutrients, cultivating steep slopes or overgrazing rangeland in order to feed themselves.

Agrarian reforms carried out over the past few decades that increased the access of poorer groups to land or abolished or reduced the rents that farmers paid to landowners are likely to have had a positive effect on health. They would also have had a positive effect on the environment when they made it unnecessary for rural households to overexploit the soil to ensure immediate survival. It is notable that health indicators have improved substantially since the 1950s in countries where major agrarian reforms were implemented—for instance in China, Cuba, and the Republic of Korea—although separating the effects of agrarian reform from those of other factors is not possible. In a review of the literature on this subject, Cooper Weil et al. noted that other studies have found evidence that farmers are more likely to invest in land improvement when ownership is more secure. They noted the unsurprising connection between size of landholding, income, consumption, and therefore health and listed various confirmatory studies (26).

FAO expresses the view that, particularly in Latin America and to a lesser extent in other developing regions, large areas of high-potential land could be reallocated to the landless and near-landless through a reform of property rights (21). Experience in agrarian reform to date suggests that maximizing the environmental and health benefits would require careful planning to ensure that landholdings were of sufficient size to provide a sustainable livelihood for those farming them.

Impact of farming on water quality

One of the most direct effects of farming on health is contamination of groundwater, aquifers, and surface waters by fertilizers, biocides, and animal wastes. Drainage water with high salinity and excess of nutrients has contributed to increases in the concentration of total dissolved solids and the eutrophication of lakes and reservoirs and, seasonally, of some shallow coastal waters. For example, in the Netherlands, agricultural chemicals are a growing threat to the quality of the drinking-water supply. Organic wastes from stables and feedlots contain large quantities of nitrogen compounds, phosphate, potassium, copper, zinc, cadmium, and other heavy metals. Only a part of these is taken up by plants, the remainder accumulating in the subsoil or leaching out to ground and surface waters.

Data provided by the Global Environment Monitoring System indicate that nitrate levels in 10% of the rivers monitored exceeded the levels established by WHO for drinking-water (10 mg/litre as N). In Europe over 90% of the rivers monitored have shown wide variations in the nitrate level, and 5% have nitrate concentrations over 200 times that found in unpolluted rivers. In South America many lakes and reservoirs are reaching hypereutrophic levels owing to the discharge of nutrients (mainly nitrogen and phosphorus) from drainage water and untreated domestic wastewater.

Forestry

Forests in all climatic zones are of great economic importance as providers of a variety of products. They also have a major protective function, especially in the tropics. Trees protect against soil erosion, improve soil fertility by reducing the salt concentration, protect cash crops by providing shade or shelter, and are a major source of animal feed (*21*).

Under the pressure of economic, political, and demographic forces, current management practices are increasingly failing to renew existing forest reserves, let alone restore those already lost. Rapid deforestation is evident in many parts of the world, developing countries in the tropics experiencing the most rapid rate of deforestation with an average loss estimated at 11 million hectares a year (*21*). Much of the land, cleared primarily for non-selective timber extraction, crop production, or cattle ranching, has soil of poor quality that erodes easily, once cleared of its protective cover. Reafforestation and afforestation offset only about 10% of the loss. Most deforestation is taking place in the tropical rainforests of Africa, Latin America, and south-east Asia.

The effects of deforestation are many and varied. Perhaps the most serious is loss of employment, income, and consumption goods by those who rely on forest exploitation. People who relied on land now deforested or protected have increasing difficulty in obtaining fuel; in India a woman may need to walk an additional 1400 kilometres a year to find firewood, since all the most accessible areas have become deforested (*40*). Similar effects occur where commercial interests control forests that were formerly a common resource; it is this kind of appropriation that underlies the *chipko* (tree-hugging) movement in India and many other citizen-led protests against logging companies (*41*). Many rural communities within range of cities have found it difficult to protect their rights to trees on their crop and pasture lands (*42*). The viability of settlements of indigenous people living in the forest may be destroyed by forest exploitation, for example through the introduction of disease and loss of livelihood. They may require resettlement, which creates many problems.

The major effect of deforestation on agriculture is that the release of rainwater becomes more erratic and irrigation water supplies are therefore threatened. Large-scale deforestation in the water catchments of major rivers is widely accepted as being responsible for excessive flooding in fertile downstream plains, giving rise to loss of life and crops and destruction of property.

Additional problems for developing countries

Agricultural change has often been particularly rapid in developing countries, often with major and unforeseen health effects involving a greater need for a health-related infrastructure. Only rarely has there been the institutional capacity to provide this. The failure to develop such an infrastructure has led to an increased risk of contamination of the food and water supply.

A particular difficulty in developing countries has been the transfer of technologies from developed countries. Such technologies need to be adapted to the climate and economic and social conditions of the country concerned. For instance, in the developed world refrigeration is an important means of prolonging the storage life of high-quality fresh and processed products. Many modern products are based on the concept of a minimum of processing plus use of refrigerated distribution and storage. But many developing countries would not be able to bear the cost of high-technology systems to ensure the integrity of products. It should be possible to transfer appropriate technology to tropical countries, but a careful cost/benefit analysis is required as well as safety precautions.

The safety of the increasingly complex technological base of the food industry requires regulations and institutional means to ensure their enforcement. In many developing countries this regulatory infrastructure of inspectors, scientists, and authorities is inadequate. An aspect of modern food processing frequently overlooked in development projects is waste. Wastes from the food-processing industry can be a major cause of pollution if not treated before disposal. They are characterized by a high content of suspended solids and the need for a high level of oxygen in water for their biodegradation. The problem is more acute for fermentation plants, whose wastes consist not only of a dense organic mass but also of a large number of viable microorganisms.

Trends

The most important factors influencing consumption and demand for food and agricultural products are population growth, especially of urban populations, income changes, income distribution, and relative prices. These are likely to remain the most important factors in the foreseeable future. As the urban population increases, so too will the dependence of poorer groups on an efficient food distribution system. Changes in the opportunity cost of women's time, household budget control, and tastes and preferences may also be important.

The continuation of high rates of population growth (even if overall average growth rates worldwide are declining), rapid substitution of live-stock products for vegetable products in the diets of richer groups, large food losses, and the loss of fertile soil through mismanagement will in the long run place severe stress on the agricultural sector. By contrast, rapid reduction in population growth, reduced losses, a continued small propor-tion of animal products in the diet, and appropriate changes in agricultural production would make it possible to meet the need for food and agricultural products in the foreseeable future.

The long-term trend is towards a decrease in real food and agricultural prices, and there is no indication that the trend will be reversed in the near future. Increases may occur because of a higher cost of energy but will tend to have most effect on more energy-intensive food or production systems. The predicted low rates of economic growth combined with excess global productive capacity in agriculture suggest that any real price increases will be small and temporary. Certain products may be subject to price rises; rapid growth in the demand for animal products may bring about a rapid growth in the demand for food grains.

As the intensity of food production increases, so too does the risk of occupational diseases and of accidents among those working in this and related sectors, unless major efforts are made by governments and inter-national agencies to increase safety and preventive measures.

The use of pesticides is likely to increase, especially in developing countries. Box 23 (page 80) illustrates the very rapid growth in world consumption. There is a trend towards the use of low-dosage, more active pesticides, although this does not necessarily mean that they are less toxic for non-target organisms. Existing and new pathogens and weeds can be expec-ted to require intensified chemical control, with the risk of an upsurge in resistance and pollution of the ecosystem.

Without a greater orientation of governments towards more effective intervention in ensuring that every person has adequate and safe food, a safe and sufficient water supply, and access to health care, the diarrhoeal diseases related to food and water will increase in many areas. So too will vector-borne diseases from irrigation, other water resource developments, and uncontrolled disposal of wastewater. Malaria, schistosomiasis, filariasis, and arbovirus fevers will continue to be major problems unless there are environ-mental control measures and effective treatment. So too will malnutrition. These problems will be reflected in static or rising mortality levels among infants and young children and in morbidity at all ages but predominantly among the poor and the aged.

Similar changes in the attitude of governments and international agencies to agriculture will also take place, especially in relation to agricultural extension services and the institutional framework within which such services are provided. A recent review of farmer innovation and agricultural research during the 1980s noted that agricultural research and official extension services have not addressed the needs of farmers working in the more unfavourable or resource-poor farming areas, often with small holdings or holdings on fragile soils (43). It also noted the increased recognition that poor farmers have often developed suitable and sophisticated practices for sustainable cultivation under difficult circumstances. The new forms of extension service and research are often labelled "farmer first". As Chambers notes (43), the main objective is not to transfer known technology but "to empower farmers to learn, adapt and do better; analysis is not by outsiders (scientists, extensionists or NGO workers) on their own but by farmers and by farmers assisted by outsiders; the primary location for research and development is not the experiment station, laboratory or greenhouse... but farmers' fields and conditions: what is transferred by outsiders to farmers is not precepts but principles, not messages but methods, not a package of practices to be adopted but a basket of choices from which to select." It is now recognized that agricultural extension services are more likely to persuade small farmers to adopt soil-conserving and water-conserving techniques if they work with such farmers in identifying their needs and resources and let them influence the nature of the extension programme. Techniques such as rapid rural appraisal or participatory rural appraisal have become increasingly used to make extension services more participatory and allow them to draw on the knowledge and experience of farmers (Box 29).

The next 20 years are also likely to bring substantial changes in the technology of food processing. Changes are now taking place with the replacement of fats and carbohydrates by macronutrient alternatives such as modified proteins and modified carbohydrates. This trend will continue in the next decade in affluent countries. Variety and nutritional value are becoming of equal importance to shelf life. Consumers want foods to be processed as little as possible but also insist on foods that are safe and of high nutritional quality. The use of encapsulation to control the release of chemical additives will permit lower concentrations to attain functional levels in foods. Such developments will increase the pressure on regulatory agencies to choose new approaches to assess the safety and nutritional value of new food products while avoiding unnecessary barriers to innovation. Advances in packaging will provide a series of barriers to block the growth of spoilage organisms. Increasing consumer concern about packaging wastes is also leading to an expansion of returnable, recyclable, biodegradable materials.

Box 29. Participatory rural appraisal and its use for health

Participatory rural appraisal is increasingly used by nongovernmental organizations (NGOs), government extension services and donor agencies, farmers and villagers participating in the determination of rural and agricultural development priorities and action. Many of these appraisals have raised health issues and many of those involved in the appraisals are developing this health procedure.

Among the many methods used in these appraisals, participatory mapping and modelling have often raised health issues. The maps or models are prepared by a village's inhabitants by marking, drawing, and colouring (often with a stick in the ground), with minimum interference and instruction from outsiders. Among the most common maps are: resource maps of catchments, villages, forests, fields, farms, and home gardens; impact and action monitoring maps where villagers record pest incidence, use of agrochemicals, weed distribution, and erosion rates; and social maps of residential areas (including wealth rankings and household assets). In many appraisals the inhabitants have also developed detailed health maps, showing the health and welfare status of each family member or each household. Such maps have included cases of tuberculosis, malnutrition, ear infection, handicaps, and jaundice and show whether people visit the primary health care centre.

Some of the most illuminating maps combine historical detail with that of the present and future. In most appraisals, different interest groups construct different maps, which serve as a stimulus for discussion or for other methods of data gathering and evaluation. Calendars, constructed in a similar way to the maps, reveal seasonal variations in diet, food consumption, illnesses, prices, fuel, pests, and debts.

An example of health information produced by participatory rural appraisal came from a workshop in June 1990 in the village of Udayanampatti, Tamil Nadu, India. An Indian NGO (The Society of People's Education and Economic Change), which ran the workshop, had been working in the village for two years. During the workshop one working group, which comprised some 15 villagers, recorded information about past and current health facilities, traditional versus modern systems of medicine, and a list of local resources. In addition, a village map was developed showing the incidence of disease, with different coloured stickers to mark the houses in which members suffered from antenatal and postnatal problems, deafness, chronic illness, disability, malnutrition, jaundice, tuberculosis, and paralysis.

This group also developed a calendar showing the seasonality of various diseases. When combined with the information produced by other methods (for instance a review of existing secondary data, key informant interviews, and group discussions presenting findings to the villagers), this can serve not only to identify problems but also to mobilize local populations to work with outside specialists in addressing health problems as part of rural and agricultural development programmes.

Source: Mascarenhas, J. et al., eds. *Participatory rural appraisal: Proceedings of the February 1991 Bangalore PRA Trainers Workshop,* London, IIED, and Bangalore, MYRADA, 1991 (RRA Notes No. 13).

Food irradiation offers health and economic benefits, helping in particular to reduce post-harvest losses and foodborne diseases, but also improving the keeping properties of certain high-value perishable foods and thereby facilitating the promotion of international trade. Some 30 countries have approved the use of irradiation for more than 40 commodities. The Codex Alimentarius Commission has adopted a Codex General Standard for Irradiated Foods and a Recommended International Code of Practice for the Operation of Radiation Facilities used for the Treatment of Foods. Irradiation represents the most recent addition to the list of food preservation technologies. Decades of study and practice have fostered increasing confidence in the ability of irradiation to protect and preserve food and thereby to safeguard health. Misconceptions abound, however, about whether irradiated food is safe to eat and how irradiation can complement or replace other methods of preserving food. WHO recognizes the safety of irradiating any food commodity up to an overall average of 10 kGy, the Codex recommended level, and considers that food irradiation can make an important contribution to promoting safe food supplies and proper nutrition (44).

Biotechnology is also likely to have increasing influence on food production and processing. Most traditional or commonly used techniques for improving productivity in crop and animal production fall under the heading of biotechnology, including plant and animal breeding. Many countries are investing substantial resources in genetic modification, tissue culture, embryo transfer, monoclonal antibodies, and other new biotechnology techniques. The effect will be felt first in animal agriculture in the developed world. A few genetically modified products are already on the market in the United States, for instance a vaccine for pseudorabies in swine and medicine for calf scours. Embryo transfer is being used extensively and greatly increases the multiplication rate of superior cattle, while biotechnology research is aimed at such goals as improved crop yields and propagation techniques, greater disease resistance, biopesticides, and nitrogen fixation. A joint FAO/WHO Consultation reported in 1991 on strategies for assessing the safety of foods produced by biotechnology (45).

Strategies

While current efforts to make farming, fisheries, and forestry more environmentally sustainable are encouraging, there is a need for a more integrated approach within the sector, for instance linking farming, forestry, and water resource management, and between this and other sectors. Such an integrated approach must have among its key goals the promotion and protection of human health and the avoidance of undesirable environmental change from expansion of food production, processing, and marketing. The prevention of chronic diseases associated with food and agriculture has only recently begun to be incorporated into agricultural policy in developed countries and has hardly been considered at all in developing ones.

There have been many instances of failure to take account of the health consequences in the design and implementation of agriculture and fisheries policies and programmes, perhaps most especially in irrigation development. Agricultural policies often fail to prevent or limit the negative effects on human health and on scarce land and forest resources. Lack of an integrated approach to the development of farming and forestry results in failure to recognize the importance of protecting wildlife habitats and maintaining biological diversity and genetic resources.

Certain broad strategic principles and actions are of relevance to most countries. For agriculture these include:

- The promotion of good agricultural practice such as crop rotation, avoidance of excessive use of fertilizers, use of correct dosages of chemicals for pest control, and correct use of agricultural tools and machinery as advocated by FAO.

- The formation of agricultural extension services addressing the real needs and priorities of farmers and foresters, which implies the use of participatory techniques such as rapid or participatory rural appraisal in determining the content and implementation (Box 29, page 94) and serving the needs of all those involved in production, especially women, whose role in production is often given little attention.

- Greater use of integrated pest control, the combination and development of traditional environmental, biological, and chemical pest control methods. This will reduce the reliance on chemicals and lessen the risks arising from human exposure to them and to water pollution from the agricultural run-off. It can also reduce the risk of resistance to chemicals.

- Advances in agricultural biotechnology to include (1) breeding strains of plants and animals resistant to pests and diseases, (2) endowing crop plants with the ability to produce their nitrogen needs or use other mineral nutrients in the soil more efficiently, (3) utilizing microorganisms that increase soil fertility and (4) developing biopesticides for specific pests. Application of such innovations could reduce the dependence of agriculture on agrochemicals and veterinary drugs that are at present sources of environmental pollution and hence of health hazards.

- The promotion of safety devices for those working in this sector and for accident prevention (e.g., gloves, goggles, ear protectors, readily available water for washing, protective clothing suited to the local climate).

- The prevention of occupational infectious disease by, for example, the immunization of human beings or animals against diseases such as tetanus, yellow fever, and rabies and the provision of adequate water supplies and sanitation.

- The education and teaching to read of workers, especially women and children, whose labour is a major input into production.

- The creation of income-generating employment for the alleviation of poverty, and for agricultural development. This requires the generation of income away from the farm and the setting up of public works programmes to ensure that all individuals and households have the means to obtain at least adequate amounts of food. Such programmes can be targeted to achieve an income or provide food for those suffering from drought or seasonal hunger. They can also help to promote sustainability and development goals, for instance through special emphasis on water catchment management, reafforestation, and other measures that help make production more sustainable and reduce the vulnerability of poorer groups to floods or droughts.

- The development of food production and agriculture in close association with national water development and resource management schemes.

- An understanding of the complementarity of urban and rural development. A shift to more intensive production and higher-value crops is often linked to rapid local urban development and diversification. Local urban development in turn may help make producer services and inputs cheaper, add to local value through crop processing, storage, and packaging, and provide employment away from the farm for rural households.

- A much greater commitment to dealing with desertification. Land degradation, including desertification, has now become an environmental hazard that undermines the world's ability to produce food, with major health consequences. In addition, desertification—through the increase of dust in the atmosphere, the increase of ground surface albedo, changes in the energy balance at the ground–atmosphere interface, etc.—may have far-reaching global climatic effects. By reducing vegetation in extensive areas of the world's drylands, desertification causes the disappearance of plant and animal species.

Healthy nutrition requires promotion through sound food and nutrition policies. These range from almost exclusive concentration on public education to a full recognition that the availability, price, and nutrient composition of food have a profound effect on human nutrition and are a major respon-

97

sibility of governments. Several conclusions can be drawn from national experience:

- The first priority is to ensure the adequacy and safety of the total food supply and equitable distribution according to individual needs. National food and nutrition policies need to be developed according to each country's political, cultural, social, and economic circumstances, the health of the population, the possibility of producing or importing food and food ingredients, the diseases to be prevented, and the characteristics of the population groups at high risk from malnutrition and foodborne and food-related diseases.

- Health-promoting and environment-protecting elements should be incorporated into government economic policies on food production, processing, distribution, and sale. Such policies should be based on a better understanding of the links between diet, nutrition, and health and on the latest information on the appropriate composition of diets.

- Consumer organizations and community-based voluntary organizations and informal groups should be involved in the development of policies for promoting healthy nutrition. The greater the knowledge of health-promoting behavioural change and the feeling of responsibility for health among consumers, the greater the potential for self-directed behavioural changes in diet, smoking, and exercise that have positive health benefits for the individual and society.

- In developing countries food and nutrition policies should seek to prevent the diet-related diseases observed in affluent societies. An increasing number of countries are passing through what is called the "nutrition transition" phase, the co-existence of communities where the malnutrition–infection complex prevails, entailing high infant and early childhood mortality and malnutrition rates, and communities with higher incomes that already suffer from conditions common in affluent countries such as obesity, cardiovascular disease, and cancer. Countries in the nutrition transition phase need to consider both types of malnutrition—deficiency and excess—in their nutrition policy.

- The food industry is now supplying a global as well as a national and local market. Accordingly, a key component in dealing with global strategies should be the development of epidemiological and toxicological databases to identify cases of accidental contamination and decrease the risk of various chemicals. These global databases should be readily accessible and quality controlled to ensure that they are used and reliable.

Recommendations

Each country should develop policies and programmes to ensure that all households receive an adequate and affordable diet and that at the same time food production is sustained. Many governments do not have the capacity to implement food and nutrition programmes that ensure that all people have access to a safe and nutritionally balanced diet and to safe drinking-water. They require national policies to coordinate such diverse goals as increasing incomes for poorer households (including small farmers and agricultural labourers), providing sufficient food supplies at reasonable cost, ensuring adequate returns to farmers, and promoting more sustainable farming techniques. Food policies must progress beyond short-term crisis management and an often almost exclusive concentration on increase in production. Dietary deficiencies cannot be solved by simply increasing food production or by educational programmes.

The need to increase food production should be accompanied by a strong emphasis on appropriate restoration and enhancement practices, including better integration between farming, forestry, and water management. Special efforts are required in fisheries and aquaculture to maximize the returns and benefits while ensuring a sustainable production base. Particular attention should be paid to the potential health and environmental effects of the high rates of population growth and low rates of growth in food and agricultural production forecast for many countries, especially in sub-Saharan Africa.

Agricultural research and extension services should be based on more decentralized, participatory models engaging farmers fully and addressing both health and environmental issues. The methodologies and techniques for such an approach are now well developed under such titles as rapid rural appraisal and primary environmental care. Health concerns need to be further integrated within these techniques.

Farming and allied rural work should become more economically rewarding and intellectually satisfying in order to sustain productivity increases and increase employment. Land ownership, tenancy rights, and input and output pricing policies should be such that farmers and foresters are encouraged to save and invest surplus earnings in increased productivity. Since capital is scarce, knowledge must become a substitute; most ecologically sound techniques, such as integrated pest management and integrated nutrient supply, are knowledge-intensive.

Priority should be given to the environmental health problems related to sustainable food and fish production in the following areas:
— Food safety with as priority the elimination or reduction of food contamination by pathogens such as salmonellae, *Campylobacter,* and *Listeria.* With respect to chemicals in food, the priority is for testing

and monitoring, and the development of improved regulations and techniques to control pests effectively with fewer chemicals and less damage to the environment (e.g., integrated pest control).

— Increasing the food supply, with special attention to (i) reducing post-harvest losses and subsequent waste and spoilage, using all the available and appropriate technologies to ensure sustainability; (ii) appropriate use of the potential of biotechnology for increasing the quantity, quality, and safety of food.

— Comprehensive and sustainable water policies for domestic, irrigation, and industrial water supplies, the management of surface water and wastewater, and safe and convenient water supplies and improved sanitation for farmers and rural households.

— Health promotion and disease control incorporated into the planning, construction, management, and operation of water resources and land development for agriculture and aquaculture.

Governments should examine the effects on health of their policies and programmes for agriculture, food, fisheries, water, and environmental protection, coordinating the policies and programmes to ensure good health and avoid harmful environmental effects. The development of food and nutrition policies and their integration into agricultural practice should involve not only government departments other than those traditionally responsible for them but also nongovernmental organizations (including consumer organizations), health care workers, and the community at large.

The integration of health goals within agricultural, nutrition, and food policies will require changes in taxation, credit, trade, exchange rates, and agricultural prices and controls; measures will be needed to improve the distribution of benefits and incentives, to ensure food safety and to improve diet and nutritional status. National policies should include measures to discourage the excessive consumption of fats, oils, sugars, and other dietary components that contribute to overweight and chronic disease. Any substantial increase in the production of grain-fed animals would have serious environmental effects in many parts of the world, making production less sustainable and diverting it from meeting nutritional needs.

In view of the environmental and health effects associated with the production, processing, and consumption of tobacco, efforts to reduce the public demand for tobacco products and to identify and introduce suitable replacement crops should be pursued more vigorously.

More resources should be devoted to improving public understanding of the issues at stake. An improved scientifically based assessment is needed of the risks and benefits of agricultural production methods, food preservation and distribution, and food consumption as compared with the other risks of everyday life. Emphasis should also be placed on nutrition education at the grassroots level for health workers, women, and children.

Recommendations for research

Governments and international agencies should develop the systematic collection, analysis, and monitoring of information on the health and environmental effects of current trends in food consumption and agricultural production. Such information is clearly essential for any policy seeking to modify undesirable trends.

Research and development priorities within each nation should be established in the light of both local and national needs, since food and agriculture problems and opportunities vary according to cultural, regional, climatic, economic, and other circumstances. Developing countries should be encouraged to concentrate on their own practical problems rather than copy patterns of research from developed countries. What are needed are new and complementary approaches:

— to develop simple low-cost methods to protect water quality, improve food storage and preservation, increase agricultural yields, minimize pollution, and reduce the prevalence of foodborne and waterborne diseases; and

— to compile and evaluate traditional practices in these areas and, where suitable, adapt them to present-day conditions and needs.

Research should be carried out on how to reconcile the goals of increased food production and reduction in tropical diseases in ways that lessen the harmful effects on the environment. The drive towards increased food production to meet the needs of a growing population may compound the problem of tropical diseases, especially when it increases irrigation and deforestation. Important health effects follow from changes in or more intensive application of pesticides in response to increased resistance on the part of the target pest. The problem is how to intensify agricultural production without worsening the tropical disease situation or to develop agricultural practices that minimize or eliminate tropical diseases.

More attention should be paid to improving understanding of individual and community behaviour and motivation in relation to food and agriculture, and of new agricultural and food processing technologies and their effects on health, nutrition, and the environment. Research is needed on:

— how to guide the food and agricultural sectors, communities, and households towards practices that promote good health without adverse environmental and agricultural effects;

— how to develop high-yield but low-input sustainable agriculture, focusing on ecological principles to improve pest management, conserve soil, water, and nutrients, recycle wastes, and utilize local sources of water efficiently;

— how to take effective government action to improve health and nutrition and to ensure safety and sustainability in food and agricultural production;

— how to provide a better understanding and greater acceptance by the public of the benefits and risks of new technologies before they are widely applied, so as to secure their utilization to the best effect.

References and notes

1. United Nations Advisory Committee on Coordination. *First report on the world nutrition situation.* Geneva, 1987.

2. Conway, G.R. & Barbier, E.B. *After the green revolution: sustainable agriculture for development.* London, Earthscan Publications, 1990.

3. Paulino, L.A. *Food in the Third World: past trends and projections to 2000.* Washington, DC, International Food Policy Research Institute, 1986 (Research Report, No. 52).

4. National Academy of Sciences. *Postharvest food losses in developing countries.* Washington, DC, 1978.

5. Bourne, M.C. Preharvest and postharvest losses of crops. In: White, P.L. & Selvey, N., eds., *Malnutrition: determinants and consequences*, New York, Liss, 1984, pp. 327–335.

6. Pariser, E.R. Post-harvest food losses in developing countries. In: Price Gittinger, J. et al., eds. *Food policy: integrating supply, distribution and consumption*, Baltimore, MD, Johns Hopkins University Press, 1987.

7. Stren, R.E. *The ruralization of African cities: learning to live with poverty.* Toronto, 1986 (Project Ecoville working paper No. 34).

8. Mazingira Institute. *Urban food production and the cooking fuel situation in urban Kenya. National report: results of a 1985 national survey.* Nairobi, Kenya, 1987.

9. Esrey, S.A. & Feachem, R.G. *Interventions for the control of diarrhoeal disease: promotion of food hygiene.* Geneva, World Health Organization, 1989 (unpublished document WHO/CDD/89.30; available on request from Diarrhoeal Disease Control, World Health Organization, 1211 Geneva 27, Switzerland).

10. Cohen, M.L. *Prepared statement in hearings before the Committee of Agriculture, Nutrition and Forestry, US Senate.* Washington, DC, Government Printing Office, June 1987, p. 28.

11. Archer, D.L. & Kvenberg, J.E. Incidence and cost of foodborne diarrhoeal diseases in the US. *Journal of food production*, **48**(10): 887–894 (1985).

12. Sutherland, P.S. *Listeria monocytogenes*. In: *Foodborne microorganisms of public health significance*. Pymble, Australian Institute of Food Science and Technology, 1989.

13. Lovett, J. *Listeria monocytogenes*. In: Doyle, M., ed. *Foodborne bacterial pathogens*. New York and Basel, Marcel Kekker, 1989.

14. Outbreak of hepatitis A—Shanghai. *Weekly epidemiological record*, **63** (13): 91–92 (1988).

15. Eyles, M.J. Viruses. In: *Foodborne microorganisms of public health significance*. Pymble, Australian Institute of Food Science and Technology, 1989.

16. UNEP/FAO/WHO. *Assessment of chemical contaminants in food*—Report on the results of the UNEP/FAO/WHO Programme on Health-related Environmental Monitoring, 1988 (available on request from Division of Environmental Health, World Health Organization, 1211 Geneva 27, Switzerland).

17. Pitt, J.I. & Hocking, A.D. Mycotoxigenic fungi. In: *Foodborne microorganisms of public health significance*, Pymble, Australian Institute of Food Science and Technology, 1989.

18. *Legumes and human nutrition*. Rome, Food and Agriculture Organization of the United Nations, 1964 (FAO Nutritional Studies, No. 19).

19. Leach, G. *Energy and food production*. London, International Institute for Environment and Development, 1975.

20. Conway, G.R. & Pretty, J.N. *Unwelcome harvest: agriculture and pollution*. London, Earthscan Publications, 1991.

21. Food and Agriculture Organization of the United Nations. *The state of food and agriculture 1989*. Rome, 1989.

22. World Resources Institute. *World Resources 1990–91*. Oxford, Oxford University Press, 1990.

23. *Global estimates for health situation assessment and projections*. Geneva, World Health Organization, 1990 (unpublished WHO document WHO/HST/90.2; available on request from Division of Epidemiological Surveillance and Health Situation and Trend Assessment, World Health Organization, 1211 Geneva 27, Switzerland).

24. Bonsall, J.L. Pesticides and health in developed countries. In: Turnbull, G.J., *Occupational hazards of pesticide use*, London, Taylor and Francis, 1985.

25. Copplestone, J.F. Pesticide exposure and health in developing countries. In: Turnbull, G.J., *Occupational hazards of pesticide use*, London, Taylor and Francis, 1985.

26. Cooper Weil, D.E. et al. *The impact of development policies on health: a review of the literature*. Geneva, World Health Organization, 1990.

27. Hunter, J.M. Bot-fly maggot infestation in Latin America. *Geographical review*, **80** (4): 382–398 (1990).

28. Bull, D. *A growing problem: pesticides and the Third World poor.* Oxford, Oxfam Press, 1982.

29. Bakir, F. et al. Methyl mercury poisoning in Iraq. *Science*, **181**: 230–241 (1973).

30. Bhat, R.V. Pesticides: a necessary evil. *Medico Friends Circle bulletin (Poona)*, **19**: 1 (1981).

31. Sharma, M. et al. The Basti tragedy. *Health for the millions*, **16**: 19–20 (1990).

32. Hunter, J.M. Exacerbation of red water disease (schistosomiasis haematobium) in the Upper Region of Ghana. *GeoJournal*, **5** (4): 303–313 (1981).

33. Marques, A.C. *Main malaria situation in the Brazilian Amazon.* SUCAM/Brazilian Ministry of Health, 1988 (unpublished paper).

34. Sawyer, D. & Sawyer, D. *Malaria on the Amazon frontier: economic and social aspects of transmission and control.* Belo Horizonte, Federal University of Minas Gerais/ CEDEPLAR, 1987.

35. Wilson, J.F. *Human issues in malaria control: population, community mobilization and indigenous peoples.* Consultant paper for the World Bank, 1987.

36. Surtees, G. Mosquitoes, arboviruses and vertebrates. In: Stanley, N.F. & Alpers M., eds. *Man-made lakes and human health*, London, Academic Press, 1975.

37. Gratz, N. The effects of water development programmes on malaria and malaria vectors in Turkey. In: *Effects of agricultural development on vector-borne diseases*, Rome, Food and Agriculture Organization of the United Nations, 1987 (Document ALG/MISC/87.12).

38. Goonasekere, K.G.A. & Amerasinghe, F.P. Planning, design and operation of rice irrigation schemes—the impact on mosquito-borne disease hazards. In: *Vector-borne disease control in humans through rice agro-ecosystem management.* Los Baños, Philippines, International Rice Research Institute, 1987.

39. Feder, G. & Chalamwong, Y. *Land ownership security and land values in rural Thailand.* Washington, DC, World Bank (Staff Working Paper No. 790).

40. Agarwal, A. Between need and greed—the wasting of India; the greening of India. In: Agarwal, A. et al., *The fight for survival: people's action for environment*, Delhi, Centre for Science and Environment, 1987.

41. Bhatt, C.P. The Chipko Andolan: forest conservation based on people's power. *Environment and urbanization*, **2** (1): 7–18 (1990).

42. Toulmin, C. *Drylands and human settlements.* London, International Institute for Environment and Development, 1990 (internal paper).

43. Chambers, R. Reversals, institutions and change. In: Chambers, R. et al. *Farmer first: farmer innovation and agricultural research*, London, Intermediate Technology Publications, 1989, pp. 181–195.

44. *Food irradiation: a technology for preserving and improving the safety of food.* Geneva, World Health Organization, 1988.

45. *Strategies for assessing the safety of foods produced by biotechnology. Report of a joint FAO/WHO consultation.* Geneva, World Health Organization, 1991.

4.
Water

Introduction

The provision of safe water and the management of wastewater have had a central role in reducing the incidence of many waterborne or water-related communicable diseases. One of the major achievements of the past 150 years is the extent to which the diseases associated with water have become of very minor significance in the mortality and morbidity of most developed countries and of some developing countries (especially for richer groups living in major cities). But the diseases associated with contaminated water remain among the most serious public health problems for much of the world's population. Water shortages are imposing serious constraints on the expansion of food production and industry, and the provision of adequate sanitation in many countries or regions within countries. Countries or regions with relatively low per caput levels of freshwater withdrawal will find it difficult to meet increasing demands for fresh water from growing populations with growing per caput levels of consumption and from agriculture and industry.

There are three crucial concerns in the relationship between water and health. The first is the constraints faced by water-poor countries and their impact on human activities. The second is the maintenance of water quality in the face of growing demand. The third is the direct link between health and water, especially concerning diseases associated with insufficient and poor-quality water and with inadequate provision for the disposal of wastewater.

Water and production

Over the last three centuries the growth in the volume of water withdrawn from freshwater sources for human use has been much more rapid than the growth in population. The volume of water withdrawal has increased more than 35 times (1), whereas human population has only increased sevenfold.

Current water use levels are stabilizing in many developed countries but still growing in most developing ones. They are likely to continue to grow rapidly well into the future if developing countries are to reach the per caput annual withdrawal levels of developed countries. Many of the wealthiest industrialized countries have annual freshwater withdrawals of over 500 m^3 per person, while a few have over 1000 and the USA has over 2000. Some developing countries also have among the world's highest figures for per caput withdrawals, for instance Argentina, Chile, Egypt, Iraq, and Pakistan, but many of the poorest countries have withdrawals of between 20 and 50 m^3 per person per year (2).

Most freshwater withdrawal is for agriculture. Irrigated agriculture accounts for around 70% of the total world use of fresh water (3). The industrial sector, including the energy sector, accounts for between 40% and 80% in developed countries and for only a few percent in most developing countries. Domestic and municipal water needs acount for around 7% of total withdrawals, although the proportion is higher in most developed countries. For instance, it is estimated that domestic and municipal water needs will account for 16% of withdrawals in Europe by the year 2000 (4).

Sustaining food production demands sustainable water supplies. Demands on water for food production will have to rise if food production is to keep pace with population growth and with changes in dietary preferences that imply more water-intensive food production. Since 1950 the area under irrigation has nearly tripled; one-third of the world's food is grown on irrigated lands, which comprise only 18% of total cropland (3).

Despite the fact that the volume of fresh water available worldwide is only a small fraction of the total global water (97% of which is saline), it still greatly exceeds present and projected future needs. However, its geographical distribution is very uneven. Box 30 shows the potential availability of water as a function of latitude; the maximum availability is around latitude 50° S, where the land area is small and the population sparse. Latitudes 40° N to about 70° N contain most of the water-rich countries such as Canada, Norway, the Russian Federation, and the United States. Brazil, Ecuador, and Indonesia, situated between the equator and latitude 30° S, can also be considered water-rich.

Most of the countries in latitudes 10° N to 40° N lack water—China, Egypt, Haiti, India, and Saudi Arabia. In most water-poor countries the inadequacy of the potential supplies is aggravated by the seasonal distribution of the rainfall—long dry seasons followed by heavy floods; thus most of the flood waters that pass through India and Bangladesh during the monsoon season are not available for use during the floods and water scarcity is a problem in many areas during the dry season (3). In addition, the classification of countries as water-rich or water-poor on the sole basis of the level of precipitation per unit area can be misleading, since many water-poor countries draw on large inflows of water from other countries, as Egypt does intensively with the Nile, and the Netherlands with the Rhine. In Egypt the

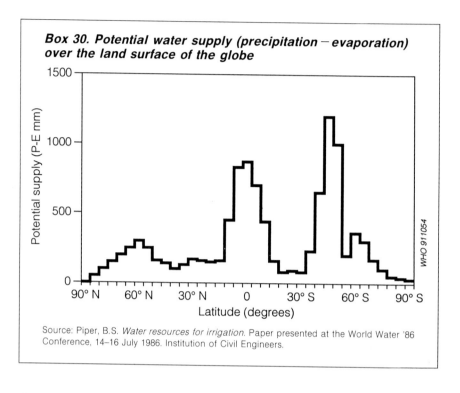

Box 30. Potential water supply (precipitation — evaporation) over the land surface of the globe

Source: Piper, B.S. *Water resources for irrigation.* Paper presented at the World Water '86 Conference, 14–16 July 1986. Institution of Civil Engineers.

river inflow provides 50 times more water than the rainfall (*3*). A more telling indicator of water scarcity is the intensity with which the local river run-off is used (Box 31).

A distinction can be made between four different causes of water scarcity (*5*):

— aridity—a permanent shortage of water caused by a dry climate
— drought—an irregular phenomenon occurring in exceptionally dry years
— desertification—a drying up of the landscape and degradation of land resources resulting from activities such as deforestation and over-grazing as well as from drought
— water stress owing to increase in the numbers of people using fixed levels of run-off.

The first two are linked to the climate, the third to changes induced by human activities, the fourth to both.

Availability of water in areas with already high levels of per caput water withdrawals can usually be increased very substantially by better water management and increased efficiency in the use of water (especially in irriga-tion). The efficiency of the world's irrigation systems is low, in many developing countries as low as 20%. Water losses are very high in distribu-

---

Box 31. Comparisons of the intensity of use of river run-off

1. Places where local river run-off is used most intensively:
   Europe: Belgium, Germany, Italy, Netherlands, Romania, Spain
   Americas: Cuba, United States
   Asia: southern and south-western parts of the former USSR, Islamic Republic of Iran, south of the Arabian peninsula, Pakistan, north-western and southern parts of India and states adjoining the Ganges, large parts of China, Japan
   Africa: Mali, Morocco, South Africa, Sudan

2. Places where local run-off resources substantially exceed current withdrawals: Scandinavia, northern and eastern regions of the former USSR, the greater part of Canada and Alaska, the Himalayan and Tibetan mountains, soouth-east Asia and the equatorial and subequatorial regions of Africa and South America

Source: World Resources Institute. *World resources, 1990–91.* Oxford, Oxford University Press, 1990.

---

tion canals because of seepage and lack of maintenance. The proper maintenance of dykes and ditches and appropriate lining of canals would yield considerable water gains.

About one-third of the planet's land surface is either semi-arid or arid, i.e., it receives less than 250 mm of rain a year. Arid areas have a very low natural productivity, but some support low-density herding or seasonal agriculture. With prudent irrigation in areas with the right soil and climate, the productivity can be increased in most semi-arid areas to levels at which commercial agricultural exploitation is profitable. Most arid or semi-arid areas are open to further degradation, especially through loss of vegetation cover. Where this is changed by human activities—such as logging and clear felling, inappropriate agricultural practices, or overgrazing by goats or cattle—the process is known as desertification. The most acutely endangered areas are in the semi-arid zones of Africa and Central Asia (6).

Many cities experience water shortages and draw to a considerable degree on groundwater aquifers at a rate above the natural rate of recharge. In many cities this has led to severe subsidence problems. In some coastal cities, it has also led to saline intrusion into the aquifers (7).

Cities can usually increase the supplies available very considerably by encouraging water conservation in water-intensive industries, ensuring that consumers pay realistic prices for water, and carrying out better maintenance and leakage prevention in existing water distribution systems.

Water losses within urban distribution systems continue to be very high, especially in developing countries. A survey in 1986 of 15 large Latin

American cities found that unaccounted-for water ranged from 39% to 67%, while in Geneva, Switzerland, unaccounted-for water was estimated at only 13% in 1989 (*8*). In the city of São Paulo, Brazil, an intensive programme to reduce losses in water distribution systems reduced the unaccounted-for water from 36% in 1977 to 27% in 1982; the savings permitted an increase of about 46% in the number of house connections without the need to increase water production (*9*).

Growing industrial production in many developing countries brings a rapidly growing demand for water by industry. Most of this demand is concentrated in cities, one important exception being large thermal power stations located outside cities, which need a great deal of water for cooling. The industrial sector, especially in developing countries, can achieve substantial water savings if water consumption is managed properly. Modern industrial systems need less water for processing and thus produce less wastewater. End-of-pipe water treatment is often replaceable by in-plant control, which can reduce effluents and often permit recycling of process water as well as reclamation and reuse of by-products along the industrial lines of production.

The countries facing the most serious water problems are those which were water-poor even before they developed water-intensive agriculture and industry. Increased water supplies are needed to meet their domestic needs and expand agricultural and industrial production.

Maintaining water quality

Inadequate supplies of water increase the problem of maintaining water quality, especially when there are multiple sources of water pollution. In most countries the four most important sources of water pollution are sewage, industrial effluents, storm and urban run-off, and agricultural run-off. In certain countries mines and oil production systems are also a major source of water pollution.

In the developed world non-point sources of water pollution present the chief problem, since point sources such as industrial effluents and the outflow of sewers and storm drains are usually treated before being returned to water bodies. This is not so for agricultural and urban run-off. With the growth in treatment of effluent from sewers, drains, and industries, non-point-source pollution becomes a more serious problem. OECD has noted the deterioration of groundwater because of local and non-point pollution and the increasing nitrate pollution of waterways (Box 32).

Agriculture is a major contributor to the deterioration of water quality; by the clearing of land, the use of fertilizers and pesticides, and irrigation. Ten percent of the rivers monitored under the Global Environment Moni-

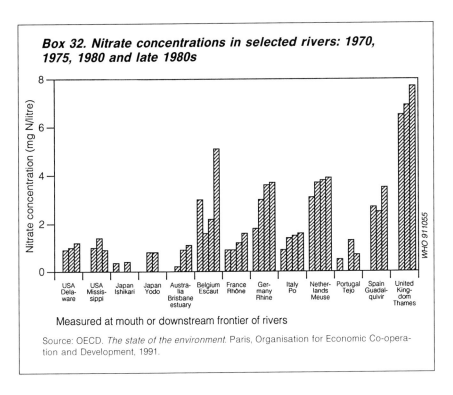

Box 32. Nitrate concentrations in selected rivers: 1970, 1975, 1980 and late 1980s

Measured at mouth or downstream frontier of rivers

Source: OECD. *The state of the environment.* Paris, Organisation for Economic Co-operation and Development, 1991.

toring System (GEMS) have nitrate concentrations that exceed the WHO guideline value for drinking-water. In Europe over 90% of the rivers monitored have shown varying nitrate concentration and 5% have concentrations over 200 times the background concentration found in unpolluted rivers. In the United States farm run-off is the principal source of pollution in 64% of the rivers and 57% of the lakes severely or moderately impaired by non-point sources (*3*). In South America many lakes and man-made reservoirs are reaching hypereutrophic levels owing to the discharge of nutrients (mainly nitrogen and phosphorus) from drainage water and untreated domestic wastewater. The upper Tiete river in the state of São Paulo in Brazil receives large volumes of drainage water, which contributes to the eutrophication of a number of reservoirs constructed downstream of São Paulo for flow regulation and hydropower generation (*9*).

A number of conditions favour the leaching of nutrients from rain-fed arable land. In areas of intensive crop production, with a heavy application of chemical fertilizers and a surplus of annual precipitation over evapotranspiration, nutrients such as nitrate and potassium can easily be leached owing to their high mobility in water, whereas other chemicals used in agriculture are less mobile and move more slowly downwards. In the long run they too can reach the groundwater.

Box 33. Nitrates in drinking-water and their impact on health

High levels of nitrates in drinking-water are a cause of concern because they may lead to serious, even fatal, consequences in infants below six months of age, nitrates being reduced to nitrites and, once absorbed, combining with haemoglobin to form methaemoglobin, which is unable to bind with and therefore transport oxygen from the lung to the tissues. The result is severe cyanosis (blue baby syndrome), which may lead to death when the methaemoglobin content of the blood rises above 20% of total haemoglobin concentration. Adults and schoolchildren are not harmed by exposure to the prevailing drinking-water concentrations of nitrates and nitrites.

Nitrites formed through reduction of nitrates can combine with other substances to produce nitrosamines and other powerful carcinogenic compounds. It has therefore been suspected that long-term exposure to nitrates may increase the incidence of various forms of cancer (e.g., gastric cancer), but epidemiological studies have so far failed to confirm this.

Sources: *Nitrates, nitrites and N-nitroso compounds.* Geneva, WHO, 1978 (Environmental Health Criteria No. 5); Conway, G.R. & Pretty, J.N. *Unwelcome harvest: agriculture and pollution.* London, Earthscan, 1991.

Concentrations of pesticides much higher than the WHO guidelines have been found in many rivers, lakes, and groundwater stores. For instance, in countries such as Colombia, Malaysia, and the United Republic of Tanzania, the levels of dieldrin in drinking-water are much higher than the WHO guideline value (*10*). In Colombia the levels of DDT are also higher than the WHO guideline value for drinking-water (*10*).

Water shortages can be overcome through the use of treated urban wastewater in agriculture. This has considerable potential and, if carefully managed, health risks are minimized (*10, 11*). Without careful management there are often serious health risks; for instance, the use of wastewater may lead to groundwater contamination, especially with nitrates, although this can be minimized by matching the application of the wastewater to the crop uptake. The use of some wastewaters for crop irrigation may lead to a build-up of toxic materials in the soil (heavy metals, refractory organic matter, specific ions such as boron, sodium, and chloride) and salinity, although this can be avoided by irrigation only with wastewater of predominantly domestic origin. Adequate soil drainage is also very important for minimizing soil salinization.

Water quality in urban areas in developing countries

The problem of maintaining water quality is particularly acute in the more urbanized areas in developing countries. Maintaining water quality is hampered by two factors: failure to enforce pollution controls at the main point sources (especially industries), and inadequacy of sanitation systems and of garbage collection and disposal. Box 34 gives some examples of water pollution in different cities in the developing world.

Box 34. Examples of water pollution in selected cities

India

Of India's 3119 towns and cities only 209 have partial sewerage and sewage treatment facilities and 8 have full facilities. On the river Ganges alone, 114 cities each with 50 000 or more inhabitants dump untreated sewage into the river each day. DDT factories, tanneries, pulp and paper mills, petrochemical and fertilizer complexes, and rubber factories use the river as a sink for their liquid wastes. The Hooghly estuary receives untreated industrial wastes from more than 150 major factories in Calcutta and raw sewage is deposited in the river continuously from 361 outfalls. The Yamuna river passing through Delhi receives nearly 200 million litres of untreated sewage each day.

Karachi (Pakistan)

The Lyari river which runs through Karachi, Pakistan's largest industrial city, is an open drain from both the chemical and the microbiological point of view, a mixture of raw sewage and untreated industrial effluents. Most industrial effluents come from an industrial estate with some 300 major industries and almost three times as many small units. Three-fifths of the units are textile mills. Most other industries in Karachi also discharge untreated effluents into the nearest water body.

Bogotá (Colombia)

The Tunjuelito, a tributary of the Bogotá river, is highly polluted. Many tanneries and plastic-processing plants pour untreated wastes into it and the dissolved oxygen in the water is almost depleted. The wastes include heavy metals such as lead and cadmium. Other rivers are not so heavily polluted with chemical wastes but receive large volumes of untreated sewage.

Alexandria (Egypt)

Industries in Alexandria account for around 40% of all Egypt's industrial output and most discharge untreated liquid wastes into the sea or into lake Maryut. In the past decade, fish production in Lake Maryut declined by some 80% because of the direct discharge of industrial and domestic effluents. The lake has also ceased to be a prime recreational site because of its poor condition. Similar environmental degradation is taking place along the seafront as a result of the discharge of untreated wastewater from poorly located outfalls. The paper, textile, and food industries contribute most to the organic load.

Box 34 (continued)

Shanghai (China)

Some 3.4 million cubic metres of industrial and domestic waste pour mostly into the Suzhou Creek and the Huangpu river, which flows through the heart of the city. These have become the main (open) sewers for the city. Most of the waste is industrial since few houses possess flush toilets. The Huangpu has essentially been dead since 1980. In all, less than 5% of the city's wastewater is treated. The normally high water table also means that a variety of toxins from industrial plants and local rivers find their way into groundwater and contaminate wells, which also contribute to the city water supply.

Peninsular Malaysia

The high levels of pollution evident in many rivers are due largely to organic wastes from sewage and discharges from oil palm and rubber factories. The range and complexity of water pollution problems caused by the discharge of other industrial effluents have increased, especially in industrial centres such as Kuala Lumpur, Petaling Jaya, and Penang. The main industrial sources of pollution come from electroplating industries, tanneries, textile mills, food processing industries, distilleries, chloro-alkali plants, sulfuric acid plants, and electronic factories. Many of these industries discharge wastes containing different compounds, including heavy metals, into public water courses without prior treatment. Significant levels of toxic heavy metals have been encountered in the Juru River Basin.

São Paulo (Brazil)

The Tiete river, as it passes through Greater São Paulo, one of the world's largest urban agglomerations, receives 300 tonnes of effluents each day from 1200 industries located in the region. Lead, cadmium, and other heavy metals are among the main pollutants. It also receives 900 tonnes of sewage each day, of which only 12.5% is treated by the five sewage treatment stations located in the area.

Source: Based on Hardoy, J.E. & Satterthwaite, D. *Squatter citizen: life in the urban Third World.* London, Earthscan Publications, 1989; see note 12 for full list of sources.

The contamination of rivers, lakes, and seashores by liquid wastes from urban residents and industries often has major environmental effects on a wider region around the city. In many coastal cities, beaches are contaminated with sewage. Fisheries are also damaged and this may threaten the livelihood of thousands of people. Worsening water pollution in India threatens the livelihood of millions who rely on fishing. There have also been reports of heavy falls in the fish catch as a result of water polution in Malaysia, in lake Maryut in Alexandria, in the bay of Dakar, around the Indus delta near Karachi, and in many rivers in China *(13–15)*.

Communicable diseases associated with water

Most of the disease agents that contaminate water and food are biological and come from animal or human faeces. They include bacteria, viruses, protozoa, and helminths and are ingested with water or food or conveyed to the mouth by contaminated fingers. Once ingested, most of them multiply in the alimentary tract and are excreted with the faeces. Without proper sanitation, they find their way into other water bodies, from where they can again infect other people. Many of the organisms in this enteric group can survive for a long time outside the human body. They can thus survive in human sewage and occasionally in the soil and be transmitted to water and foodstuffs. The more resistant organisms may be transmitted mechanically by flies breeding in accumulations of domestic waste around settlements.

Most of the diseases associated with water are communicable. They are usually classified according to the nature of the pathogen, but in considering health and the environment it is more convenient to classify them in categories according to the various aspects of the environment that human intervention can alter (16). Bradley suggested that diseases associated with water can be classified in four categories: waterborne, water-washed, water-based, and water-related (17). A fifth category emerging in developed countries could be called water-dispersed.

- *Waterborne diseases.* These arise from the contamination of water by human or animal faeces or urine infected by pathogenic viruses or bacteria, which are directly transmitted when the water is drunk or used in the preparation of food. Cholera and typhoid are the classic examples (although infection is not only through ingestion of contaminated water; direct transmission through the faecal–oral cycle and food contamination also take place). Other diseases such as leptospirosis may be acquired through contact of abraded skin with infected water.

- *Water-washed diseases.* Scarcity and inaccessibility of water make washing and personal cleanliness difficult and infrequent. Where this is so some diarrhoeal diseases and contagious skin and eye infections are prevalent. All waterborne diseases can also be water-washed diseases, transmitted by faecal–oral routes other than the ingestion of contaminated water (16). This category of diseases also includes infestation with lice or mites, which are vectors of various forms of typhus. Water-washed diseases diminish whenever an adequate supply of water is available and used.

- *Water-based diseases.* Water provides the habitat for intermediate host organisms in which some parasites pass part of their life cycle. These parasites are later the cause of helminthic diseases in people as their

115

infective larval forms in fresh water find their way back to humans by boring through wet skin (schistosomiasis), being ingested with water plants, crustaceans, or fish that are eaten raw or inadequately cooked (liver and lung flukes), or by infecting a minute water crustacean (*Cyclops* water fleas) and being swallowed (dracunculiasis).

- *Water-related diseases.* Water may provide a habitat for water-related insect vectors of disease. Mosquitos breed in water and the adult mosquitos may transmit malaria, filariasis, and virus infections such as dengue, yellow fever, and Japanese encephalitis. Different mosquitos vary in their preference for different water bodies but are usually very specific in their requirements. Most malaria vectors require relatively clean water. The culicine mosquitos, which spread filariasis, prefer to breed in flooded pit latrines and other highly polluted water. *Simulium* blackflies, which spread river blindness, breed in moving water, and *Chrysops* deerflies conveying eye worm (*Loa loa*) prefer muddy swamps. The tsetse flies that spread African trypanosomiasis (sleeping sickness), although breeding on land, bite near watercourses and can be effectively controlled by clearance of the woodland that fringes the water for a distance of a few metres.

- *Water-dispersed infections.* The four categories of water-related diseases described above are primarily problems of developing countries, although some can also occur in developed countries because of indigenous transmission or introduction by immigrants and travellers. A fifth category of diseases associated with water is emerging in developed countries—infections whose agents can proliferate in fresh water and enter the human body through the respiratory tract. Some freshwater amoebae that are not usually pathogenic can proliferate in warm water and if they enter the host in large numbers can invade the body along the olfactory tracts and cause fatal meningitis. Bacteria of the genus *Legionella* have demonstrated the capacity to proliferate in the water of complex air-conditioning systems, from which they may be dispersed as aerosols and infect substantial numbers of people through the respiratory tract. It is likely that other opportunistic pathogens will appear that find a suitable habitat in new technological devices using water. Other water-related infections such as that caused by waterborne *Cryptosporidium* may achieve increased clinical importance as the numbers of immunosuppressed people increase owing to acquired immunodeficiency syndrome (AIDS) or to chemotherapy facilitating organ or tissue transplants.

Box 35 lists the water-related diseases and estimates their impact on mortality and morbidity and the size of the population at risk. The health effects of the diseases associated with water are heavily concentrated in the developing world and, within the developing world, among the poorer urban and rural households of the poorer countries. Nearly half of the population in developing countries suffer from health problems associated with water.

Diseases arising from the ingestion of pathogens in contaminated water or food have the greatest health impact worldwide. The pathogens are often symptomless in carrier individuals and sometimes in animals not susceptible to them, and they can survive for varying periods of time in water and be swallowed with it. They include those at the origin of classic epidemics—cholera, dysentery, and typhoid fever—and a considerable variety of other microorganisms, including protozoa (e.g., amoebae) and viruses (e.g., hepatitis A). They may be found in untreated water contaminated by human and animal excreta or remains, or in water handled unhygienically after treatment, as often happens in water shortages for hydrological or economic reasons. In these latter situations contamination of food is as likely as contamination of water and it becomes difficult to attribute responsibility to this or that pathway, though the primary cause undoubtedly rests with the availability of water.

Waterborne diseases are the largest single category of communicable diseases contributing to infant mortality in developing countries (1500 million episodes of diarrhoea and some 4 million deaths per year) and second only to tuberculosis in contributing to adult mortality, with 1 million deaths per year.

Only a few fatal cases of waterborne diseases are now recorded in developed countries and outbreaks are exceptional. Infrequent episodes, such as the outbreaks of cryptosporidiosis in the United Kingdom and the United States, and the brief mini-epidemic of typhoid that occurred in 1963 at Zermatt, Switzerland, following a malfunction of the water supply and disposal system, are a reminder that vigilance is still required.

Diarrhoea remains one of the most pressing health problems and is usually caused by one of a number of waterborne pathogens including *Giardia*, *Vibrio*, and rotavirus, although it can also result from non-enteric infection. The average annual incidence of diarrhoea among children under five years of age is 3.5 episodes; many children have 10 or more episodes each year. Each episode lasts from 2–3 days to 2 weeks or more and may result in severe dehydration, the severity depending on the infectious organism, the intensity of the infection, and such host factors as age, nutritional status, and immunity. The weight loss that accompanies diarrhoea usually leads to acute malnutrition, and repeated episodes lead to chronic malnutrition. The risk of dying from diarrhoea is greatly increased in malnourished children.

The cholera epidemic in Latin America, which started in Peru and then spread to several other countries, is a reminder of the speed with which

Box 35. Examples of water-related infections with estimates of morbidity, mortality, and population at risk

Disease	Morbidity	Mortality (no. of deaths per year)	Population at risk
Waterborne and water-washed			
Cholera	see Box 36		
Diarrhoeal diseases (includes salmonellosis, shigellosis, *Campylobacter*, *E. coli*, rotavirus, amoebiasis and giardiasis)	over 1500 million episodes in children under 5 years	4 million in children under 5 years	More than 2000 million
Enteric fevers (paratyphoid, typhoid)	500 000 cases; 1 million infections (1977–78)	25 000	
Poliomyelitis	204 000 (1990)	25 000	
Ascariasis (roundworm)	800–1000 million cases; 1 million cases of disease	20 000	
Leptospirosis (Weil disease) Trichuriasis (whipworm) }	no figures available		
Water-washed			
Skin and eye infections			
Trachoma	6–9 million people blind		500 million
Leishmaniasis	12 million infected; 400 000 new infections/year		350 million
Other			
Relapsing fever Typhus fever (rickettsiosis) }	no figures available		
Water-based			
Penetrating skin			
Schistosomiasis (bilharzia)	200 million	200 000	500–600 million
Ingested			
Dracunculiasis (guinea worm)	Over 10 million		Over 100 million

Box 35 (continued)

Disease	Morbidity	Mortality (no. of deaths per year)	Population at risk
Water-related insect vectors			
Biting near water			
African trypanosomiasis (sleeping sickness)	20 000 new cases annually (thought to be an under-estimate)		50 million
Breeding in water			
Lymphatic filariasis	90 million		900 million
Malaria	267 million (107 million clinical cases)	1–2 million (three-quarters in children under 5)	2100 million
Onchocerciasis (river blindness)	18 million (over 300 000 blind)	20 000–50 000	85–90 million
Yellow fever	10 000–25 000		
Dengue fever (breakbone fever)	30–60 million infected every year		

* Also foodborne.

Sources: Cairncross, S. & Feachem R.G. *Environmental health engineering in the tropics—an introductory text.* Chichester, John Wiley, 1983; White, G.F. et al. *Drawers of water: domestic water use in East Africa.* Chicago, University of Chicago Press, 1972. Figures for morbidity, mortality and population at risk from *Global estimates for health situation assessment and projections 1990,* Geneva, World Health Organization, 1990 (unpublished document WHO/HST/90.2).

certain waterborne or water-washed infectious diseases can spread (Box 36). What has received less attention from the media is the fact that cholera remains a significant cause of death in many other countries.

Among the many water-related and water-based diseases, schistosomiasis, dracunculiasis, lymphatic filariasis, onchocerciasis, roundworm, and hookworm stand out for the degree of debilitation they cause in human populations. Few people die of these diseases, but some are a cause of severe pain and suffering while others affect millions of people.

The presence in water of organisms that are themselves vectors of pathogens gives rise to risks of a different nature. Dracunculiasis is caused by the ingestion of a small crustacean (*Cyclops*) present in surface waters and

---

Box 36. Cholera in 1991

Cholera affected many Latin American countries in 1991, the first such epidemic in the region this century. It had been assumed that improvements in water, sanitation, sewage treatment and food safety had eliminated this disease just as it had in Europe and North America in the late nineteenth and early twentieth century, when large-scale cholera epidemics in major cities had helped spur major investment in improving water supplies and installing sewers.

The epidemic first appeared in Peru in January 1991, and by the end of the year more than 276 000 cases and 2664 deaths from cholera had been reported. At the same time, 39 154 cases and 606 deaths had been reported in Ecuador, and cases were also reported in other Latin American countries, plus 24 imported cases in the USA.

Cholera remains a serious problem in many African and Asian countries. It is endemic in India and Indonesia and has been reported in Iraq, although the number of cases and number of deaths at mid-July 1991 were relatively low; for all of Asia 6700 cases were reported, with 68 deaths. Cholera was also reported in many African countries. In 1991 a total of 134 953 cases were reported in 19 of these countries, with 12 618 deaths. The actual numbers of cases of cholera will be substantially higher than the number reported in these countries, since no figures are available from other countries in the region known to have been hit by the epidemic.

Source: World Health Organization, provisional figures, 1991.

---

containing the larvae of a worm of the genus *Dracunculus*. When the barely visible *Cyclops* is ingested, the larvae invade human tissues and develop into worms that can be 1 m long, giving rise to a painful and debilitating chronic disease that among other things blisters the skin. From the blisters new larvae are shed on contact with water, to infest other arthropods and, through them, more people. The number of people infected (Africa, south and west Asia) is of the order of 10 million and 100 million are at risk. Access to protected well-water prevents infection; improvements in sanitary conditions have eliminated the disease from most of Asia, the Eastern Mediterranean and large parts of Africa (*18*).

Another water-related disease is schistosomiasis. Infection occurs through contact of the skin with water polluted by human excreta containing the eggs of a parasitic worm. These eggs hatch and the larvae penetrate various species of aquatic snail, where they reproduce. They are then released in a different larval form into fresh water, from where they can infect people coming into contact with it. Depending on the fluke species involved, chronic disturbances of the bladder or the gastrointestinal tract ensue. In the urinary form, cancer of the bladder is common in untreated cases, making it the most frequent cancer in Egypt. The population at risk worldwide is estimated at 600 million, the number infected at 200 million. The proportion of those infected who die from schistosomiasis is relatively low (estimates suggest up to 200 000 worldwide each year), but the disease results in a marked reduction of productivity in the population affected, mostly farmers but increasingly urban dwellers as well. Poorly designed or poorly maintained irrigation and impoundment schemes have been responsible for the spread of the disease; the prevalence rose from 6% to 60% three years after the construction of the first Aswan dam (1906) and from 0% to 90% after the construction of the Volta dam (19, 20). The spread is due to the direct contamination of water with infected urine or stools and therefore to personal habits that are often rooted in tradition.

Other diseases are carried by insects that breed in water. The spread of malaria (270 million infected, 110 million clinical cases per year, more than 1 million deaths per year, three-quarters in children aged under 5 years) has been facilitated by the extension of perennial irrigation agriculture. The presence of large bodies of standing water in the vicinity of human dwellings increases the likelihood of infection, especially in Asia and Latin America. In sub-Saharan Africa the infection rate is already so high that it does not appear to be possible for the situation to worsen. Better management of water resources would improve matters, but the incidence of malaria can only be drastically reduced by effective and large-scale action including selective indoor spraying of insecticide and insect-repelling products, the use of personal protective measures (by children in particular), reliance on dependable prophylactic drugs (including, in the future, vaccines) and, where necessary, early treatment.

Some mosquito species breed in rain-filled discarded cans or containers near houses, including the main vectors of dengue (30–60 million infections per year with perhaps 100 000 clinical cases and 10 000 deaths) and yellow fever, a greatly under-reported disease (probably several hundred thousand cases a year with a case-fatality rate of over 50%). Blackflies (*Simulium* spp) breeding in swift-running water transmit microfilariae that give rise to onchocerciasis (river blindness) in some parts of Latin America but especially in Africa (worldwide some 18 million infected, over 300 000 blind). Environmental measures are of limited effectiveness against onchocerciasis except when settlements are moved away from the breeding grounds, but new therapeutic means used at an early stage are bringing the disease under control.

Water and sanitation

Estimates of the numbers of people lacking access to safe and sufficient water supplies and adequate sanitation provide the best figures for the numbers of people at risk from water-related diseases. Safe and sufficient water supplies and adequate sanitation would reduce infant and child mortality by more than 50% and prevent a quarter of all diarrhoeal episodes (21). Safe water supplies would also eliminate dracunculiasis. Increasing the supply of water to households would greatly reduce the incidence of water-washed diseases, and improved sanitation could disrupt the cycle by which the agents of many waterborne and water-based diseases are returned to food, water, or soil. A review of studies on the health impact of water supplies found that, in most of the cases where water supply improvements were shown to have brought about a reduction in diarrhoeal diseases, the improvements had included increased availability of water (21). Increased water availability probably also helps to control infectious skin diseases and infections carried by body lice (22, 23).

Box 37 presents the projected reduction in the morbidity of a large range of diseases achievable by improvements in water supply and sanitation.

Box 37. Potential reductions in morbidity for different diseases as a result of improvements in water supply and sanitation

Diseases	Projected reduction in morbidity (%)
Cholera, typhoid, leptospirosis, scabies, dracunculiasis	80–100
Trachoma, conjunctivitis, yaws, schistosomiasis	60–70
Tularaemia, paratyphoid, bacillary dysentery, amoebic dysentery, gastroenteritis, louse-borne diseases, diarrhoeal diseases, ascariasis, skin infections	40–50

Source: *Intersectoral action for health*, Geneva, World Health Organization, 1986.

WHO estimates for 1988 suggest that 170 million urban and 770 million rural inhabitants lack access to safe and adequate water supplies and that over 1700 million people lack adequate sanitation: 331 million urban and 1388 million rural inhabitants (24). Most urban centres in Africa and Asia have no sewerage system at all, including many cities with a million or more inhabitants (25). Most human excrement and household wastes end up, untreated, in rivers, streams, canals, gullies, and ditches. For those cities with a sewage disposal system, the system rarely serves more than a small proportion of the population, typically in the richer residential, government, and commercial areas.

These figures for the number of people inadequately served with water and sanitation are likely to understate the problem, one reason being the lack of attention given in many projects to the quantity of water needed by an individual or household for health (23). For instance, the availability of a water tap within 100 metres of a house is often considered adequate by official agencies, but it is not necessarily adequate for the water needed for washing, cooking, and personal hygiene.

Moreover, official figures for the numbers of people adequately served often overstate the number actually served. For instance, they may assume that all those with water taps in their settlements are adequately served, but there are often so few communal water taps that people have to wait for a long time in queues and this tends to reduce water consumption to below what is needed for good health. Piped water systems in many tropical cities also function only intermittently for a few hours a day, which makes it especially difficult for households relying on communal taps. The water in piped systems is often of doubtful quality because of contamination of old and leaky distribution pipes by groundwater and sewage. Many urban dwellers in illegal settlements draw water from piped distribution systems through illegal connections and these are often a major source of leaks. Leaky distribution mains present an additional hazard when the water pressure is low and pollution from contaminated groundwater or wastewater from leaking drains and sewers may enter through damaged joints or pipe fissures when the pressure drops (23).

Many households and settlements judged by governments to be adequately served by public systems may resort to other water sources because of the problems mentioned above or may not be able to afford to purchase the water they need. Official figures for many of the poorer developing countries claim that over 80% of the urban population had access to safe water in the mid-1980s, including 100% coverage in Nigeria and Liberia and 99% coverage in Togo (26). Local specialists find it hard to reconcile these figures with the reality in the urban centres in which they work. Box 38 gives some illustrations of deficiencies in water and sanitation drawn from local studies.

Improvements in the quality of the water supply and in its availability are usually possible at relatively low cost, especially if optimal use is made of local resources and knowledge. In many instances cost recovery is possible. In cities where poorer households pay private water vendors at high cost, a proper piped water system can often replace the vendors and provide these households with a more economical and convenient supply at the same price

Box 38. Inadequacies in the water supply and sanitation of some cities

Bangkok (Thailand)
About one-third of the population has no access to public water and must obtain water from vendors. Only 2% of the population is connected to a sewer system; human wastes are generally disposed of through septic tanks and cesspools, their effluents, as well as wastewater from sinks, laundries, baths, and kitchens, being discharged into stormwater drains or canals.

Calcutta (India)
Some 3 million people live in bustees and refugee settlements that lack potable water and have serious annual flooding and no systematic means of disposing of refuse or human wastes. Some 2.5 million live in similarly blighted and unserviced areas. Piped water is only available in the central city and parts of some other municipalities. The sewerage system is limited to only a third of the area in the urban core. Poor maintenance of drains and periodic clogging of the system have made flooding an annual feature.

Dakar and other Senegalese towns
Senegalese towns have no provision for the removal of household and public waste. Of the five urban centres with sewerage systems, generally only the inner urban population has access to these facilities. In Dakar, the capital, a survey in 1980–81 found that 28% of households have private water connections while 68% rely on public standpipes and 4.2% on buying water from carriers. A survey in Pikine, the outer part of Dakar, found an average of 696 persons per standpipe with 1513 in one neighbourhood. In Dakar nearly one-sixth of human solid wastes is dumped outside proper toilet facilities.

Dar es Salaam (United Republic of Tanzania)
In a survey of 660 households drawn from all income levels in 1986–87, 47% had no piped water supply either inside or immediately outside their houses while 32% had a shared piped water supply. Of the households without piped water, 67% buy water from neighbours and 26% draw water from public water kiosks or standpipes. Only 7.1% buy water from water sellers. The average water consumption is only 23.6 litres a day. For sanitation, only 13% of the dirty water and sewage produced is properly disposed of. Of the 660 households 89% had simple pit latrines, and only 4.5% had toilets connected to septic tanks or sewers. Most households have to share sanitary facilities. Overflowing latrines are a serious problem, especially in the rainy season, and provision for emptying septic tanks or latrines is very inadequate.

Jakarta (Indonesia)
Less than a quarter of the city's population have direct connections to a piped water system; some 30% depend solely on water vendors at a

Box 38 (continued)

cost five times that of piped water. The city has no sewerage system. Septic tanks serve about 25% of the city's population, others use pit latrines, cesspools, and ditches along the roadside. Many of the population have to use drainage canals for bathing, washing, and defecation.

Karachi (Pakistan)

Potable water has to be brought more than 160 km from the Indus and is available for only a few hours a day in most areas. One-third of households have piped water connections; most slum dwellers and squatters must either use public standposts or buy water from vendors at inflated prices.

Khartoum (Sudan)

The water supply, sewage disposal, refuse disposal, and electricity supply systems are all inadequate in both the coverage of the urban area and the maintenance of the service. The water supply system is working beyond its design capacity while the demand continues to rise. The coverage is poor, low-income groups in squatter settlements suffering most and paying the most for water, often bought from vendors. Breakdowns and cuts in the supply system are common. The municipal sewerage system serves only about 5% of the Khartoum urban area. Even that system is susceptible to breakdowns, and then waste is discharged either directly into the river or onto open land. For most people in the low-income areas there is no system of sewage disposal.

Kinshasa (Zaire)

There is no sewerage system in Kinshasa. About half the urban population (some 1.5 million people) are not served by a piped water network. Higher-income areas are often 100% connected, while many other areas have 20–30% of houses connected, essentially those along the main roads. The sale of water flourishes in areas far from the network. In these areas water is usually obtained from wells or the river.

Madras (India)

Only 2 million of the 3.7 million residential consumers within the service area of the local water supply and sewerage board are connected to the system. On average they receive some 36 litres per day per person. The rest within the service area must use public taps, which each serve about 240 persons. Another million consumers outside the service area must rely on wells, but these supplies are inadequate because of falling groundwater levels. The sewerage system serves 31% of the metropolitan population and raw sewage flows freely into the metropolitan area's natural watercourses at many points.

Source: Based on Hardoy, J.E. & Satterthwaite, D. *Squatter citizen: life in the urban Third World.* London, Earthscan Publications, 1989; see note 27 for a full list of sources.

as they previously paid to vendors (*28, 29*). A thriving informal market for water is evidence of a demand unsatisfied by the formal sector. It is also an indication of how much people would be willing to pay for an adequate conventional water supply if it were made available to them (*23*).

The cost of constructing water supplies varies widely, depending largely on the availability of water resources. For instance, for urban water systems in monsoon south-east Asia, a water supply with house connections can cost as little as US$ 60 per head, whereas in the arid Eastern Mediterranean area it is likely to cost five times as much. A typical figure for a developing country would be US$ 120 per person served (*23*).

A cheaper alternative to water piped into each house is public standposts. These cost roughly half as much to build as house connections, say US$ 60 per head. The difference is not primarily due to savings in the cost of distribution pipes, as the distribution system normally accounts for only one-third of the total cost of a water supply; rather, it is due to the fact that those who use standposts consume much less water than households with private connections, so that there is less demand on the abstraction, treatment, pumping, and storage capacity of the system. Households with taps in the yard of their homes use roughly half as much as those with house connections, so that the cost for them is nearer to the lower figure, say US$ 80 per person. To combine the construction costs with the annual operating costs of a system (typically about US$ 0.35 per cubic metre of water supplied), an equivalent annual amortization cost must be used, as in Box 39.

Box 39. Typical costs of urban water supply

Level of service	Typical construc-tion cost (US$)	Equivalent annual amount[a] (US$)	Typical water con-sumption (litres per person per day)	Annual operating cost[b] (US$)	Total annual cost (US$)
Public standpost	60	9	20	3	12
Yard tap	80	12	60	8	20
Private connection	120	18	150	19	37

[a] Converted on the basis of amortization over 10 years at 10% interest.
[b] Calculated on the basis of $ 0.35 per m³.

Source: Cairncross, S. Water supply and the urban poor. In: Hardoy, J.E. et al., eds. *The poor die young: housing and health in Third World cities.* London, Earthscan Publications, 1990, pp. 109–126.

Improved sanitation can be achieved at far less per caput cost than conventional sewerage systems and sewage treatment plants and is at the same time more effective and hygienic than the pit latrines or bucket latrines that remain the most widely used sanitation systems. The World Bank has identified a wide range of household and community systems that could greatly improve sanitation while taking due account of local physical conditions, social preferences, and economic resources (*30*). Several have a total annual cost per household of between one-tenth and one-twentieth of that of conventional sewerage systems. Most need far lower volumes of water for efficient operation. Some need no water at all. Box 40 outlines different sanitation options and their costs.

Box 40. Typical range of capital costs of sanitation systems per household (1990 prices)

Type of system	Cost (US$)
Twin-pit pour-flush latrine	75–150
Ventilated improved pit latrine	68–175
Shallow sewerage	100–325
Small-bore sewerage	150–500
Conventional septic tank	200–600
Conventional sewerage	600–1200

Note. Capital costs alone are not a sufficient basis for determining the cost of a system, since some systems are more expensive than others to operate and maintain. The total discounted capital, operation, and maintenance costs for each household must be calculated to determine the charge that must be levied for the service and establish whether households can afford to pay for the service. If the monthly cost of providing sanitation exceeds 5% of the family income, it may be deemed unaffordable. Most low-cost sanitation alternatives come within this limit even for the poorest of communities, especially urban communities.

Source: Sinnatamby, G. Low cost sanitation. In: Hardoy, J.E. et al., eds. *The poor die young: housing and health in Third World cities.* London, Earthscan Publications, 1990, pp. 127–167.

Changing disease patterns resulting from water management

Agricultural change involves alterations in the basic environment. The two main types of environmental modification are provision of increased or more controlled water for vegetation growth and opening up of additional land.

Increasing the supply and control of water is often achieved by a reservoir providing a large area of still water. If vegetation has not been cleared beforehand, there may be a phase of eutrophication, destruction of submerged trees, and proliferation of aquatic macrophytes that may last a decade or even more. In endemic areas, the snails that are the intermediate hosts of human schistosomiasis thrive on such vegetation and will tend to colonize the periphery of most tropical reservoirs, infecting those who go to the lakeside to fish and for other purposes. On the other hand, flooding of previously fast-flowing tributary streams by the rising water level tends to remove the breeding sites of *Simulium* vectors of onchocerciasis, though new habitats for them may develop on the dam spillways. Schistosomiasis will be most prevalent where the reservoir shores are gently sloping, there is much human–water contact, and waterweed is abundant.

In irrigation schemes, particularly in Africa, the Eastern Mediterranean, and the Philippines, schistosomiasis is the predominant health problem. The intermediate host snails flourish in the slower-moving water of minor canals and particularly in the ditches of the drainage systems needed to remove excess water from the fields and to avoid salinization. Schistosomiasis used to be endemic in certain limited areas of Japan. The use of effective mollusci-cides, the lining of irrigation canals to eliminate the breeding grounds of the snails, the treatment of excreta, continued care of patients, and a high level of community involvement have achieved the virtual eradication of schisto-somiasis from Japan. No clinical cases have been reported since 1977 and snails have not been sighted since 1983 (K. Uchida, personal communication).

In Asian rice cultivation the predominant diseases are malaria, schis-tosomiasis, Japanese encephalitis and leptospirosis, with smaller contribu-tions from gastrointestinal and hepatic flukes. All these diseases are focally distributed; in many areas malaria is prevalent but is unrelated to agricultural activity. Similar problems occur with irrigated rice systems elsewhere, though different arboviruses prevail, especially in the Americas, and lym-phatic filariasis plays a variable role.

Malaria is also strongly but locally associated with water impoundments, particularly in Asia and Latin America. Vectors may breed at the margins of reservoirs.

In south-east Asia and countries of the former USSR, there are reservoirs presenting a major problem with *Opisthorchis* infection. This human liver fluke is ingested with uncooked and inadequately fermented freshwater fish that have been infected by fluke larvae emerging from freshwater snails. Not only does the parasite damage the human bile duct, it is also carcinogenic; the mortality from bile duct carcinoma is significant.

The trend towards multiple cropping depending on both irrigation and appropriate crop varieties can increase threefold the period during which the ricefields provide breeding habitats in the absence of measures to restrict the survival of mosquito larvae. Selection of crop rotations within the year can reduce the time when free surface water is present.

Livestock changes may affect vector-borne disease patterns in a complex manner. Increased animal populations may divert mosquito biting activity away from humans, especially if the livestock pens are located between the breeding sites and the human settlements. On the other hand, the stock may act as amplifiers, permitting a great proliferation of arboviruses normally transmitted at a lower level among wild birds or mammals. Subsequently the infection may spill over into the human population, as can occur with Japanese encephalitis virus, which is amplified in domestic pig populations. Livestock populations, by increasing food supplies for mosquitos and tsetse flies, may also encourage larger vector populations than would otherwise be the case; however, little quantitative data are available on this subject. In east Asia domestic animals are susceptible to schistosomiasis and have a role in maintaining the parasite life cycle in endemic areas.

Increased mechanization may reduce the transmission of water-related diseases, for example decreasing the snail population by permitting clearance of vegetation from canals. Indirectly it may lead to larger fields, better levelling, the drainage of marshy areas, and a sharper separation of land and water, all of which will generally decrease the prevalence of vectors of disease.

Most mechanical equipment also tends to reduce the personal contact of farm workers with the aquatic environment. Thus schistosomiasis transmission will be reduced, as will transmission of leptospirosis, which has rodent reservoirs but no invertebrate vector. Improved agricultural methods other than mechanization may also reduce schistosomiasis in those working in water, and better clothing will reduce insect bites.

As agricultural activity and cultivation methods become more sophisticated and higher yields are systematically sought, a more evenly cultivated landscape will result, the patches of water will be reduced, and many disease vectors will decrease. There may, however, be large populations of a few vectors whose ecological preferences happen to coincide with the spreading patterns of agriculture.

The process of deforestation creates a moving boundary zone between the forest and cultivated land. In South America, malaria is most intense in the arable areas; mucocutaneous leishmaniasis is more a feature of the jungle itself and is transmitted to intruding loggers and other people. Large tracts of south and south-east Asia have the most intense malaria transmission along the forest fringes of the hilly areas that often coincide with national borders. *Anopheles dirus,* which breeds in pools in the partly cleared forests, is an extremely effective vector of falciparum malaria. Population movements are often accompanied by such illicit activities as smuggling and gem mining and facilitate transmission, and there is little enthusiasm for government control activities.

Gem and tin mining creates many pools to act as mosquito larval habitats. These areas appear likely to create some of the most intractable foci of Asian malaria for decades to come. The disease is often resistant to multiple drugs and prospects for control are poor, especially among the groups that operate illegally, even if vaccines are eventually developed.

The increasing incidence of dengue fever and lymphatic filariasis in many urban areas is also worth noting. In urban areas there has been an increase in the breeding of clear-water mosquitos, chiefly *Aedes aegypti*. In ditches, sullage water, and flooded pit latrines in Africa and Asia there has been an increase in *Culex quinquefasciatus*. *Aedes* was formerly controlled in cities in the Americas by rigorous domestic inspection and removal of containers to control yellow fever. This disease is now rare and is effectively prevented by immunization, but *Aedes* now causes massive epidemics of dengue fever. Where several serotypes of dengue are being intensely transmitted, as in many cities of south-east Asia, a severe and often lethal haemorrhagic shock syndrome occurs and can be a major cause of child mortality. For instance, in an epidemic in Thailand in 1987, 174 285 cases and 1007 deaths were reported, over 89% of the cases and deaths in infants and children under 14 years of age (*31*). The increasing *Culex* populations of urban Asia and East Africa are not only a massive biting nuisance, they also transmit lymphatic filariasis, which is on the increase in tropical cities. The causes of, and solutions to, the *Aedes* and *Culex* problems are primarily environmental. Insecticides in water cisterns may assist in combating *Aedes*, and expanded polystyrene heads can prevent *Culex* breeding in flooded pit latrines.

Wastewater is often the medium through which pollutants or pathogens can affect humans. Where water is scarce, the use of urban sewage and wastewater for irrigation is taking place on an increasing scale. Often, the sewage is partially treated and this makes it necessary to set firm limits on the crops grown and to institute appropriate techniques for water application such as "drip" and "bubble" irrigation.. Even then there are increased health risks for farmers and consumers, although health education can reduce them. In east and south-east Asia raw excreta are often used to fertilize ponds used for aquaculture. The main health hazards arise when water is used for other domestic purposes or when fish infected with human parasites from faeces are eaten inadequately cooked or raw. Similar problems result from virus contamination of marine shellfish by sewage.

Strategies

The fact that fresh water is limited both in quality and in quantity in most places indicates the need for comprehensive water management involving representatives of all water users. Among the objectives of such management are to ensure that the best use is made of available supplies (including protection from pollution) and to limit conflicts over access to fresh water.

Good water management should be based on recognition of the importance of safe and sufficient supplies for health and on the fact that fresh water is a scarce and finite resource and has a cost that, wherever possible, its users should bear.

Sound financial practices play an important and often neglected part in achieving better water management. They include pricing structures that reflect real costs and encourage efficient use; users of large amounts of water (including large industrial and agricultural concerns) are often charged well below cost and are encouraged to overuse water, while a high proportion of the population lack access to piped water. A central aim of sound financial practice is to ensure that revenue from water sales is sufficient to maintain the water supply and management system. This involves demand management, cost containment to reduce wastage and ensure appropriate allocation of fresh water resources to competing uses, and cost recovery to manage demand and ensure the sustainability of the service.

Consideration should be given to:

— management of quantity by revising the allocation of water to different users
— safeguarding quality by clear and enforceable pollution control
— encouraging all techniques and technologies promoting economical use of fresh water, its recycling or reuse, and reduction of water pollution
— managing water distribution and wastewater collection and treatment on a more equal basis
— involving all sectors and groups in the community in the decision-making process.

In the many regions or settlements where there is a risk of floods, a central component of water resources management is a combination of mitigation of their effects and disaster preparedness, i.e., measures taken to limit the effects of floods when they happen (or to reduce their scale) and to ensure prompt action to limit adverse effects on health.

An example of a methodology for reaching consensus at community level on the use of available water resources (or other natural resources) is primary environmental care, which was developed to promote sustainable development at the community level (*32, 33*). Inspired by the principles that underlie primary health care, it is based on an analysis of the factors contributing to the success of 80 innovative projects concerned with environmental health management. It proposes nine principles to guide outside agencies in their work with local communities to meet human needs, manage resource use within sustainable levels, and ensure environmental protection (Box 41).

Box 41. Primary environmental care

Primary environmental care (PEC) is a process by which local groups or communities organize themselves with varying degrees of outside support to apply their skills and knowledge to the care of their natural resources and environment while satisfying livelihood needs. Primary environmental care has three integral elements: satisfaction of basic needs; protection and optimal utilization of the environment; and empowering of groups and communities.

Development projects that followed PEC guidelines produced improvements in water supply and sanitation, agricultural yields, and natural resource management, better health care and family planning, and improved access to housing, employment, and income-generating activities. An analysis of 80 successful projects suggested nine guidelines for success:

- **Build on local knowledge and resources.** In rural areas, poor households often rely on a mix of agricultural produce, wild plants and animals, remittances, and trading. At the strategic level, it is impossible to predict their needs and preferences, especially in resource-poor areas where there is great spatial and social diversity (*34*, *35*). In urban areas using the knowledge, resources, and capacity of low-income groups has resulted in the installation of community water and sanitation systems in low-income settlements with all costs recovered, cheap and effective drainage and garbage collection systems, and construction of housing more appropriate for comfort, safety, and control of disease vectors (*36–39*).

- **Build on and work with local social organization and management systems.** Local organizations are often crucial for sustainable resource use and development because they can act as institutions for resource management and control. They include water management committees, water user groups, neighbourhood groups, youth and women's groups, housing societies, farmer experimentation groups, church groups, mothers' groups, and grazing management groups. They enforce rules, provide incentives, and impose penalties designed to achieve rational and effective use of resources. Existing organizations are resources to be strengthened and developed, not ignored (*40*, *41*).

- **Build on locally available resources and technologies.** Resource-poor rural areas without an infrastructure that are far from roads and markets and have an uncertain climate and poor soil typically produce some five times less food per unit area than irrigated and lowland areas near cities. Yet the potential for improving resource use without recourse to external aid is great. The development of appropriate pesticide, nutrient, and water management practices can lead to a doubling or tripling of the yield of crops, livestock, and trees.

Box 41 (continued)

- **Use participatory methods for planning, implementation, monitoring, and evaluation.** Outside agencies and professionals working in participatory ways have repeatedly found that low-income rural and urban inhabitants have a great deal of knowledge that will help to introduce innovations. They are no longer seen simply as informants but also as teachers, extension workers, activists, and monitors of change.

- **Mutually agree the correct entry points for initiating projects.** PEC projects start as small and cheap. They have an uncomplicated design and do not try to over-innovate. Successfully introduced technologies are commonly low-risk, easy to teach, and provide clear, direct benefits in the coming season or year.

- **Permit project flexibility.** PEC approaches show that it is impossible to predict the results of participatory planning and development without sustained contact with potential beneficiaries. A common feature of successful projects has been an early period of experimentation. Discussion, often long, allows outsiders to learn and replan. Many successful projects have changed priorities and adapted practice to meet needs. For example, in Kenya a forestry project to teach farmers tree planting and raising was changed when it was learnt that 30% of farms already had micro-nurseries (*42*).

- **Maintain an open-ended approach to the duration of the project.** PEC projects are of realistic length so as to achieve real social and natural resource change and development. Projects less than five years in duration have a much greater chance of failure than those of 5–10 or more years (*43*). The need to give sustained support is increasingly being recognized as an important complement to the long-term sequential view of resource use and management taken by communities.

- **Encourage multiplication strategies.** As PEC projects start small, considerable attention is paid to replication beyond the active project boundaries. The best educators are the rural or urban beneficiaries themselves, so innovative extension methods promote group demonstrations, visits, workshops, and farmer-to-farmer extension to achieve effective multiplication.

- **Encourage the appropriate attitude in project professionals.** PEC implies new roles for project staff and local people. Outsiders establish rapport, convene, catalyse, facilitate, and inquire; choose, adapt, and improve methods; watch, listen, and learn.

Sources: Pretty, J. & Sandbrook, R. *Operationalizing sustainable development at the community level: primary environmental care.* Paper presented to members of the DAC working party on development assistance and the environment, London, OECD, IIED, 1991; and Borrini, G., ed. *Lessons learnt in community-based environmental management*, Rome, Istituto Superiore di Sanità, 1991.

The control of bacterial and parasitic waterborne diseases remains a priority, but contamination of water by heavy metals and other chemicals should also be prevented or minimized.

Major developments over the past 20 years in the application of new or revised techniques in water supply and sanitation have produced a range of options that permit cost-effective solutions appropriate to local conditions, cultures, and circumstances and can greatly improve health and environmental conditions. Experience with health care systems and basic services in the past ten years suggests that multisectoral intervention has much greater impact and cost-effectiveness, for instance when improved water supply and sanitation are combined with health care and hygiene education and, where needed, drainage. What is lacking in most developing countries is a strategy and the institutional framework to benefit from this experience.

The International Drinking Water Supply and Sanitation Decade (1981–90) made considerable progress in enhancing the importance given by many governments to water supplies and sanitation, although the ambitious targets set for the decade have not been met. Perhaps as important as the increased coverage of the population achieved in these ten years has been the great increase in knowledge about the range of techniques and technologies and the most effective means of improving water and sanitation in ways appropriate to local conditions, resources, and people's preferences. The decade also brought improved coordination between development assistance agencies.

At the same time, a number of obstacles were brought to light, the removal of which would significantly increase the performance of existing water supply and sanitation facilities. Among these factors were insufficient provision and use of funds, poor management, inappropriate system design, poor operation and maintenance standards, inadequate legal frameworks, and overlapping responsibilities.

Among the key lessons from the Decade (*18, 23, 44*) is the need for:
— more attention to strengthening the ability of communities or local government to run and maintain (and where possible build or improve) water or sanitation systems; for aid projects this means that they should be implemented within the existing administrative framework and not by the creation of autonomous or semi-autonomous project implementation units
— more emphasis on integrating water and sanitation improvements with other improvements, including environmental hygiene and primary health care
— involving local populations in decisions about the type of intervention, the design, implementation, and evaluation of projects and the sharing of capital and recurrent costs

— survey and analysis of local environmental hygiene conditions, prevailing disease patterns, and relevant socioeconomic factors as inputs into the design and implementation of interventions

— more emphasis on the needs of those who have the primary responsibility for infant and child care, cooking, washing, and domestic hygiene (in most instances women), and for their full involvement in decisions about the nature and level of the projects planned, cost, types of repayment, and provision for maintenance

— specifying the role of nongovernmental organizations; NGOs, including many in developing countries, have often proved successful in promoting low-cost and effective approaches.

Box 42 describes a water supply project in Ethiopia that reflects this approach.

Improvements in the quality and availability of the water supply are usually possible at relatively low cost, especially if the best use is made of local resources and knowledge. Certain points are worth noting:

• Better maintenance and repair of existing water systems can often significantly increase the water supply. Many water supply systems lose 60% of the water from leaks in the pipes; reducing the leakage rate from 60% to 12% (the typical figure for systems in the United Kingdom or the United States) would more than double the amount of water available for use (*23*). Just 20% of the leaks often account for 80% of the water losses (*45*).

• The design of water systems needs to be based on an analysis of local problems that assesses which combination of actions would make best use of local resources. Various approaches that may be considered unconventional by engineers trained in developed countries may prove to be the cheapest and most effective options; for instance, in some localities government support to make water vendors more efficient and to improve water quality might be the most cost-effective option. In others, making use of local water sources for small independent networks for particular city areas may be more cost-effective than extending the water mains system. In areas with sufficient rainfall, grants to households to install guttering and rainwater tanks may be a cheap way of improving supplies (*23*).

Perhaps one of the most important advances over the past 20 years is in knowledge of how to work with low-income groups and their community organizations. They should be actively involved in designing, implementing, and running water supply and sanitation schemes, with women taking a primary role since they usually manage household water supplies and suffer most from inadequate provision. An institutional framework should be developed to ensure effective partnership between local governments and

---

Box 42. The Dodota Water Supply Project in Ethiopia

Dodota is a district covering 300 km^2 in the Arsi region of Ethiopia; it had some 60 800 inhabitants in 1988. The mean annual rainfall is about 600 mm and the area often suffers from drought. In 1980, at a meeting between representatives from local women's associations and staff from SIDA's Women in Development programme, unanimous agreement was reached that drinking-water was their primary need. A project was developed with cooperation between the national women's association, the regional rural development unit (ARSI), and SIDA. The project involved developing two springs and laying pipelines to a series of small reservoirs, which then served distribution systems in three small towns and various villages. The local population did much of the work; people from each peasant association dug the trenches for the pipes and taps in their own village and made a small contribution to the cost of the project. A training programme was set up to teach the women to operate and manage the water system. Each peasant association had to elect a member for training. In all, 131 women were trained to administer and manage the project, keep the books, collect fees from those drawing water, and construct and maintain the pipelines.

An evaluation of the project found high levels of satisfaction among the local people and substantial increases in per caput consumption, even though those using the water system had to pay (although a low price). Many of those who had lived far from a perennial water source thought that they now paid less for water then they had done previously; some had been forced to buy water during the dry season, others had invested in donkeys and containers, which also cost more than they now paid. Many people also used the water they purchased for other purposes—for small numbers of goats and calves or for growing vegetables and trees or making alcohol for sale. There was less stomach trouble and almost no diarrhoea, especially among the children, and local people stated that their children grew faster and began to walk at a much earlier age. People also said that they washed themselves and their clothes more frequently and that the new water supplies meant major savings in time spent collecting water. The total cost per person was about US$ 30.

Source: Poluha, E. et al. *Concern and responsibility: an evaluation of the Dodota water supply project in Ethiopia.* Stockholm, Swedish International Development Authority, 1990.

---

community organizations. Box 43 describes this shift from community development through community participation to community management.

Recommendations

Governments and international agencies should make a renewed commitment to improving water supply and sanitation and carefully review current

Box 43. From community participation to community management in water and sanitation

One of the key lessons of the 1980s is that, to promote a healthy environment, water and sanitation programmes must be formulated around various other interventions including preventive health care, hygiene education, nutrition improvement, and promotion of literacy. During the 1980s an increasing number of development assistance agencies joined in a coordinated programme to meet the goals of the United Nations International Drinking Water Supply and Sanitation Decade. Most governments and international agencies had as their primary goal expansion of the number of people reached with water and sanitation; most resources went to the construction of new systems. Expansion of the coverage became the criterion for success and little attention was paid to whether the systems functioned as designed or, indeed, whether people actually used them. Considerable efforts were devoted to the development of new handpumps, excreta disposal systems, and water treatment processes, but relatively little effort or money went to understanding the linkage between improved health and improved water and sanitation or developing health-related design criteria. The conventional "top-down" programming and project implementation left in its wake thousands of unusable, costly installations in the form of derelict water treatment plants and broken handpumps, and communities with the same, if not worse, health conditions as before. Addressing the health problems associated with inadequate water and sanitation might need broadly based strategies, but these were difficult to implement and rarely fitted the more narrow objectives of the government or aid agency departments responsible for water and sanitation.

Ironically, the lack of financial and human resources to promote rapid expansion of the coverage eventually forced governments and external agencies to adopt radical new approaches. Changes arose from the realization that many more facilities could be built with existing resources and their use and maintenance improved if the intended beneficiaries were involved at all stages of development and operation. Water and sanitation agencies also began to recognize the key roles that could be taken by women, community leaders, and other groups with recognized competence and authority. There was a growing emphasis on the social and institutional aspects rather than on the construction of systems.

This shift can be seen in the terminology used in water and sanitation programmes. Twenty years ago "community development" was used to describe the generation of local contributions. At the start of the Decade the emphasis shifted to "community participation". The current terminology refers to "community management", as a process in which there is local acceptance of responsibility for and control of water and sanitation services. Communities need to be motivated and adequately supported if they are to fulfil these roles. Considerable strengthening of hygiene education is needed to orient users of water supply and

---

Box 43 (continued)

sanitation facilities to their potential health benefits and to promote proper use and maintenance practices.

Over the course of the Decade new approaches in institution building, human resources development, and hygiene education have focused on underserved populations, mainly in rural and urban fringe areas where major investments in water and sanitation remain scarce. In many countries there has also been increased reliance on non-governmental organizations to expand the coverage. NGOs have proved to be especially effective in promoting appropriate low-cost technologies in areas where they have had sufficient field staff to provide the necessary support.

Technologies should be designed to foster a healthy environment that not only improves water quality and reduces disease transmission, but also lessens the human (usually women's) burden of carrying water. Training programmes that incorporate both technical and health issues are needed at all levels from university professionals to community workers to sensitize water and sanitation personnel to the overriding health objectives of these services. Schoolchildren and adults need user education to understand their responsibilities towards their water and sanitation system. A related element is community involvement, especially that of women, in the planning, implementation, and operation of their systems. Governments need to find better ways of integrating the various ministries and local organizations, and development assistance agencies must support health-related issues in countries by promoting sustainable projects, expanded community involvement and management, effective coordination between government agencies, and the integration of technologies, training, and health education. Community-based development requires that the chosen technology should be appropriate to local conditions, and this has encouraged better communication between local institutions, national governments, and outside donors.

Sources: Warner, D.B. & Laugeri, L. Health for all: the legacy of the water decade. *Water international*, **16**: 135–141(1991); Beyer, M. *Water and sanitation in UNICEF, 1946–86*, New York. UNICEF, 1987 (History Monograph Series).

---

policies to see if they have benefited from the lessons learnt from the International Decade. Such lessons should include better integration of water supply, sanitation, drainage, and hygiene education, and greater attention to the maintenance of a water and sanitation infrastructure.

Box 44 lists the recommendations of a WHO working group on operation and maintenance.

Governments, especially those in the arid and semi-arid areas of the world, should consider wastewater to be an integral part of their water resources. Its use for irrigation adds nutrients and humus-like organic matter

---

Box 44. Recommendations on making water supply investments more effective

1. To ensure long-term sustainability, water should be managed as a commodity in exactly the same way as any other resource. Its use and exploitation should be on a financially sound and cost-effective basis subject to the same legal and regulatory controls as other resources to ensure its conservation, protection and wise utilization.
2. The supply of water to consumers should normally be based on the principle of *effective demand*, which can be defined as the standard of service that the users are willing to maintain, operate and finance to ensure adequate public health standards. The effective demand has to satisfy the priorities of the community at large.
3. Water systems should be managed and operated following the principles of good business practices. The form of management will vary depending on the local situation, i.e. rural, urban, semi-urban, location, age structure etc. The responsible agency should be autonomous but should manage the system under technical, financial and administrative guidelines set by the national government. The agency should be fully accountable to its consumers.
4. Greater emphasis should be given to sanitation development and to closer links with water supply and solid and liquid waste management in the planning of new programmes. The basic needs of the poor should be recognized. Governments should require agencies to provide services at preferential tariffs to such groups or institute subsidies to promote public health.

Source: *Proceedings of the meeting of the Operation and Maintenance Working Group.* Geneva, World Health Organization, 1990 (unpublished document, WHO/CWS/90.14; available on request from Division of Environmental Health, World Health Organization, 1211 Geneva 27, Switzerland).

---

to the soil, thus contributing to increased crop yields while reducing the need for synthetic fertilizers. It also saves groundwater and precludes the discharge of wastewater to rivers and lakes, thus protecting sources of water supply.

Recommendations for research

Research should be aimed at the development of appropriate water and sanitation systems technically adapted to local skills, materials, and equipment and economically feasible, culturally acceptable, and environmentally sound. In particular, the following subjects should be studied:

— practical water treatment systems for the removal of iron, fluoride, and manganese ions and the control of hardness and corrosiveness

— water conservation methods such as rainwater harvesting, fog condensation, and underground dams
— stabilization ponds for wastewater, designed to reduce evaporation losses and optimize land use
— treatment technology for the use of wastewater for irrigation, e.g., slow and rapid sand filters, horizontal or up-flow roughing filters, secondary settling units for removal of helminths
— the integration of latrines and simple biogas systems that use animal and human wastes
— handpumps: the problems of pollution from zinc, galvanized parts, and nitrates, and of the depression of groundwater tables.

Research should identify and test appropriate combinations of public and private sector agencies, NGOs, community organizations, and women's groups in the planning, financing, operation, and maintenance of water supply and sanitation systems in peri-urban and rural areas. In particular, the following subjects should be considered:

— the development of institutional structures and resource transfer mechanisms needed to provide services to low-income communities
— the development of methodologies to assess the capacity and performance of institutions in operating and maintaining water supply and sanitation systems
— the design of legal instruments to enforce public health regulations
— the organization of community participation in water supply and sanitation systems.

Research should identify the water supply and sanitation systems that, within local constraints, maximize health benefits and minimize risks, and develop the database needed to establish guidelines on health-related matters. In particular, it should

— carry out epidemiological studies on the use of wastewater, sludge, and excreta in agriculture and aquaculture
— evaluate the effectiveness of the methods of human exposure control applied to systems using wastewater for irrigation
— develop guidelines for the safe use of domestic/industrial wastewater for irrigation, taking into account both chemical and biological contamination.

Research should aim at defining levels and mechanisms of cost recovery that can be effectively implemented in order to contribute to the financial sustainability of the service institutions; and at developing alternative models, including tariff-setting and financial planning, for supporting the sector when its cost cannot be covered by its beneficiaries.

References and notes

1. L'Lvovich, M.I. & White, G.F. Use and transformation of terrestrial water systems. In: Turner, B.L., ed. *The earth transformed by human action: global and regional changes in the biosphere over the past 300 years.* Cambridge, Cambridge University Press, 1990.

2. World Resources Institute. *World resources 1990–91.* Oxford, Oxford University Press, 1990.

3. World Resources Institute. *World resources, 1988–89.* New York, Basic Books, 1988.

4. *The state of the environment.* Paris, Organisation for Economic Co-operation and Development, 1991.

5. Clarke, R. *Water—the international crisis.* London, Earthscan Publications, 1991.

6. Kassas, M. Drought and desertification. *Land use policy,* **4**: 389–400 (1987).

7. Douglass, M. The environmental sustainability of development—coordination, incentives and political will in land use planning for the Jakarta metropolis. *Third World planning review,* **11** (2): 211–238 (1989).

8. Hueb, J.A. *El programa de control de perdidas como estrategia para el desarrollo de instituciones de agua potable e saneamiento.* Lima, CEPIS, 1986 (Hojas de Divulgación Tecnica No. 34).

9. SABESP/CNEC. *Master plan for utilization of the hydraulic resources for the São Paulo metropolitan area.* São Paulo, 1986.

10. WHO Commission on Health and the Environment. *Report of the Panel on Food and Agriculture.* Geneva, World Health Organization, 1992 (unpublished document WHO/EHE/92.2).

11. WHO Technical Report Series, No. 778, 1989 (*Health guidelines for the use of wastewater in agriculture and aquaculture:* report of a WHO Scientific Group).

12. **India**: Centre for Science and Environment. *The state of India's environment 1982: a citizen's report.* Delhi, 1982; **Karachi**: Beg, M. et al. Land-based pollution and the marine environment of the Karachi coasi. *Pakistan journal of science, industry and resources,* **27** (4): 199–205 (1984); **Bogotá**: Castaneda, F.C. The risks of environmental degradation in Bogotá, Colombia. *Urbanization and environment,* **1** (1): 16–21 (1989); **Alexandria**: Hamza, A. An appraisal of environmental consequences of urban development in Alexandria, Egypt. *Environment and urbanization,* **1** (1): 22–30 (1989); **Shanghai**: Sivaramakrishnan, K.C. & Green, L. *Metropolitan management—the Asian experience.* Oxford, Oxford University Press (for the World Bank), 1986; **Peninsular Malaysia**: Maheswaran, A. Water pollution in Malaysia: problems, perspectives and control. In: *Development and the environment crisis—a Malaysian case.* Penang, Consumers Association of Penang, 1982, and Sahabat Alam. *Environmental news digest,* No. 4, 1986; **São Paulo**: see reference *9*.

13. Kebe, M. The West and Central African action plan. *The Siren*, No. 37, July 1988, pp. 31–34.

14. Sahil. Marine pollution and the Indus Delta. *House journal of National Institute of Oceanography (Karachi)*, **1**: 57–61 (1988).

15. Smil, V. *The bad earth: environmental degradation in China*. New York, M.E. Sharpe, and London, Zed Press, 1984.

16. Cairncross, S. & Feachem, R.G. *Environmental health engineering in the tropics—an introductory text*. Chichester, John Wiley and Sons, 1983.

17. White, G.F. et al. *Drawers of water: domestic water use in East Africa*. Chicago, University of Chicago Press, 1972.

18. Warner, D.B. & Laugeri, L. Health for all: the legacy of the water decade. *Water international*, **16**: 135–141 (1991).

19. van der Schalie, H. Aswan dam revisited—the blood fluke thrives. *Environment*, **16**: 18–26 (1974).

20. Rosenfield, P.A. *The management of schistosomiasis*. Washington, DC, Resources for the Future, 1979 (Research Paper R-16).

21. Esrey, S.A. et al. *Health benefits from improvements in water supply and sanitation: survey and analysis of the literature on selected diseases*. Washington, DC, USAID, 1990 (WASH Technical Report, No. 66).

22. Prost, A. & Négrel, A.D. Water, trachoma and conjunctivitis. *Bulletin of the World Health Organization*, **67** (1): 9–18 (1989).

23. Cairncross, S. Water supply and the urban poor. In: Hardoy, J.E. et al., eds., *The poor die young: housing and health in Third World cities*, London, Earthscan Publications, 1990, pp. 109–126.

24. *The International Drinking Water Supply and Sanitation Decade: review of decade progress* (as of December 1988). Geneva, World Health Organization, 1990 (unpublished document).

25. Hardoy, J.E. & Satterthwaite, D. *Squatter citizen: life in the urban Third World*. London, Earthscan Publications, 1989.

26. UNICEF. *The state of the world's children 1990*. Oxford, Oxford University Press, 1990.

27. **Asian cities**: Sivaramakrishnan, K.C. & Green, L. *Metropolitan management—the Asian experience*. Oxford, Oxford University Press (for the World Bank), 1986; **additional information on Bangkok**: Phantumvanit, D. & Liengcharernsit, W. Coming to terms with Bangkok's environmental problems. *Environment and urbanization*, **1** (1): 31–39 (1989): United Nations. *Population growth and policies in mega-cities: Bangkok*. New York, Department of International Economic and

142

Social Affairs, 1987 (Population Policy Paper No. 10); **additional information on Karachi**: Sahil. Marine pollution and the Indus Delta, *House journal of National Institute of Oceanography (Karachi)*, **1**: 57–61 (1988); United Nations. *Population growth and policies in mega-cities: Karachi*. New York, Department of International Economic and Social Affairs, 1988 (Population Policy Paper No. 13); **additional information on Manila**: Jimenez, R.D. & Velasquez, A. Metropolitan Manila: a framework for its sustained development. *Environment and urbanization*, **1** (1): 51–58 (1989). **African cities**: chapters in Stren, R.E. & White, R.R. eds., *African cities in crisis*, Boulder, CO, Westview Press, 1989, especially: Ngom, T. Appropriate standards for infrastructure in Dakar, pp. 176–202; Kulaba, S. Local government and the management of urban services in Tanzania, pp. 203–245; El Sammani, M.O. et al. Management problems of Greater Khartoum, pp. 246–275; and Mbuyi, K. Kinshasa: problems of land management, infrastructure and food supply, pp. 148–175.

28. Adrianzen, T. & Graham, G.G. The high cost of being poor; water. *Archives of environmental health*, **28**: 312–315 (1974).

29. World Bank. *Urban policy and economic development: an agenda for the 1990s*. Washington, DC, 1991.

30. Kalbermatten, J.M. et al. *Appropriate technology for water supply and sanitation: a review of the technical and economic options*. Washington, DC, World Bank, 1980.

31. *Global estimates for health situation assessment and projections 1990*. Geneva, World Health Organization, 1990 (unpublished WHO document WHO/HST/90.2; available on request from Division of Epidemiological Surveillance and Health Situation and Trend Assessment, World Health Organization, 1211 Geneva 27, Switzerland).

32. Pretty, J. & Sandbrook, R. *Operationalizing sustainable development at the community level: primary environmental care*. Paper presented to members of the DAC working party on development assistance and the environment, London, International Institute for Environment and Development, 1991.

33. Borrini, G. *Lessons learnt in community-based environmental management*. Rome, Istituto Superiore di Sanità, 1991.

34. Agarwal, A. & Narain, S. *Towards green villages*. Delhi, Centre for Science and Environment, 1989.

35. Pretty, J.N. *Rapid catchment analysis for extension agents: notes on the Kericho training workshop for the Ministry of Agriculture*. London, International Institute for Environment and Development, 1990.

36. Arlosoroff, S. et al. *Community water supply; the handpump option*. Washington, DC, World Bank, 1987.

37. Schofield, C.J. et al. The role of house design in limiting vector-borne disease. In: Hardoy, J.E. et al., eds. *The poor die young—housing and health in Third World cities*, London, Earthscan Publications, 1990.

38. Sinnatamby, G. Low cost sanitation. In: Hardoy, J. E. et al., eds. *The poor die young—housing and health in Third World cities.* London, Earthscan Publications, 1990.

39. *Community participation and women's involvement in water supply and sanitation projects.* The Hague, International Water and Sanitation Centre, 1988.

40. Murphy, D. Community organizations in Asia. *Environment and urbanization*, **2** (1): 51–60 (1990).

41. Rahman, M. A., ed. *Grassroots participation and self-reliance.* New Delhi, Oxford and IBH Publications, 1984.

42. Chavangi, N. A. & Ngugi, A. W. *Innovatory participation in programme design; tree planting for increased fuelwood supply for rural households in Kenya.* Paper presented at a workshop on farmers and agricultural research, Institute of Development Studies, University of Sussex.

43. Uphoff, N. Paraprojects as new modes of international development assistance. *World development,* **18**: 1401–1411 (1990).

44. Beyer, MG. *Water and sanitation in UNICEF, 1946–1986.* New York, UNICEF, 1987.

45. Bachmann, G. & Hammerer, M. 80 percent of losses come from 20 percent of leaks. *World water,* **7** (10): 48–50 (1984).

144

5.
Energy

Introduction

The central role of energy in economic and social development has long been recognized and a great deal of effort has been devoted to developing technologies for the extraction, production, and use of all types of energy. The aim has always been to reduce costs, make systems more efficient, and provide access to previously untapped energy sources. In recent decades reducing the adverse environmental and health effects has also become an aim.

Wealth is dependent on the availability of energy; the wealthiest countries and households within countries have the highest per caput levels of energy consumption. Increasing demand for energy may mean a change in energy sources, for example from biomass fuels such as wood, dung, and crop wastes, widely used in poorer societies, to fossil fuels, and within fossil fuels from coal to oil and natural gas. Such a change is usually associated with rising income and more commercialized energy sources. Increasingly, industrial and service-based production structures and higher per caput income also imply an increasing demand for electricity because of its greater flexibility of use. Most electricity is generated by fossil-fuelled power stations, hydropower or, in a number of developed countries, nuclear power. These changes have important implications for health and for the environment.

Fossil fuels account for nearly 90% of the world's commercial energy production. The developed countries, with some 25% of the world's population, account for more than 70% of the world's fossil fuel consumption. Box 45 shows the level of fossil fuel consumption by region in 1985. The concentration of fossil fuel consumption in Europe, North America, and the USSR is the result both of the energy intensity of production systems (in industry, agriculture and, to a lesser extent, services) and of the consumption levels of their populations, especially in the heating or cooling of homes and the use of automobiles. The per caput energy consumption of commercial fuels will need to increase considerably in the poorer countries if they are to develop the more productive and stable economic bases on which developed

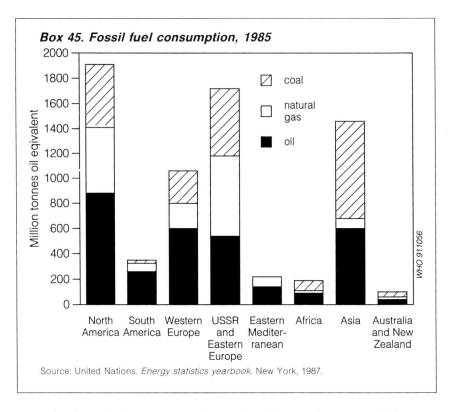

Box 45. Fossil fuel consumption, 1985

Y-axis: Million tonnes oil eqivalent (0–2000)

Legend: coal, natural gas, oil

Categories: North America, South America, Western Europe, USSR and Eastern Europe, Eastern Mediterranean, Africa, Asia, Australia and New Zealand

WHO 911056

Source: United Nations. *Energy statistics yearbook*. New York, 1987.

countries depend. A strong commitment by all countries to the efficient use of energy can keep such an increase within bounds.

Energy use and health

The largest consumers of fossil fuels are the countries of North America and Europe. The average per caput commercial consumption of fossil fuels in developed countries is about ten times that of the developing countries. The difference is much larger between some of the richest countries and the poorer ones; commercial energy consumption in Norway, the United States, and Canada is 40–50 times that of the poorer African or Asian countries. Part of the difference may be explained by the greater need in colder climates for space heating, although air-conditioning of buildings may make space cooling as energy-intensive as "space heating".

There are significant differences between countries in the industrial world that have no simple relationship to levels of industrialization or wealth. For instance Japan, with one of the world's highest per caput GDPs, has one of the lowest levels of energy consumption relative to its GDP among OECD countries (Box 46).

Box 46. Energy requirements per unit of GDP and trends over time

Country	Energy intensity[a] (TOE/1000 $)	Change in energy intensity[b]	
		1980	1988
Japan	0.27	84	69
Switzerland	0.28	107	103
Italy	0.32	87	77
France	0.37	92	84
Federal Republic of Germany	0.41	89	77
United Kingdom	0.41	80	67
OECD average	0.41	89	75
USA	0.44	88	73
Spain	0.45	123	116
Australia	0.47	98	87
Netherlands	0.48	98	87
Sweden	0.52	90	89
Greece	0.58	123	137
Canada	0.64	93	80
Turkey	0.79	163	161

[a] Energy efficiency is calculated by dividing the total energy consumption (measured in tonnes of oil equivalent, TOE) by the GDP at 1985 prices and exchange rates.
[b] Relative to 1970 (= 100).

Source: OECD. *The state of the environment.* Paris, Organisation for Economic Co-operation and Development, 1991.

The relationship between economic growth and energy demand has weakened in most OECD countries, higher energy prices and energy conservation policies of governments both contributing to this (*1*). So too has structural change in most economies, for instance the increasing importance of services and light manufacturing industry and the declining importance of many heavy industries with among the highest energy inputs per unit value of output. The increasing energy intensity in Greece, Spain, and Turkey between 1970 and 1988 in terms of energy consumption per unit of GDP is worth noting.

Apart from the indirect relationship between energy and health, many energy-dependent processes offer direct benefits to health. The large reduction in health risks from food contamination in the developed world owes much to improved food handling, storing, packaging, and cooking, all of which are dependent on fossil fuels or electricity. Domestic and commercial refrigerators have brought major benefits in terms of safer storage of food. Cooking stoves bring many advantages; cooking food in an earthenware pot over an open fire may fail to eliminate pathogens because of inadequate heating and may also consume up to eight times more energy than metal cooking pots on a gas stove.

The provision of health care is highly energy-dependent. Hospitals cannot function effectively without uninterrupted sources of electricity, and this implies a need for emergency generators. Hospitals and health care centres cannot be effective in the absence of motorized vehicles, including ambulances and other public service vehicles. Health care personnel (including midwives and health educators) need transport to reach patients, and the distribution of drugs and medical equipment is dependent on transport systems. Many other basic services important for good health are energy-dependent, including diagnostic and surgical procedures, the production of drugs and the provision of piped water and services to collect and safely dispose of household and human wastes.

Environmental and health effects of energy production and use

Almost all forms of energy production and use have the potential to produce environmental changes that may give rise to direct or indirect adverse effects on human health. Such changes may arise as a consequence of routine practices in the production and use of energy, or as a result of an accident. The health effects are seen at different points in energy production and use, for instance at the extraction of energy or tapping of energy sources, the transmission of energy to users and its use, including for some fuels the emission of pollutants and the disposal of wastes or residues. The scale and nature of the health risks and their location vary considerably, depending on the energy source.

Fossil fuels and air pollution

Fossil fuels are the largest source of atmospheric pollution, and the growth in pollution has paralleled the growth of modern industry, power plants, the domestic use of coal, and the expansion of road transport. Complete combustion of fossil fuels produces carbon dioxide and water together with some oxides of nitrogen generated by the fixation of atmospheric nitrogen at high temperatures. Incomplete combustion leads to black smoke, comprised of finely divided particles of carbon or complex hydrocarbons, or to carbon monoxide and a range of partially oxidized organic compounds. However, all fossil fuels have minor components and impurities, which account at most for 1–2% by weight but which also contribute substantially to the emission of pollutants. Fossil fuels contain organic or inorganic sulfur compounds in varying amounts; while removal at source is practicable for natural gas and possible for the lighter fractions of oil, it is more difficult for coal. Most of the sulfur present in fossil fuels is emitted as sulfur dioxide. Other inorganic impurities, particularly in coal, include traces of a wide range of metals. The more volatile metals such as mercury are emitted in the vapour phase. Others are largely present in the ash residue but may to some extent be emitted with the gases.

The health effects of air pollution derived from energy use depend considerably on which energy source is chosen and the extent to which available technologies are used to control emissions. For instance, China has emerged as the largest single consumer of domestic coal. Eastern Europe probably uses more brown coal than any other part of the world. In China and in several East European countries the use of low-quality fossil fuels in factories and power plants, combined with inadequate controls on emissions, results in serious air pollution problems. The domestic use of similar fuels may aggravate the situation.

Large furnaces achieve more complete combustion of coal than is possible domestically, and the use of high chimney stacks and greater velocity of flue gases can disperse pollutants more effectively over greater distances thus minimizing the local effects; but this creates pollution problems further away. Old or poorly operated plants may still produce black smoke through incomplete combustion, contributing to fine particulate loads in the atmosphere near the source. Although residual ash is commonly removed from the flue gases by electrostatic precipitation, finer particles may escape. Inorganic components of the ash or semi-volatile metals accompanying it include lead, cadmium, mercury, molybdenum, and arsenic (2). These metals may present health hazards, as in parts of Czechoslovakia, where arsenic-containing coal has caused considerable contamination of the environment around power stations.

Most of the world's population is exposed to a mixture of air pollutants that may represent a health risk. More than 1000 million urban residents worldwide are exposed to outdoor air pollution levels higher than those recommended by WHO. Well over that number are exposed to indoor air pollution from coal or unprocessed biomass fuels burnt on open fires or unvented stoves. While information exists on the general magnitude of exposures associated with demonstrable effects on health, few definitive exposure/response relationships have been established. Acute effects from short-term exposure have been easier to define than chronic effects. Moreover, drawing up any consistent set of exposure/response relationships from the epidemiological studies carried out in different parts of the world is

Box 47. Some urban air pollutants and their effects on health

Traditional ('reducing') pollutants from coal/heavy oil combustion

SMOKE (SUSPENDED PARTICULATES) (some contributions from diesel traffic also) — Can penetrate to lungs, some retained; possible long-term effects. May irritate bronchi also

SULFUR DIOXIDE — Readily absorbed on inhalation: irritation of bronchi, with possibility of bronchospasm

SULFURIC ACID (mainly a secondary pollutant, formed from sulfur dioxide in air) — Hygroscopic: highly irritant if impacted in upper respiratory tract. Acid absorbed on other fine particles may penetrate further to produce bronchospasm

POLYCYCLIC AROMATIC HYDROCARBONS (small contributions from traffic also) — Mainly absorbed on to smoke: can penetrate with it to lungs

LONDON SMOG COMPLEX

Short-term effects: sudden increases in deaths, in hospital admissions, and in illness among bronchitic patients. Temporary reductions in lung function (patients and some normals)

Long-term effects: Increased frequency of respiratory infections (children). Increased prevalence of respiratory symptoms (adults and children). Higher death rates from bronchitis in polluted areas

Possible carcinogenic effects: May play some part in the higher incidence of lung cancer in urban areas

Photochemical ('oxidizing') pollutants from traffic sources, or other hydrocarbon emissions

HYDROCARBONS (volatile: petrol, etc.) — Non-toxic at moderate concentrations

NITRIC OXIDE — Capable of combining with haemoglobin in blood, but no apparent effect in humans

NITROGEN DIOXIDE / OZONE [Mainly secondary pollutants formed in photochemical reactions] — Neither gas is very soluble: some irritation of bronchi, but can penetrate to lungs to cause oedema at high concentrations. Urban concentrations too low for such effects, but evidence of reduced resistance to infections in animals

LOS ANGELES SMOG COMPLEX

Short-term effects: Primarily eye irritation. Reduced athletic performance. Possibly small changes in deaths, hospital admissions

Longer-term effects: Increased onsets of respiratory illnesses (children), increased asthma attacks (adults). No clear indication of increased bronchitis

Aldehydes, other partial oxidation products, peroxyacetylnitrate — Eye irritation, odour

Box 47 (continued)

Others from traffic

CARBON MONOXIDE (other sources contribute, and smoking an important one)

Combines with haemoglobin in blood, reducing oxygen-carrying capacity

Possible effects on central nervous system (reversible unless concentrations very high). Some evidence of effects on perception and performance of fine tasks at moderate concentrations. Enhances onset of exercise angina in patients. Urban concentrations too low for specific effects

LEAD (some industrial sources contribute to air lead; human intake often dominated by lead in food or drink)

Taken up in blood, distributed to soft tissues, and some to bone

Possible effects on central nervous system (longer time scale than in case of carbon monoxide, and not necessarily reversible). Indications of neuropsychological effects on children within overall environmental exposure range, but role of traffic lead uncertain

Source: Holland, W.W. et al., eds. *Oxford textbook of public health, 2nd ed. Vol. 2. Methods of public health.* Oxford, Oxford University Press, 1991.

complicated by the different mixtures of pollutants (and different methods for measuring particulates) as well as by differences in exposure to other factors such as tobacco smoke.

The usual urban mixture of air pollutants contains oxides of nitrogen and sulfur from burning of either coal or oil, suspended particulates of various kinds, including true smoke from the incomplete combustion of coal and from diesel vehicles, and inorganic compounds from the combustion of fossil fuels. Secondary reactions in the air result in the formation of acid sulfates. The major sources of urban air pollution are overwhelmingly coal-fired or oil-fired power stations, motor vehicles (cars, buses, motorcycles, trucks, and other vehicles with internal combustion engines), home cooking and heating (particularly if coal or biomass fuel is used), and industry. The relative contribution of the different sectors varies considerably from period to period and from city to city, and often from season to season. In many cities in the developed world, air pollution from industry is less of a problem, as the economic base is predominantly services and light manufacturing and there is little or no heavy industry. Box 47 lists the air pollutants produced by fossil fuels.

Air quality has improved in a number of cities in the developed world; trend analysis shows that emissions of sulfur dioxide, carbon monoxide, lead, polycyclic aromatic hydrocarbons, and particulates have all in general decreased in OECD countries from 1970 levels. This reflects stricter regulations on emissions, changes in energy structures and fuel prices, change from domestic consumption of coal to central provision of electricity and gas, the introduction of more efficient technologies, and the economic slowdown evident in the first part of the 1980s in Europe (1). By contrast, nitrogen oxides have tended to increase or, at best, remain stable, owing mainly to the growth in automobile traffic and in total mileage driven (1). Box 48 illustrates trends in air pollution in Milan, Italy, and shows the decline in sulfur dioxide concentrations from 1970 to 1989 (although still high at the end of the period) and the growth in nitrogen dioxide concentrations.

Air quality has deteriorated steadily in many cities in the developing world as both populations and pollution-generating activities continue to grow rapidly. The main contributors and their relative importance vary greatly from city to city. In cities with high concentrations of heavy industry, the industries themselves are usually the main contributor. In many cities, congested streets and poorly maintained motor vehicle engines contribute a great deal to air pollution.

Airborne lead remains a major problem in many cities where lead is still used as an additive in petrol, often in high concentrations; it can contaminate the soil and dust near busy roads, posing health risks to small children who breathe in such particulates or ingest them if they put soil in their mouths.

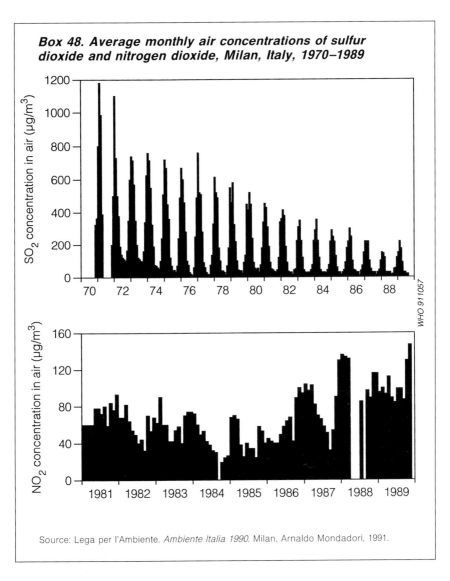

Box 48. Average monthly air concentrations of sulfur dioxide and nitrogen dioxide, Milan, Italy, 1970–1989

Source: Lega per l'Ambiente. *Ambiente Italia 1990.* Milan, Arnaldo Mondadori, 1991.

Lead may affect the neurological development of children. A WHO study of inner city schoolteachers in Mexico City revealed blood lead levels 2–4 times higher than in areas where low-lead fuel was in use (*3*). The data in Box 49 show lead pollution to be one of the most serious long-term environmental problems facing urban populations, if the results are confirmed in larger samples and in different circumstances. It would also be one of the easiest problems to solve, at least in part, by encouraging the use of unleaded petrol, as has already been done in some countries. However, because lead is retained in the top surface layer of the soil, it may continue to be a significant source

---

Box 49. Lead

Exposure to lead in childhood is associated with alterations of neurophysiological function, with effects that persist into early adulthood. Needleman et al. (1991) re-examined neurobehavioural function in a homogeneous group of young adults from well-to-do families who had been examined 11 years previously at the age of seven for both neurobehavioural performance and lead levels in their deciduous teeth. At both ages the lead levels were negatively correlated with performance. Young adults exposed to higher levels of lead in their infancy tended to be under-achievers; they had a lower standing in school, increased absenteeism, lower vocabulary and grammatical reasoning scores, poorer eye–hand coordination, and longer reaction times. None of the subjects presented clinical symptoms of lead poisoning either as children or as young adults. This is an example of a harmful exposure with lasting consequences on the mental development of children that only a decade-long follow-up and a complex statistical analysis of a host of functional tests was able to reveal.

Source: Needleman, H.L. et al. The long-term effects of exposure to low doses of lead in childhood. *New England journal of medicine*, **322**: 83–88 (1991).

---

of exposure in small children for a considerable time, even after the use of leaded petrol has been discontinued. On the other hand, leaded petrol is not the only source of lead in the human environment. Lead in the paint in old buildings and continued use of lead piping in areas supplied with acidic water are an even greater source of exposure for children in many poor neighbourhoods.

Various other pollutants may have serious health effects. High levels of sulfur dioxide in combination with smoke and particulates in urban air have been associated with increased mortality, particularly from cardiorespiratory disease, and more admissions to hospital with respiratory disease. At commonly found lower levels, increased frequencies of respiratory symptoms in adults and children have also been reported. Transient impairment of respiratory function has been induced by exposure to sulfur dioxide, asthmatics being particularly sensitive. Although reports are fragmentary, they provide a consistent picture of respiratory effects due to exposure to these pollutants (4).

Emissions from vehicles can have a disproportionate effect on exposure to primary pollutants because they tend to concentrate close to the ground. They have also become very important in relation to the formation of secondary (photochemical) pollutants. Road vehicles are the main contributors to oxides of nitrogen in such areas.

The major secondary pollutant is ozone formed within photochemical smog. The problem was first recognized in Los Angeles and it is now found widely throughout heavily populated urban centres, where it is closely linked with emissions from motor vehicles (5). Photochemical oxidants such as ozone and peroxyacetyl nitrates can cause discomfort and respiratory illness in sensitive individuals, who are estimated to constitute 1–5% of the total population. The concentration of photochemical oxidants rises during the day in the presence of strong sunlight, and in many regions of the world tends to reach its maximum some distance downwind of source areas, large regions having relatively uniform values. Within cities the concentrations may be lower in busy streets close to traffic than elsewhere.

In many cities the concentrations of air pollutants are already high enough to cause morbidity in susceptible individuals and premature mortality in the aged, particularly in those with respiratory problems. In Latin America, recent studies suggest that air pollution levels are sufficiently high in São Paulo, Rio de Janeiro, Belo Horizonte, Bogotá, Santiago, Mexico City, Monterrey, Guadalajara, Caracas, and Lima-Callao to justify high priority being given to control (6).

It is difficult, however, to assess the degree to which human health is being impaired by air pollution in cities around the world. Information on air quality levels is scarce, particularly in the poorer and less urbanized developing countries. In addition, direct epidemiological evidence of adverse health effects is also relatively limited.

Comparing the health of people living in highly polluted areas with those in less polluted areas shows a strong association between the incidence of acute respiratory infections and pollution levels. In industrial districts and areas where pollution is high, morbidity increases substantially in the dry winter months, when dust levels are 2–3 times greater than during wet periods. Box 50 gives an example of the link established between air pollution and reduced lung function in children in Cubatão, Brazil.

The extent to which air pollution poses a risk to the general public depends on a number of factors, including:

— the hazard of the compound released or of derivatives formed by chemical processes occurring within the air, including the stability and persistence of the agent within the environment and its ability to penetrate indoors;

— the amount of pollutant released and the height at which it is released; tall chimney stacks tend to protect local people but disperse the pollutant over a wider area;

— the atmospheric conditions leading to dilution and dispersal of the pollutant, including worst-case inversion conditions and geographical considerations; local topographical and climatic conditions can

---

Box 50. Air pollution and health: the case of Cubatão

Cubatão is a city in southern Brazil that has a high concentration of industry and significant pollution problems. Three studies that have been carried out related air pollution to health.

The first, in 1983, took a sample of children from each school and measured their lung function. The tests were chosen because they are relatively easy to do. Comparisons of lung function against a standard (for age and height) found a very high proportion of children with abnormally low lung function and a clear correlation between the children with the lowest lung function and the school areas with the highest levels of industrial air pollution. In 1983 the state environmental body began to impose environmental controls, fining many industries and closing others down because they contravened the regulations.

In 1985 the lung function tests were repeated. It was expected that there would be improvement since the levels of particulate matter, NO_x, and SO_2 had gone down. This proved to be the case except in eight schools where there was no improvement or lung function showed further deterioration. These were schools near to the industries where air pollution levels were still high.

A third study sought to measure lung function every day taking two cohorts of children, one already tested, another new. Children with bronchial problems or otherwise not in good health were excluded. The lung function of the children was normal but in each succeeding year the results, although still normal, were worse than those in the previous year. The conclusion was that, if air pollution was not drastically reduced, the children's lung function would reach abnormal levels.

Source: Hofmaier, V.A. *Efeitos de poluição do ar sobre a função pulmonar: un estudo de cohorte em criancas de Cubatão.* São Paulo, School of Public Health, 1991 (Doctoral thesis).

---

exacerbate the situation, as in Mexico City, where thermal inversions trap pollutants within the valley in which the city is located;
— the distance from the source;
— the composition, activities, and location of the general population in relation to the time of release (e.g., they might be exercising; children might be present);
— the presence of particularly susceptible individuals in the exposed groups.

A distinction must be drawn between acute air pollution episodes and high concentrations of pollutants prevalent throughout the year. Acute episodes brought about by high emissions and specific meteorological conditions can trap pollutants in the atmosphere and cause exceptionally high concentrations. They can last up to a week or more and are particularly serious in cities where topographical features help trap pollutants, for instance Los Angeles and Mexico City.

In regard to annual averages, an assessment of air pollution in over 50 cities throughout the world in developed and developing countries (7) showed that, in well over half of them, the levels of sulfur dioxide and suspended particulate matter, the pollutants most commonly measured, regularly exceeded the guidelines established by WHO. On the basis of these data, an estimated 1000 million people are living in cities where the WHO guidelines for sulfur dioxide and suspended particulate matter are exceeded.

Acute air pollution episodes occur at different times of the year. During the coldest months the combustion of fossil fuels can result in heavy emissions of sulfur oxides and suspended particulate matter. Warmer weather often causes acute episodes of photochemical oxidant pollution, especially in congested areas with high concentrations of motor vehicle traffic. Although the data are limited, the WHO/UNEP assessment showed that the WHO maximum one-hour guidelines for nitrogen dioxide and for ozone were exceeded in half of all the cities for which data were available. When episodes occur in conjunction with heat waves and high humidity, as in Athens and other cities during recent summers, premature mortality occurs among the aged, especially those with respiratory problems.

In addition to the major problems arising from high levels of urban air pollution, there is the question of whether exposure to low levels of pollutants, such as now occurs in many developed countries, is associated with long-term effects on health. Carcinogens such as benzo[a]pyrene must be presumed to constitute a risk, though a very small one at present levels of exposure. Associations have been described between levels of urban air pollution and lung cancer rates, but causal relationships are difficult to establish in the presence of important confounding factors such as tobacco smoking, socioeconomic status, and occupation, and given the inadequacy of data on the actual exposure to specific carcinogenic agents in the air.

Fossil fuels—other effects on health

Occupational exposure entails serious hazards to health during the production of energy, as in most industries. The deep mining of coal has historically been associated with accidents from cave-ins and gas explosions and the transport of the coal in and around the mine. Coal-mining has also caused illness, most notably pneumoconiosis but also asthma from the inhalation of dust (8). Modern developments have changed the picture in many countries (9) through improved working practices and dust suppression, but the risks of injury related to haulage and to increased mechanization have changed less. There are also some special hazards associated with the processing of coal. For example, the manufacture of smokeless fuel or of coke for steel mills or the gasification of coal may expose the workforce to tar rich in polycyclic aromatic hydrocarbons; earlier in this century it was the occurrence of skin tumours that drew attention to the carcinogenicity of these compounds (*10*). While this problem has been largely contained, the increased risk of lung cancer among workers in these industries has been widely recognized. Hazards associated with the petroleum and natural gas industry are concentrated in the phase of exploration and the development of new oilfields. This is especially so in offshore developments, in which diving accidents and storm or explosion damage to offshore platforms pose hazards additional to those arising on land.

Two important indirect environmental health effects of fossil fuel combustion, the contribution to global warming and to acid precipitation, are discussed in Chapter 8. A third possible effect is in regard to the well-being of future generations. If people continue to use fossil fuels at current rates, since they are readily available and inexpensive, they may be handicapping future generations, which not only may be forced to pay much more to extract less accessible oil and gas or develop new, more expensive energy sources, but also will have to pay more for all petrochemicals and other goods derived from oil (including medicines, fertilizers, and pesticides).

Hydropower

The health effects of hydropower are mostly indirect and relate to the environmental changes arising from the construction of large hydroelectric dams. These may bring many benefits other than producing electricity. The water impounded by dams is often used not only to produce power but also to control floods and to provide water for drinking and irrigation. However, there may be large health costs, mostly affecting poorer rural households. These include accidents, illness, and deaths among dam construction workers and displacement of people to make way for the dam. Many large dams have involved the removal and resettlement of tens of thousands of people. These displaced persons often suffer psychological stress owing to the loss of lifetime occupations and relationships, the disruption of ordinary life, and the break-up of families (*11*). Other health problems are associated with the disruption of food supplies, and the lack of a healthy housing and living environment in the areas where the displaced people are resettled.

The process of generating hydropower does not produce wastes or other by-products harmful to human health. However, when the water supply is obtained by damming a stream or river, the accumulation of a large, almost stationary body of water may, in tropical countries, enhance the spread of vector-borne diseases (Chapters 3 and 4). The retention of river water by large dams may have downstream effects such as a reduction in the nutrients essential for agriculture and aquaculture and in the replenishment rate of aquifers. In areas where people depend on wells for their daily supply of drinking-water, the lowering of the groundwater table may cause serious water shortage.

Nuclear power

The normal operation of nuclear power plants produces environmental pollution of less consequence than that of many other fuel cycles. The average individual yearly radiation dose from discharges to people living within 50 km of a power station is estimated to be about 1/1000 of the dose received from natural background radiation. More than 80% of the occupational exposure to radiation in the nuclear fuel cycle is associated with reactor operations; the highest individual doses are incurred by those engaged in maintenance and repair work, especially of heat exchange installations. Exposures to radiation received during uranium mining now (as compared with previous years) are generally small, as are those in other parts of the fuel cycle. There are problems, however, with the public's acceptance of nuclear power, stemming mainly from concern about nuclear power plant accidents. Furthermore, appropriate methods for the final disposal of high-level radioactive wastes have yet to be implemented. These factors contribute to considerable public anxiety about risks to health for both present and future generations from the nuclear power cycle.

Epidemiological studies provide no definite evidence of radiation effects in populations residing close to nuclear facilities. An increase in childhood leukaemia was observed in the United Kingdom around two nuclear installations where reprocessing of spent fuel is carried out, but other studies in France and the United States have not revealed any such increase. A recent case-control study related to one of the nuclear installations in the United Kingdom associated the childhood leukaemias with paternal occupational exposure rather than with discharges to the environment. It also noted that the fathers could have been occupationally exposed to noxious agents other than radiation; clearly, further research is required.

Electricity

Electricity has a central role in all developed countries since it provides the energy for virtually all communications, lighting, and mechanical work (apart from road transport). Most of the health risks arise from the production of electricity and vary according to the energy source. Most electricity production is from fossil-fuelled or nuclear power stations or hydroelectric dams, and the health risks associated with its production have been described above. Energy in the form of electricity brings little or no risk to the household, industrial, or commercial user, as long as the wiring has been installed correctly and is not interfered with.

However, the expansion of the electricity supply system has led to increased exposure of the population to electromagnetic fields. Many industrial and household appliances produce such fields and some medical diagnostic devices may expose patients and medical workers to fairly intense fields. Only since 1979 has it been suggested that exposure to electromagnetic fields may increase the risk of some cancers, in particular leukaemia, lymphoma, and nervous system tumours. The evidence is weak and its interpretation is as yet uncertain but it cannot be dismissed, particularly in view of the likely global increase in the use of electricity.

Accidents

The accident at Chernobyl has created public anxiety about the health effects of nuclear-energy-related accidents. At Chernobyl improper experimentation and operator error induced a surge of reactor power that could not be controlled, leading to a rapid rise in temperature, explosion of the core, and an intense graphite fire. An additional factor was the absence of containment in this type of reactor. This accident resulted in the immediate death of 31 emergency workers, the contamination of large areas of the European part of the then Soviet Union, and the evacuation of approximately 100 000 people from the 30-kilometre exclusion zone around the power station. Possible long-term effects on health are still being investigated.

There can be accidents at any stage in the energy cycle and in all energy systems, as a result of human error, structural or mechanical failure or natural phenomena such as hurricanes or earthquakes. It is difficult to assess their health effects because no single national or international agency systematically collects such data. A study of data on severe accidents in the energy industry between 1969 and 1986 by the Swiss Reinsurance Company and from published literature found that the most severe accidents involved coal-mining operations, fires, explosions of oil and natural gas, failure of hydroelectric dams, and core damage with significant radionuclide release in nuclear power plants (12). Such events, even if the likelihood of their occurrence is very low, can result in a large number of fatalities, mostly to workers. But it is difficult to draw definite conclusions about the relative risks to health from severe accidents in different energy systems. Natural gas and hydropower appear to present the largest accident risk, this contrasting sharply with the relatively small risk to public health from their routine operation. There is little information about the possible long-term health effects of energy-related accidents.

There are also energy-related accidents within the home or workplace. Portable heaters or cookers and open fires are major causes of burns, scalds, and accidental fires, especially in many low-income settlements in urban and rural areas of developing countries. Fatal carbon monoxide poisoning may result from the use of certain unvented types of heaters.

Additional problems in developing countries

Various problems have been described already, such as the air pollution in cities that have developed as centres of heavy industry and in urban areas of developing countries where biomass fuel or poor-quality coal are the only available energy sources. Many developing countries have other fundamental problems—absence of an energy infrastructure and distribution network, inadequate maintenance systems, and scarcity of qualified personnel. Virtually all of them are unable to allocate sufficient resources to pollution control.

The most serious health problem associated with energy in developing countries arises from the use of coal and unprocessed biomass fuel. While outdoor air pollution creates comparable problems in developed and developing countries, indoor air pollution from incomplete combustion of unprocessed biomass fuel and coal is a problem mainly confined to developing countries and is a serious health risk for large numbers of people, causing much respiratory disease. An estimated 700 million women in the world are likely to be affected by indoor air pollutants arising from the use of biomass fuel, making this the largest single "occupational health" problem for women.

Governments in developing countries also face special difficulties in implementing what may be termed a health-promoting energy policy. The considerable health implications that the price and availability of different fuels have for poorer groups have been described. Yet health is not a priority concern for governments in their energy or macroeconomic policies.

Indoor pollution from fossil fuels

Fossil fuels are widely used for space or water heating in the home or for cooking in many countries. They deserve particular attention because of the poor combustion conditions that often occur and the fact that hundreds of millions of people are regularly exposed to potentially harmful emissions.

Coal fumes are a major source of indoor air pollution when coal is used for cooking or heating on open fires or in poorly designed stoves with inadequate attention to venting of flue gases. Bituminous coal poses particular problems for domestic use since it is difficult to achieve complete combustion, this leading to potentially harmful smoke emission. The production of sulfur dioxide from the sulfur present in most solid fuels is inevitable. Inadequate provision of chimneys and ventilation and the occasional downdraft can expose occupants to very high concentrations of pollutants. There are examples of this type of pollution in parts of China, where studies have linked exposure to increased risk of lung cancer (*13*). These domestic stoves can also be a major contributor to air pollution outside the home; one estimate suggests that burning domestic fuel generates about half of Delhi's air pollution, while in China "the burning of raw coal in millions of small inefficient stoves is a very burdensome air pollution source through the colder half of the country" (*14*). About 500 million Chinese regularly use coal for cooking and for heating their homes.

The use of oil products for heating or cooking in the home presents fewer problems than does coal. Most appliances are capable of burning the fuel efficiently with only small emissions of partial combustion products, and since the grades of oil generally used for domestic purposes contain little sulfur, emissions of sulfur dioxide are usually negligible. However, health problems inside buildings often arise from faulty flues or the use of equipment with no flues. In rural areas in many parts of the world, unflued oil stoves of various types used for cooking contaminate indoor air. The risk is not only from oxides of nitrogen but also from carbon monoxide, which can reach lethal concentrations if not properly vented.

Indoor pollution from biomass fuels

Biomass fuels include wood, logging wastes and sawdust, animal dung, and vegetable matter containing grass, leaves, crop residues, and agricultural wastes. Biomass fuels have the potential advantage of being a renewable energy resource. In rural subsistence economies they are usually plentiful initially but, in the absence of replanting, population pressure and land use can cause the demand to exceed the supply. On combustion, unprocessed biomass fuels produce less energy per unit mass than fossil fuels.

Nearly half the world's population rely mainly or exclusively on biomass fuel for their daily energy needs. It is usually burnt in open fires or in a simple clay or metal stove. The stove is often at floor level, so adding to the risk of accidents, especially of burns to children, and jeopardizing food hygiene. Often there is no chimney. In cool regions (including high altitudes in tropical countries), the combination of open fires or inefficient stoves, absence of chimneys, and poor ventilation leads to severe indoor air pollution with adverse effects on human health (*15, 16*).

The combustion of raw biomass products produces hundreds of chemical compounds (17), including suspended particulate matter, carbon monoxide, oxides of nitrogen and sulfur, hydrocarbons, aldehydes, acenaphthylene, benzene, phenol, cresol, toluene, and more complex hydrocarbon compounds including polyaromatic hydrocarbons. Although indoor concentrations vary considerably, it is very common for the WHO health guidelines to be exceeded by several orders of magnitude. Using improved stoves with ventilation and exhaust chimneys can reduce the emissions of suspended particulate matter by up to 60%, of carbon monoxide by up to 86% and of aldehydes by up to 30% (M.R. Pandey, unpublished data, 1990).

The most serious health risks are from burns and smoke inhalation, the severity of risks from the latter depending on the length and level of exposure. Although data on exposure levels are limited, it is estimated that exposure to pollutants is 60 times greater in indoor environments in the rural areas of developing countries than in the urban areas of developed countries (16). The principal adverse effects on health are respiratory, but in poorly ventilated dwellings, especially when biomass fuels such as charcoal or coal are used to heat rooms in which people sleep, carbon monoxide poisoning is a serious hazard (18). Exposure to carcinogens in emissions from biomass fuel combustion has been confirmed in studies in which exposed subjects wore personal monitoring equipment (19). Women who spend 2–4 hours a day at the stove have high levels of exposure to total suspended particulates and benzo[a]pyrene. This must be presumed to create some risk of respiratory cancer.

Chronic effects include inflammation of the respiratory tract caused by continued exposure to irritant gases and fumes. This reduces resistance to acute respiratory infection, and infection in turn enhances susceptibility to the inflammatory effects of smoke and fumes, establishing a vicious circle of pathological change. These processes may lead to emphysema and chronic obstructive pulmonary disease, which can progress to the stage where impaired lung function reduces the circulation of blood through the lungs, causing right-sided heart failure (cor pulmonale) (20).

In many developing countries, girls and women tend the fires and do the cooking, inhaling larger concentrations of pollutants over longer periods than men. The prevalence of chronic bronchitis increases by 100% in those chronically exposed to biomass fuels (21). Exposure may also result in reduced lung function and, at a later stage, an up to six times greater prevalence of cor pulmonale, particularly in cold hilly regions. Tobacco smoking may be an added factor (22). Women are the main victims of this form of chronic obstructive lung disease, as shown by observational and epidemiological studies in India (S.R. Kamat, personal communication) and in several south-east Asian countries, parts of Africa, and Central and South America (16, 18, 23, 24).

Infants and children may be heavily exposed because they remain with their mothers while fires are tended and cooking is done. This exposure, combined with malnutrition, may retard growth and lead to smaller lungs and a greater prevalence of chronic bronchitis (S.R. Kamat, personal communication).

Other effects arise when the cook crouches close to the fire and sustains heat damage to the conjunctiva and cornea, which become chronically inflamed. Prolonged exposure may lead to keratitis, causing impaired vision and probably also increasing the risk of recurrent infection, cataract, and, ultimately, blindness (25).

Various possibilities exist to limit indoor air pollution arising from the use of biomass fuels. Processed biomass fuels, such as charcoal or biomass fermented or digested in a tank to manufacture wood alcohol or biogas, produce more energy per unit of fuel than raw biomass and cause less air pollution. The adverse effect of biomass fuels burned indoors can be lessened by improved stove design and simple improvements in ventilation. However, in the past 15 years many outside interventions have produced so-called improved stove designs and new biogas plants that met neither local needs nor the criterion of affordability (26).

Another effect related to the use of biomass fuel is the time and effort needed to collect it. In developing countries, women are largely responsible for gathering fuel, and where fuel is scarce its collection often requires exhausting journeys to and from the sources of supply.

Yet another effect of biomass use arises if biomass fuels are used without reforestation to replace them. This not only depletes an energy resource, it also releases additional carbon dioxide into the atmosphere while reducing the capacity of the biosphere to remove it. It depletes the vegetation ground cover, which may lead to severe soil erosion; this in turn makes it impossible for local people to maintain a livelihood. In many rural areas environmental degradation may be to a greater extent caused by the commercially organized gathering of biomass to meet the demand for fuel in urban communities, but it is the rural communities that suffer first and most from the non-sustainable use of biomass.

Trends

Fossil fuels—oil, coal, and natural gas—account for 90% of the world's commercial energy production. Most transport systems rely on oil, and most electricity production is from fossil-fuelled power stations. Oil remains the world's dominant fuel, supplying nearly 38% of global energy needs despite conservation efforts and a switch to alternatives. Coal, which fuelled modern industrial growth, has slipped to second place, accounting for 30% of all the energy consumed. Natural gas accounts for 20%.

The projected increase in global primary energy production over the next two decades varies, depending on assumptions about population growth and changes in per caput energy use. However, even if it is assumed that greatly increased efficiency in the production and use of energy will make an acceptable standard of living possible for less energy per person than is currently estimated, a world population substantially larger than the current population is likely to need more than the present level of global energy. The production of electricity is expected to increase rapidly over the next two decades, since electricity is a flexible, convenient, and clean form of energy for domestic and industrial use, particularly in urban areas.

While technologies to use energy more efficiently and mitigate the negative health effects are available, their use will require financial resources that are not readily available in many countries. Without major efforts by all countries and international institutions in research and development, and without policy changes and more rational planning, the next two decades are likely to see a substantial increase in the use of fossil fuels, particularly cheaper low-grade coal, with a resulting increase in air pollution and continued use of biomass fuel in unsustainable ways, as its use outstrips replanting.

A number of major factors will influence trends in the use of energy and the energy sources used. Two of the most significant are social and economic development in developing countries and population growth. At present the average per caput consumption of commercial energy in developing countries is one-tenth the average for developed countries; this average for developing countries will rise considerably as stronger, more stable economies develop and human needs are met. Many essential public health measures are energy-dependent, for instance health care centres serving both the rural and the urban population, water supplies, sanitation, waste disposal systems, and public transport systems. Although stronger economies and basic services do not require per caput consumption figures approaching those now common in the developed world, they imply a much higher average than is current, and for an increasing population. High levels of consumption in developed countries reflect patterns of use that evolved when oil, coal, and gas were relatively abundant and cheap. With the increasing shortage of cheap energy and the slow growth in the number of households, per caput consumption in developed countries should decline, especially if governments provide strong incentives for more efficient use.

The use of petrol-driven vehicles for transporting people and goods is growing rapidly throughout the world, particularly in developing countries.

A considerable amount of work has been done to increase the efficiency of vehicle engines, to reduce hazardous emissions, to develop alternative fuels, and to create transport systems that meet urban needs without necessitating the widespread use of private cars. Future health effects arising from energy use in the transport sector will be much influenced by the extent to which new technologies are applied. In Brazil the use of cars powered by alcohol or an alcohol-gasoline mixture is widespread and has led to a considerable reduction of carbon monoxide in urban air. Wastes from alcohol production were initially discharged into waterways, causing major water pollution problems. This has now ceased and the wastes are used as agricultural fertilizer.

The world has sufficient energy sources (oil, coal, natural gas, uranium, hydropower, and solar energy) to meet needs in the short term. But the sources are not uniformly distributed among countries or regions. The majority of the world's population live in regions with little or no access to energy other than biomass fuel or low-grade coal.

Supplies of non-renewable sources (generally much the cheapest energy sources) are finite. The point at which the world will experience shortages of fossil fuels is still debated. Reserves of coal remain very considerable; on the basis of current costs, patterns of use and knowledge of reserves, it is estimated that coal supplies will last another 200 years, although most of the high-quality coal has already been mined. Much of what remains (lignite and brown coal) contains more sulfur. Current oil reserves are sufficient to last about 30 years at current rates of consumption, and although rising oil prices will stimulate more exploration and permit higher-cost sources to be tapped, most of the high-quality and readily available oil deposits have been or are being utilized. Reserves of natural gas will last 40 years at current consumption rates. As the demand for clean energy rises in the developed world, there are fears that the developing world will increasingly resort to more polluting fuels such as brown coal and high-sulfur oil. The next two decades are likely to see a wider availability of more affordable technology increasing the efficiency and controlling the emissions to the environment from combustion of these fuels.

As the costs of energy from fossil fuels increase, the next few decades may also see the development of alternative renewable sources of energy as well as the direct use of solar energy, which will bring fewer hazards to the environment and to health. There may also be more effective measures to conserve energy and increase the efficiency of its utilization in both developed and developing countries. Solar energy is the most widely available source and is already being tapped in many countries. However, its use will be limited by the cost of transforming solar radiation into usable forms of energy. There will also be limited space in many countries for large solar collector arrays.

Of the renewable energy sources, hydropower and geothermal energy can only be harnessed in particular locations. There remains in many developing countries a considerable amount of untapped hydropower potential, and the trend is likely to be towards smaller systems that avoid the major social and environmental costs of large hydropower installations. The use of renewable biomass for commercial purposes is also limited by the availability of land, much of which is needed for growing food. But much could be done to encourage the replanting of vegetation for use as fuel in rural areas of developing countries. This would have the added benefit of preventing soil erosion.

The next two decades are likely to see an intensification of research and development in the developed world on solar and wind power to increase the scope of their use on a commercial scale. The outcome of such research will be important for developing countries, where the cost of importing oil or developing nuclear power is often prohibitive. In the meantime, exploitation of existing technologies for decentralized energy production could greatly improve the quality of life and standards of health care in rural areas in developing countries.

There are large variations in the amount of research and development devoted to different technologies and energy sources, and thus in the acceptance, reliability, and cost of different types of energy production, use, and mitigation technologies. Technologies related to the production and use of fossil fuels and mitigation of related hazards are well established; those related to the production and use of solar and renewable biomass resources are still in the formative stage.

Projections of future trends in the use of nuclear energy are difficult to make. Experience with the use of nuclear fuels is limited compared with that of fossil fuels, and there are a number of reservations in the public's mind. Fuel availability is not a problem; uranium will last for many centuries since its use is limited and spent fuel can be used to breed plutonium, which can also be used as a nuclear fuel. But continuing efforts to develop an intrinsically safe nuclear reactor and acceptable and practicable methods for the disposal of high-level radioactive wastes are needed to overcome these reservations. In addition, the very high capital costs of nuclear power stations and the high level of technical skill and institutional development needed to utilize this source of energy make it poorly suited to the needs of most developing countries.

In the developing world introducing energy-efficient industrial processes and techniques could help mitigate the adverse health effects of industrialization. It has been estimated that, if energy-efficient technologies, particularly in end-use devices, were adopted in developing countries, only a modest growth in per caput energy would be needed to raise their average standard

167

of living to the level achieved in Europe in the mid-1970s. It should also ensure cost-effectiveness in achieving a rise in living and health standards.

Strategies

Meeting energy needs for development while minimizing the direct and indirect costs to health and the environment requires a series of actions and a range of technologies. The actions and technologies vary greatly from country to country, depending not only on the demand for energy but also on human (technical), financial, and energy resources as well as on environmental conditions. The importance of electricity to social and economic development and the likely rapid growth in demand for it mean that special attention needs to be paid to reducing the potential hazards of electricity production and particularly the use of fossil fuel.

Each country must develop a strategy for its own specific needs, making the best use of its own resources while taking into account the effects on the local, regional, and global environment. The aim is to find the right combination of indigenous or most readily available natural resources and technologies to produce the required energy at a reasonable cost, both in financial terms and in terms of health and the environment. In all countries good industrial practice, increased efficiency, avoidance of unnecessary and wasteful use of energy, greater awareness among producers and consumers, and appropriate incentives should be basic features of any strategy.

A number of priorities need emphasis within national strategies:

- Reducing the effects on health of indoor air pollution caused by the domestic use of coal and biomass fuel, a problem mainly to be found in developing countries. A better design for cooking or heating stoves and better ventilation would solve many of the environmental health problems; such stoves are more likely to be accepted if they produce significant fuel savings. Once people are aware of this immediate benefit, they are more likely to accept the secondary benefit of a healthier indoor environment. In some countries there is also a considerable potential for the conversion of raw biomass into safer and more efficient fuel, although exploitation of biomass fuels should not be at the expense of environmental degradation and diminished food production.

- Reducing air pollution from fossil fuel use. Technologies already exist that greatly reduce the emission of airborne pollutants at source. Catalytic converters can reduce the emission oxides of nitrogen, carbon monoxide, and volatile organic compounds from motor vehicles fuelled with lead-free petrol. In many countries reducing air pollution from motor vehicles demands a high priority as this is an increasing component of total air pollution. Fitting power stations with scrubbers can reduce sulfur dioxide emissions by up to 95%, and equipping them with catalytic converters can significantly reduce emissions of oxides of nitrogen. Similarly, electrostatic precipitators and bag filters can trap large amounts of particulates (dust, ash, and soot) in factory or power plant exhaust gases. It is generally easier and less costly to employ such control technologies in new plant than to attempt to modify existing equipment. New technologies have been developed, such as fluidized bed combustion, capable of burning raw or processed fuels much more efficiently and also greatly reducing pollution emissions. An increasing number of countries are also developing co-generation plants. A conventional thermal power station only converts into electricity between 24% and 35% of the heat from burning fossil fuel or from the nuclear reaction; the rest is waste heat. Smaller power stations within factories or close to residential areas can make use of the waste heat for hot water and space heating in buildings, up to 80% of the chemical energy in the fuel being converted to useful energy.

- Controlling the carbon dioxide output into the atmosphere. While a region or country may have little choice in the type of fuel it uses for energy production, a number of strategies are available to minimize carbon dioxide emissions. Improvements in the efficiency and conservation of energy hold most promise; the greatest potential is in countries with the highest fossil fuel consumption and the most developed energy supply systems. It is reasonable to assume that, in order to meet needs for social and economic development, developing countries will increase their production and use of energy mainly by recourse to the most readily available and cheapest source of energy, i.e., coal. More carbon dioxide will therefore be produced by these countries than previously, while the reverse will be true in the most developed countries. But sustainable development cannot be achieved without taking into account potential environmental health hazards and the need to conserve a finite resource. Thus it is in the longer-term interests of developing countries to adopt measures for increasing efficiency in use and conservation of energy. The demand for and consumption of energy can also be reduced considerably by modifying lifestyles and work practices. For example, reducing the use of private cars in city centres by adopting efficient public transport systems would contribute significantly to lowering carbon dioxide emission as well as to reducing air pollution and improving fuel conservation.

169

- Giving higher priority to research, development, and the use of renewable energy sources. Most of the above environmental health effects stem from the combustion of fossil fuels, but there is another strong incentive for utilizing alternative renewable sources of energy: reserves of fossil fuels are finite. It is to be expected that the research and development needed to make use of renewable sources of energy (solar, wind, geothermal, hydropower, waste incineration, and renewable biomass both for domestic and commercial use and as an alternative source of fuel for transport) will be concentrated in developed countries.
- Paying greater attention to preventing major accidents and to action limiting the health and environmental effects of accidents, if they happen. It is also important to acquire and disseminate as much information as can be gained on the environmental health consequences of major accidents. Intensive efforts are required by all governments to reduce the likelihood of serious accidents and to mitigate possible environmental health effects. Increasing the safety of mines, dams, and nuclear power plants deserves special priority.

Recommendations

Environmental health assessment should be an essential component of decision-making in relation to new energy developments. This means, particularly in rapidly growing urban centres, recognizing the importance of the siting of heavy industry dependent on energy production or power plants and of related arrangements for waste disposal, including the use of appropriate technologies for mitigating or preventing adverse environmental health effects.

The growing importance of fossil-fuelled transport as a source of air pollution in cities throughout the world should be recognized and efforts should be made to plan more effective systems of public transport. The indirect costs of adverse health effects should be weighed against the direct costs of introducing control technologies.

Developing countries should implement national energy strategies that give due consideration to the health and environmental aspects and promote the most efficient use of fossil fuels. Most developing nations will have to increase the use of primary energy if their economies are to develop to the point where they can support a healthy and prosperous population and the services such a population needs. In most instances fossil fuels are the cheapest option; they are also the most healthy option if measures are taken to control air pollution, especially among those currently using biomass fuels. A careful technological choice in which health and environmental factors are given sufficient attention along with preventive planning, stress on efficiency, an appropriate regulatory framework, and good management can greatly reduce adverse effects on health and limit greenhouse gas emission.

Within each country, knowledge and practical skills should be developed to foresee and identify environmental health hazards and take action to reduce the risks from energy production and use in rural and urban domestic and industrial settings. This includes accident prevention and preparedness. The objective can only be achieved by an understanding of potential environmental health hazards and of what needs to be monitored in the environment and in human subjects, and practical arrangements and skills for carrying out the necessary investigations will be required.

Bilateral and multilateral collaboration will help to implement the above recommendations by providing appropriate training and transfer of technology relevant to the needs, culture, and resources of individual countries.

The use of readily renewable biomass should be developed, as of particular relevance to many developing countries. By this means large-scale rural environmental degradation can be prevented, with its profound indirect effects on human health. Priority should be given to the domestic use of ventilated stoves and/or processed biomass as a means of reducing the effects of indoor air pollution on the health of large numbers of women and children in developing countries.

The education of women should be improved, due respect being given to long-established cultural habits, to ensure that future generations understand the issues better and participate in decisions concerning energy efficiency, conservation, and environmental health. Without this understanding at grassroots level the maximum benefits to health will not be achieved. Although social and economic development is important in providing a stable base for the development of society, it is not the only factor involved in achieving optimal health status.

The role that individual energy-related pollutants play in the causation of adverse health effects, should be established as clearly as possible, to improve knowledge of the environmental pathways from source of emission to target organ and to determine the nature and magnitude of human exposure through simple and reliable monitoring techniques emphasizing personal monitoring.

Recommendations for research

New methodologies for the quantitative assessment of health benefits and costs should be developed to facilitate the choice of the most appropriate energy sources. They should include quantification of the benefits of energy to health, an estimation of the cost of preventing adverse effects, and an estimation of the cost of ill health induced by polluting emissions.

The benefits to health from an increased use of electricity are indisputable, and further socioeconomic development will be accompanied by increased production and distribution of electricity by overhead power lines and the use of various electrical appliances in the home and office. Epidemiological studies indicate the possibility of adverse effects from exposure to electromagnetic fields, but the data are inconclusive. Additional investigations, both epidemiological and experimental, should be carried out on human exposure to electromagnetic fields. Epidemiological studies should as far as possible define exposure through actual measurements.

Pollution control technologies appropriate to the requirements of developing countries should be developed, to enable these countries to meet their increasing needs for energy from fossil fuels at the smallest environmental and health cost.

Research should be carried out to make renewable energy (e.g., solar, wind, geothermal, small-scale hydroelectric) and energy conservation technologies more widely applicable. Since nuclear power is likely to continue to be a significant energy source in some countries, efforts should continue to develop an inherently safe reactor and satisfactory methods for the disposal of high-activity wastes.

Because petrol-driven vehicles constitute a major source of pollution in developing as well as in developed countries, more efficient vehicles, vehicles that are not dependent on petrol, and more convenient and efficient systems of public transport should be developed.

References and notes

1. *The state of the environment*. Paris, Organisation for Economic Co-operation and Development, 1991.

2. Morris, S.C. et al. *Health and environmental effects of the national energy plan: a critical review of some selected issues*. Upton, Brookhaven National Laboratory, 1980 (BNL 51300).

3. Friberg, L. & Vahter, M. Assessment of response to lead and cadmium through biological monitoring; results of a UNEP/WHO global study. *Environmental research*, **30**: 95–128 (1983).

4. Bates, D.V. Air pollution in the developed world. *La recherche*, forthcoming.

5. Photochemical Oxidants Review Group. *Ozone in the United Kingdom*. Harwell Laboratory, 1987.

6. Romieu, I. et al. Urban air pollution in Latin America and the Caribbean: health perspectives. *World health statistics quarterly*, **23** (2): 153–167 (1990).

7. UNEP/WHO. *Assessment of urban air quality*. Nairobi, UNEP, 1988.

8. Algranti, E. *Doenças respiratórias associadas à mineração do carvão*. São Paulo, University of São Paulo School of Public Health, 1991 (Doctoral Thesis).

9. *Coal and the environment*. London, Her Majesty's Stationery Office, 1982.

10. Cook, J.W. et al. The isolation of a cancer-producing hydrocarbon from coal tar. *Journal of the Chemical Society*, **136** (1): 395–405 (1933).

11. Goldsmith, E. & Hildyard N. *The social and ecological effects of large dams. Volume I: Overview. Volume II: Case studies*. Camelford, Wadebridge Ecological Centre, 1984.

12. Watt Committee on Energy. *27th Consultative Conference—Risk and the energy industries*. Birmingham, University of Birmingham, 1990.

13. Chapman, R.S. et al. Assessing indoor air pollution exposure and lung cancer risks in Xuan Wei, China. *Journal of the American College of Toxicology*, **8**: 941–948 (1989).

14. Smil, V. *The bad earth: environmental degradation in China*. New York, M.E. Sharpe, 1984.

15. Smith, K.R. Dialectics of improved stoves. In: Kristoferson, L. et al., eds., *Bioenergy: contribution to environmentally sustainable development*, Stockholm, Stockholm Environment Institute, 1990.

16. Smith, K.R. Air pollution: assessing total exposure in developing countries. *Environment*, **30** (10): 16–20, 28–35 (1988).

17. Smith, K.R. *Biofuels, air pollution and health—a global overview*. New York, Plenum, 1987.

18. Chen, B.H. et al. Indoor air pollution in developing countries. *World health statistics quarterly*, **23** (2): 127–138 (1990).

19. Smith, K.R. et al. Air pollution and rural biomass fuels in developing countries; a pilot village study in India and its implications for research and policy. *Atmospheric environment*, **17**: 2343–2362 (1983).

20. Pandey, M.R. et al. Indoor air pollution in developing countries and acute respiratory infection. *Lancet*, **1**: 427–429 (1989).

21. Malik, S.K. Preliminary report on exposure to domestic cooking fuels and chronic bronchitis. *Indian journal of chest diseases and allied sciences*, **27**: 171–174 (1985).

22. Pandey, M.R. et al. Chronic bronchitis and cor pulmonale in Nepal. Domestic smoke pollution and acute respiratory infections in a rural community of the hill region of Nepal. *Environment international*, **15**: 337–340 (1989).

23. Kossove, D. Smoke-filled rooms and lower respiratory disease in infants. *South African medical journal*, **61**: 622–624 (1982).

24. Woolcock, A. J. et al. Studies of chronic lung disease in New Guinea populations. *American review of respiratory disease*, **102**: 575–590 (1970).

25. Siwitabau, S. *Rural energy in Fiji: a survey of domestic rural energy use and potential.* Ottawa, International Development Research Centre, 1978 (IDRC Research Report 157e).

26. Sarin, M. Improved stoves, women and domestic energy. *Environment and urbanization*, **3** (2): 51–56 (1991).

6.
Industry

Introduction

Industrialization has been the cause of many changes in the use of energy and water resources, in the pattern of human settlements, and in the social and economic context of health (1). Industrialization in developed countries has underpinned the change from predominantly rural and agrarian societies to predominantly urban societies where no more than a small percentage of the labour force work in agriculture. It has also provided the basis for unprecedented increases in wealth and personal mobility for a considerable proportion of the world's population, mostly in developed countries. At the same time it has greatly increased the demand for non-renewable resources and strained the capacity of natural systems to absorb the by-products of industrial waste and industrial society.

In far too many instances, lives have been lost, health damaged, and serious injuries inflicted because environmental hazards have been ignored or identification of the hazards has taken too long. By understanding and identifying the risks early and establishing ways of assessing and controlling existing and new hazards, public health can be improved and the benefits associated with industrialization enjoyed without degradation of human health and of the environment.

The increasingly productive economies of developed countries have resulted in increased personal incomes for most of the population, greater educational opportunities, improved standards of living (including much improved environmental health) and, although with exceptions, enhanced personal freedom. Three changes are worth highlighting for their effects on health: increased individual incomes; increased national wealth; and an economic infrastructure that serves health needs.

Increased incomes have permitted large improvements in diet, housing, and access to health services. Although increasing affluence and associated lifestyles often bring new health problems, the net effect of increased individual prosperity in the developed world over the last 100 years has been an important factor in improving health. Increased prosperity within a country enables governments to improve the quality of environmental health, health services, and education. The unit costs of the infrastructure and of most services are also lower when people live in dense concentrations.

However, there can be a health price for these economic changes, as was evident during the industrial revolution in Europe and North America. Industrialization has had and continues to have a significant environmental health impact in most countries, especially in Eastern and Central Europe and in many developing countries. Growth in industrial output can be accompanied by a decline in health in the absence of government action to control industrial pollution, provide health and safety in the workplace, and ensure a good-quality living environment. Pollution emissions and resource requirements can also be high (see Box 51).

Box 51. The environmental impact of industry in OECD countries

Among countries of the Organisation for Economic Co-operation and Development (OECD), industrial output represents around one-third of the aggregate GNP. The pollution emissions or resource requirements of industry in 1987 were:
— 15% of water consumption (excluding water used for cooling)
— 25% of nitrogen oxide emissions
— 35% of final energy use
— 40–50% of sulfur oxide emissions
— 50% of contributions to the greenhouse effect
— 60% of biological oxygen demand and of substances in suspension
— 75% of non-inert waste
— 90% of toxic substances discharged into water.

It should be noted that only a few industrial sectors are responsible for most raw material consumption and pollution, especially the food and agricultural processing industry, metal extraction and processing, cement works, pulp and paper, oil refining, and the chemical industry.

Source: *The state of the environment.* Paris, Organisation for Economic Co-operation and Development, 1991.

Both in the past and today there are many examples of prosperous industrial centres where the negative effects on health are very small. The health risks arising from industrial production are much influenced by the nature of the production and the extent to which society is willing to enact and enforce rules and regulations for the safe design of installations and protection of workers and the general public. The challenge facing governments is to keep to a minimum the adverse health and environmental effects while promoting and sustaining economic development.

Industrial activities and their health hazards

The term industry covers a great range of activities, each with the potential to affect the health of workers, their families, and the wider public. It includes heavy industries (for instance smelters) and light industries (for instance electronic goods assembly). It is used in this report to include services (tourism, catering, laundries, banks, finance) in which most of the economically active population of developed countries now work. It ranges from small informal enterprises with only one or two workers up to large factories with thousands of employees. The health hazards associated with industrialization include not only those of the production process but also those of the raw materials, fuels, and wastes as they are obtained, transported, and handled, and the effects on health of the products and wastes.

The adverse health effects range from those caused by relatively high exposures of small populations within particular factories (or parts of factories) to those of the general public under, usually, lower levels of exposure.

Occupational exposure

At the workplace a variety of factors influence the level of risk for the working population. They include the extent of exposure to hazards, which in turn is affected by the process design and the safety precautions taken and by the extent and quality of support services and their ability to respond rapidly and effectively to injury or disease. The extent to which workers and management alike understand the industrial process and the control technologies and safety equipment is also important.

Estimates based on the current occupational injury rates in a number of countries suggest that there are 32.7 million occupational injuries per year and 146 000 deaths (2). Although no global estimate can be made at present, the prevalence of some common occupational diseases among exposed populations is as follows: silicosis, 3.5–43.2%; coal miner's pneumoconiosis, 8.3–43.8%; byssinosis, 5.0–30.0%; lead poisoning, 1.7–100.0%; mercury poisoning, 2.6–37.0%; noise-induced hearing loss, 1.7–70.0%; occupational skin diseases, 1.7–86.0%; and low back pain, 2–5% (2). Box 52 gives an example of what has been termed the worst industrial disaster in the United States, the Hawks Nest tunnel and the silicosis associated with it.

The health risks to many workers in small workshops or rooms in houses pose special problems, as such workers are usually not covered by regulatory systems. For instance, in Jamaica the recycling and repair of lead-acid batteries in informal enterprises has led to the exposure of both workers and the community to lead (3). In the Amazon region of Brazil the use of mercury by informal gold miners to separate pure gold from impurities by subjecting

---

Box 52. The Hawk's Nest tunnel

More than 700 people are thought to have died as a result of building a tunnel for the Hawk's Nest hydroelectric plant at Gauley Bridge in Virginia, USA, during the 1930s. This estimate has been constructed from an examination of vital statistics in West Virginia.

In Fayette County, where the tunnel was being built, the death rate among black males rose greatly from 1930 to 1937. Black underground workers outnumbered white workers three to one, whereas black men were only one-fifth as numerous in the general population. A similar pattern appears in the deaths of white males in the county, with variations. Female death rates were stable over these years in both the county and the state. The death rate for black males was markedly higher in every year than that for whites, but with an even greater relative increase from 1930 to 1937. In general the county death rate rose markedly for black males in 1930 and for white males in 1931; during the same period it declined gradually in the state.

Judging from the rates in three comparable mining counties near-by, 284 more black and white men aged 10–59 years died in Fayette County than were expected to in 1931–35. Comparisons with rates for the entire state suggest an excess of 278 deaths. It cannot be proved that the excess of deaths among men from Fayette County in the 1930s resulted from work on the tunnel, but it is clear that something shortened the lives of an unusual number of working-age men during the drilling of the tunnel or in the five years that followed. Respiratory disease was the major single contributor to the increased death rate of males in the county in the crucial years; white male deaths ascribed to non-tuberculous respiratory disease or silicosis exceeded normal expectations by 85%, while black male deaths from respiratory causes were two-and-a-half times the expected number.

If it is assumed that migrant whites and blacks who moved away after completion of the project suffered at least the same rate of mortality as did local whites, in all, 581 of the 922 black workers and 183 of the 291 white workers would have died. Within five years of its completion the Hawk's Nest tunnel would have claimed a total of 764 victims to silicosis. This estimate may well be too small. The above estimates are for deaths occurring before the end of 1937. Silicosis might well have brought a slower death to workers for many years afterwards.

Source: Cherniack, M. *The Hawk's Nest incident: America's worst industrial disaster.* New Haven, CT, Yale University Press, 1986.

---

the mixture to high temperatures results in serious mercury poisoning. Many people working at home or in small informal enterprises use chemicals that should only be used under carefully controlled conditions with special safety equipment (Box 53).

Box 53. Occupational safety in informal enterprises: the price of cheap glue in Turkey

Over 50 deaths were documented among Turkish leather workers from leukaemia and destruction of the bone marrow as a result of the introduction of a cheaper benzene-containing glue in making shoes, handbags, and other leather goods. Most of this work is done in small shops. The new glue, introduced around 1965, has benzene as its primary solvent. This compound's capacity to destroy human bone marrow has been known since the nineteenth century. The solvent's evaporation during the bonding of the leather caused concentrations which, when eventually measured, were found to be several hundred times higher than the maximum recommended. The epidemic took over a decade to develop and would not have been detected until many more had died were it not for the observations of Dr M. Aksoy, who headed the only haematology programme in Istanbul. The result of his observations was a government ban on this glue. Dr Aksoy continues to watch leukaemia on a long-term basis. An active industrial hygiene or a worker surveillance approach to the problems of small industries could have saved many lives and reduced long-term leukaemia risk for an estimated 28 000 Istanbul leather workers, as well as workers elsewhere in Turkey who were using this glue but whose fate was not documented.

Source: Aksoy, M. et al. Types of leukaemia in a chronic benzene poisoning. *Acta haematologica*, **55**: 65–72 (1976).

Health risks to the public

For the public living and working outside the factory gate, the health risks vary considerably, depending on the distance from the factory, the relationships with the factory workers, and susceptibility to pollutants. For instance, workers' families may be subject to high levels of exposure to hazardous substances, such as lead and asbestos brought home on workers' clothing or acquired by making regular visits to the workplace. Infants and children may be particularly at risk because of their greater susceptibility. Exposure is often higher for people who live close to particular industries or make use of water sources contaminated by industrial wastes.

Industrial pollution has many indirect health effects. Industrial liquid wastes for instance may damage river, estuarine, or coastal fisheries, resulting in much reduced fish catches and therefore lower incomes in the fishing industry and decreasing the availability of a food source that is often a significant part of the protein intake of poorer groups (4). Industrial products such as lead in ceramic pots and in crystal glass can also be a source of hazards. Industrial emissions also contribute to the rise of greenhouse gas concentrations and thus to global warming (Chapter 8).

Accidental releases

Accidental releases of toxic substances often result in health risks both at the workplace and in the wider environment. The industrial accident at Bhopal, when methyl isocyanate emitted from a Union Carbide plant caused several thousand deaths and over 50 000 injuries, is one of the best known examples (5). Such accidents occur not only from the accidental release of toxic chemicals in factories but also during their transport, while they are being stored, or as a result of explosions, fires, and collisions.

Toxic chemicals and hazardous waste disposal

Certain industrial and institutional wastes are categorized as hazardous or toxic because of the special care needed for their storage and disposal to ensure that they are isolated from human contact and stored in ways that prevent them from contaminating the human environment. Most toxic wastes come from the chemical industry but others, including the metal, petroleum, transport, electrical equipment, and leather and tanning industries, also produce significant quantities of hazardous waste. Sewage sludge and hospital wastes are also considered hazardous.

The nature of hazardous wastes varies considerably. Some are highly flammable, as are many solvents used in the chemical industry; some are highly reactive and can explode or generate toxic gases on contact with water or another chemical; some, such as sewage sludge or hospital waste, may contain disease-causing agents. Some wastes are highly toxic, for instance cyanide, arsenic, and many heavy-metal compounds, and many are carcinogenic.

The nature, amount, and wide distribution of hazardous wastes and their potential danger to health have been recognized only in the past 15 years. The United States provides an example of the magnitude of the problem they create. Because little consideration was given to the regulatory aspects of hazardous wastes during the nineteenth and much of the twentieth century, there are now some 50 000 land sites in that country where hazardous wastes may have been dumped without control and without provision to ensure that the wastes do not pollute the groundwater. The cost today of having to deal with the result of many years of inadequate control runs into thousands of millions of dollars. The controlled disposal of hazardous wastes cost US$ 19 000 million in 1988 (6).

Other examples of the careless disposal of industrial wastes, including heavy metals, are to be found worldwide. The discharge of mercury-contaminated wastes into water, which received such publicity through the hundreds of deaths and thousands of cases of disablement it caused at Minamata, Japan (Box 54), also gave rise to serious problems in many North American water bodies and has been noted at Alexandria, Bangkok, Bombay, Cartagena, Managua, Perai and various Chinese cities (7–11). Significant build-ups of mercury, lead, cadmium, copper, and chromium have been reported in recent years in almost every industrializing country in south-east Asia (12, 13).

The Kalu river, which runs through two of Bombay's industrial suburbs, receives liquid effluents containing heavy metals from over 150 industrial units. This causes high levels of mercury and lead in the water near the village of Ambivali and the villagers are increasingly exposed as the heavy metals enter the food chain through cattle browsing on riverbank vegetation (14). On the south-east Pacific coast of Latin America, heavy metals have been detected in practically all areas that receive industrial and municipal wastes, and high concentrations of mercury, copper, and cadmium have been found in some fish species (15). Lead and cadmium concentrations in drinking-water were found to exceed the guideline values in about a quarter of the 344 stations that monitor water pollution within the Global Environment Monitoring System network (16). High mercury and cadmium concentrations have also been found in rivers and underground waters in China and, on occasion, in fish (17). The widespread use of mercury to remove impurities from gold in Brazil and the discharge of waste into water bodies has resulted in mercury contamination of the food chain, posing a risk for local populations who eat a lot of fish.

Health hazards can also arise from inadequate attention to the safe disposal of equipment containing dangerous materials such as polychlorinated biphenyls in transformers and heavy metals in electric batteries. An extreme example of this was in Goiania, Brazil, when an abandoned cancer therapy machine was broken up and radioactive caesium-137 was released. Some 240 people were contaminated, many died, and of those who survive many will be at increased risk of developing cancer (18).

Knowledge about the health risks of toxic chemical wastes is still inadequate. A review of research on the public health aspects of toxic waste disposal sites in the United States (20) stated that "although studies on the health of populations in the vicinity of disposal sites have found only inconclusive evidence thus far implicating exposure to toxic wastes in the occurrence of disease, the following adverse health effects have been suggested: (a) decreased weight at birth, (b) increase in the frequency of congenital malformations and abortions, and (c) increase in the occurrence of certain forms of cancer."

Box 54. Minamata disease

Minamata disease is a chronic neurological disorder caused by methyl-mercury. The disease first broke out around Minamata Bay, in south-west Japan, and was officially attributed by the Japanese Government to methylmercury in 1968. Mercury oxide was used in the production of acetaldehyde by Chisso Company and discharged in the plant's waste-water as organic mercury. It was biologically concentrated in fish and shellfish consumed by people living around Minamata Bay. Patients recorded in accordance with the Japanese Pollution-Related Health Damage Compensation Law as suffering from Minamata disease to-talled 2248 around Minamata Bay as of March 1990. Of these, 1004 had died by that date.

The causes of death among Minamata disease patients varied. In a study of deaths among people with the disease, and non-exposed controls, 47 deaths were attributed to Minamata disease among 334 exposed people, none among the controls. The distribution of other causes of death differed little between the two samples (*19*).

In July 1966 the Chisso Company established a closed circulation system. It stopped the production of acetaldehyde in 1968. The Kuma-moto prefectural government conducted a project to dredge and re-claim the parts of the bed of Minamata Bay where mercury was in excess of an agreed standard. The project, which continued from 1974 to 1990, covered 1 510 000 m^2 of seabed and cost 47.9 thousand million yen, of which 30.5 thousand million were charged to the responsible company. Chisso Company paid about 90.8 thousand million yen as compensation to recognized patients.

The review also suggested that "further study will be required... to con-firm the validity of these effects and to determine whether other risks also may exist".

Identifying the health impact

It is in the workplace that the health impact of industrial pollutants is best understood. Diseases caused by chemicals have been observed in most organs of the body after high exposure in the workplace. Examples are different chronic lung diseases (silicosis, asbestosis, byssinosis), kidney diseases (cad-mium, mercury), diseases of the central nervous system (organic solvents, lead, mercury, manganese) and malignant diseases of different organs (asbes-tos, arsenic, nickel, aromatic amines, benzene). Most manifestations of dis-ease, such as lung cancer or chronic obstructive pulmonary disease, associat-ed with environmental factors are not caused only by exposure to that specific factor, and it is difficult to determine the extent to which exposure to environmental agents has contributed. For instance, the effect on health of exposure to a particular chemical must be separated from that of other occupational exposures, including to noise, vibration, and psychological stress, or ill health deriving from diet or pathogens in the home (21). (See Chapter 7 for a discussion of noise and its effects on health.)

There is increasing evidence that some environmental factors may affect the resistance of the body by increasing the susceptibility to disease, but identifying such effects is difficult. Indeed, there are so many factors that contribute to any individual's state of health that it is difficult to identify the contribution of environmental agents as distinct from other factors.

The difficulty of identifying the effect on health of particular pollutants is still greater outside the workplace. Clear-cut examples of diseases caused by exposure to chemicals in the general population are few. Very large numbers of people are exposed to lower concentrations, which are often so low that they do not differ much from background concentrations. There are examples, however, of exposure outside the factory gate approaching the worst occupational exposure. This is so for cadmium exposure from mining in China and Japan and from lead and cadmium emissions from smelters in Upper Silesia, Poland (Box 55).

Concern about the potential effects of long-term exposure to a number of chemical and biological agents is widespread, but verifying the effects is difficult for several reasons:

— the long period before the effect becomes manifest complicates epidemiological studies, especially when populations are mobile and population and exposure records inadequate
— chronic diseases have a multiplicity of causes and it is often difficult to determine the extent to which a particular agent or process is responsible
— there is a poor understanding of the basic mechanisms involved in the pathogenesis of human chronic disease
— diseases are wrongly classified.

In addition, there is virtually no information concerning the levels, trends, and causes of chronic diseases in developing countries.

Among the different techniques used to consider the health effects on the wider population, three are worth stressing: experimental studies; extrapolations from workplace exposures; and epidemiological studies. Epidemiological studies are expensive and take time, especially if aimed at detecting relatively small health effects developing in the long term. Their sensitivity can be improved by concentrating on particular groups within the population known to be susceptible, for instance asthmatics, schoolchildren, or older people.

Experimental studies are necessary both to assess the safety of the chemical and physical agents to which people are exposed and to provide

Box 55. Pollution in Upper Silesia, Poland

The Upper Silesian area, with Katowice at its centre, is the most industrialized region of Poland. With about four million inhabitants, it covers some 2% of the territory of Poland but holds about a quarter of Poland's industrial production, including all non-ferrous metals, most coal, and over half of lead, zinc, and steel production.

The region is heavily polluted, mainly as a result of emissions from industrial sources, although air pollution from domestic coal-burning stoves is also significant. The non-ferrous metal industries, especially plants producing lead and zinc, are responsible for a substantial proportion of the pollution.

In Katowice district there are four non-ferrous metal plants, two that have operated for more than a century and two built in the 1960s. One of the older plants had a particularly high output of lead into the air and, as a result, about 300 children living in the plant's immediate vicinity were found to be suffering from lead poisoning. At the end of the 1970s the processing of lead battery scrap was discontinued at this plant, which meant a substantial reduction in lead emissions to the atmosphere.

It is the newer plants, built in the 1960s and designed with inadequate pollution control equipment, that have proved the most damaging to the environment. One of these, the Miasteczko plant, was responsible for high emissions of lead, cadmium, and zinc into the atmosphere, although in recent years the lead and cadmium emissions have fallen substantially (see table).

Lead and cadmium emissions from the Miasteczko plant (kg per year)

	1987	1988	1989	1990 (first half)
Lead	86 029	83 311	62 926	18 057
Cadmium	1 045	1 040	745	138

A secondary effect of the Miasteczko plant has been high dust deposition. This has meant serious heavy metal contamination of soils with concentrations considerably exceeding the permissible standards. Part of the soil contamination in this region can be attributed to the geological formation and to the mining of lead and zinc over many years plus inadequate management of mining wastes. Tests on vegetables taken from gardens in the neighbourhood showed levels of lead and cadmium several times higher than maximum permissible concentrations.

In the period 1977–1985 the provincial health and epidemic control station conducted tests on the lead and cadmium content in the blood of those living in the vicinity of the plant. Throughout the test period the mean concentration of lead in the blood was about twice as high as that in persons living in a village away from industry and main roads. Some of those tested were found to exhibit the early detectable symptoms of toxic lead effects, the frequency of such symptoms and their intensity being greater in children than in adults. In further tests carried out between 1981 and 1985 on 709 children more than 20% had raised concentrations of lead and cadmium in the blood (above 35.0 µg/dl and 2.0 µg/dl respectively) and in 10% the zinc protoporphyrin levels were more than 3.0 µg/g of haemoglobin.

Source: Jarzebski, L.S. *Case study of the environmental impact of the non-ferrous metals industry in the Upper Silesian area.* Paper prepared for the Panel on Industry, WHO Commission on Health and Environment, 1991.

understanding of the measures needed to predict and prevent adverse effects on the environment and human health.

Extrapolations from occupational exposure have often led to the identification of serious health risks for the wider public. For instance, information about the health-damaging effects of occupational exposure to such toxic substances as lead and asbestos have been used to calculate the health risk to the wider public. Identification of a serious health problem among workers in a particular industry serves as a warning that a wider population may be affected; thus the discovery of high lead levels in workers' blood by an industrial hygienist in a lead foundry in Bahía, Brazil, led to investigations of lead in the blood of children in nearby residential areas. Their blood levels were also found to be very high as a result of lead emissions from the factory. This led to action by the company both to reduce occupational exposure and emissions and to provide treatment for workers and the public affected (22).

Additional problems in developing countries

Most developing countries have ineffective legal and institutional structures to deal with the issue of pollution control in the workplace, in the immediate surroundings of industries, and in the district, city, or region. One recent paper noted that "few health standards are applied to limit work-place exposures; in most …countries, the standard-setting process is either just beginning or has not yet begun. In those nations where standards regulating work practices or toxic exposures do exist, the standards are often not enforced, either for political or economic reasons or because of a lack of trained inspectors" (23). In addition, the licensing requirements for new industries rarely include environmental impact, and this makes predictions of health effects particularly difficult for industries using new chemicals or processes that are unfamiliar to government regulatory authorities (21).

The standards set are also often inappropriate because they are modelled on those in developed countries and have not been adjusted to take into account differences in climate, nutritional status, genetic predisposition, work schedules, and exposure levels (24). Developing countries rarely coordinate effectively the monitoring and regulation of the production, transport, and disposal of hazardous wastes. In some countries no regulations on the subject have been put into force (21). In Mexico in 1985, for example, there were no regulations governing the disposal of hazardous wastes (25). After the incident at Bhopal, India enacted stiff legislation to strengthten the Government's power to regulate the handling of hazardous substances from manufacturing and transport to use and disposal. However, as in most developing countries, the funds and infrastructure needed to enforce this legislation are lacking (26, 27). Box 56 presents an example drawn from

185

Box 56. An example of the health and environmental cost of liberal pollution control

The Government of the Republic of Korea chose a number of locations for concentrated industrial development, to help accommodate its rapidly expanding industrial production. The concentration of industrial investment at the Ulsan/Onsan industrial complex, which by 1985 provided 13% of the nation's manufacturing output, brought a rapid influx of population and thus rapid growth in the population of Ulsan City; the city's population grew from 100 000 in 1962 to about 600 000 at present. The population within the boundaries of the industrial complex grew from some 500 households in 1962 to about 6000 at present. Local residents complained of a variety of health problems, particularly of the nervous system, which they attributed to industrial pollution. Adverse effects of industrial pollution on local agricultural production and fisheries were noted.

An investigation of the industries that were a direct result of investment by foreign corporations revealed that these were applying emission control measures in keeping with local Korean legislation but less stringent than in their home countries, so that in effect they were transferring potentially polluting industries to the Republic of Korea.

Source: WHO Commission on Health and Environment. *Report of the Panel on Industry.* Geneva, World Health Organization, 1992 (unpublished document WHO/EHE/92.4).

Ulsan, Republic of Korea, of the high cost to health and the environment of inadequate attention to pollution control.

Many developing countries face additional problems. One is pollution control in sites with a high concentration of industry, including many export-processing zones. Health risks are greater because of the high concentration there of heavy industries, as a result of government support for specialization (21). Although such a concentration can provide economies of scale in the treatment of wastewaters and thus promote good environmental practice, in the absence of such action the health hazards are greater, particularly as population densities in or around these special industrial estates tend to be very high.

The disposal of hazardous wastes also poses special problems in developing countries, although the amount produced is less than in developed countries. Most wastes are either disposed of as liquid wastes that run untreated into rivers, streams, or other nearby water bodies, or are deposited on land sites with few safeguards to protect those living nearby or neighbouring water sources from contamination. Very few developing countries have effective government systems to control the disposal of hazardous wastes; indeed, in most there are no regulations dealing specifically with such wastes, let alone a system to implement them. Such systems need a competent, well-staffed regulatory authority with the ability to make regular checks in each industry using or generating toxic chemicals, and with power to penalize offenders. This authority needs the backing of the central government and the courts. To achieve effective control of toxic wastes, industries in all countries must be required to keep accurate records of the kinds and quantities of waste, the dates of disposal, and the methods by which it is disposed of. Enterprises that specialize in collecting and disposing of these wastes must be very carefully monitored; so too must the specialized facilities that need to be created to handle toxic wastes. Since the safe disposal of many toxic wastes is expensive, there are large incentives not to comply with regulations.

It is not uncommon for hazardous industries or unsuitable technologies to be transferred to developing countries, since it is cheaper to transfer production there than to meet the increasingly stringent environmental and health regulations of developed countries (28, 29). Many industries manufacturing asbestos transferred production from the United States to Latin America, Brazil and Mexico being the most frequently selected countries. Asbestos textile imports into the United States from Mexico, China (Province of Taiwan) and Brazil grew rapidly between 1969 and 1976, and China (Province of Taiwan) and the Republic of Korea have been displacing Japan as a source of asbestos textiles for the United States since new regulations on this industry were introduced in Japan (28).

A further problem is the transfer of toxic or hazardous wastes from developed to developing countries. The cost of transporting these wastes to rudimentary storage sites in developing countries is a mere fraction of the cost of complying with government regulations for safely storing or incinerating them in their country of origin. This is discussed in more detail in Chapter 8.

Industrial accidents are usually more common in countries with relatively small and undeveloped industrial bases. The reasons include inadequate planning for safety, lack of skilled and experienced engineers to service and maintain industrial equipment, and difficulties in obtaining spare parts because of foreign exchange shortages and government import controls. Plant operators, too, are often poorly trained, especially where there is a high turnover of staff.

In most developing countries, as compared with developed countries, a much higher proportion of the industrial workforce is to be found in small, informal enterprises. This increases the difficulty for government services to monitor and enforce compliance with occupational health and safety regulations. Studies of occupational health conditions and policies in Brazil (22) and Nigeria (30) showed that the workers in small-scale industries had higher injury rates than those in large-scale industries (21). In Nigeria, inspectors only visit firms that employ at least 10 persons, but the vast majority of enterprises employ fewer than 10. The Self-Employed Women's Association in Ahmedabad, India, achieved some reduction in health risks through the provision of safety equipment, improvements in working conditions, the intervention of a health team, educating women workers, and lobbying policy-makers.

Strategies

Industrialization is an essential feature of economic growth in developing countries, and such countries need economic growth. While economic growth as a result of industrialization can have many positive effects on human health, it also creates a risk of adverse effects on the worker and the general population, the latter being affected either directly or through the degradation of the environment. Appropriate strategies for the planning and control of industrial activities should aim at minimizing potential health and environmental problems and thus maximizing the benefits of industrialization. Box 57 gives lead pollution as an example of prevention being cheaper than abatement and health care.

Box 57. Lead as an example of intersectoral concern

While a number of examples of the interrelationship between environmental, behavioural, and development sectors could be cited, one contemporary example, lead poisoning, may be used as an illustration. Lead or lead compounds have been widely used in different commodities: as an antiknock additive in petrol; in batteries; in solder used in tin cans; in piping for water; and in ceramic and household paints. These uses have resulted in a demand for lead that has been met through lead smelting. The plants produce local contamination of the environment and, in some cases, worker injury. Recent advances in knowledge about the effect of lead on health have produced evidence that there may be no safe body level for lead, even though many nations accept 25 μg/dl as the primary action level and 10–15 μg/dl as a secondary level.

Funds for treating poisoned people, environmental abatement programmes, and modification of behavioural patterns are required to reduce the toxic burden of this heavy metal. Intersectoral planning can reduce these health and economic burdens and be cost-effective. The cost of health care and abatement exceeds the cost of preventive modification of industrial practices and good manufacturing practices confining the use of lead to appropriately sound and healthy purposes.

A successful approach to controlling the adverse effects of industrialization on health involves a substantial degree of coordination among international agencies, national and local governments, and private corporations or businesses. It also needs the participation of the general public, local communities, employees of industry, and the mass media. The public health professional must work with all to ensure a healthy environment and prevention or mitigation of the adverse health effects.

This approach calls for a better knowledge of the adverse effects on health and the environment of chemical pollutants, noise, the depletion of resources, and other forms of environmental degradation resulting from industrialization. An effective regulatory system, properly funded, is needed to control environmental pollution. Permits, licences, and inspections by a regulatory authority are essential, and there must be adequate numbers of public health and environmental officials.

Priority should be given to primary prevention applying appropriate control technology to eliminate or reduce pollution from industrial processes both in and out of the workplace, with a view to protecting the health of workers, the community, and the environment in general. Control technology comprises not only design and implementation but also operation and maintenance.

Control technology should be considered in the context of risk management. The decision to apply control technology should be based on the identification and assessment of hazards, and include study of the socio-economic context, of existing public health problems, and of the availability of resources, personnel, and infrastructure. This should make it possible to select the most appropriate technology for each situation.

Existing knowledge of technologies for the prevention and control of occupational and environmental hazards should be applied to anticipate and prevent hazards at each stage of the design, planning, and siting of new industries and, when necessary, to modify existing installations.

The effectiveness of control measures depends essentially on society's ability to implement them. Among the factors that have facilitated control in the developed world have been rapid and sustained economic growth, democratic pressure on governments for pollution control and worker safety, an already existing structure of local government through which control could be achieved, and ability to identify and understand the health problems and provide advice on their solution. In many developing countries the health problems arising from industrialization are tackled by weak, ineffective, and often unrepresentative local governments and within often unstable economies. Many developing countries lack the means to develop the institutional and regulatory mechanisms best suited to their needs.

The mass media have an important role in alerting and educating the public about environmental health hazards posed by industrial activity. The authorities should provide the press with adequate information in a reliable and comprehensive manner.

Three elements are of particular importance in achieving more environmentally sound industrial development:

- The incorporation of health and environmental considerations into all aspects of planning for new industry—cost-benefit analyses, siting, process design, granting of permits, transport of raw materials, product discharges to the air and water, waste generation and disposal.

- The development of techniques to control pollution more easily and flexibly within a legal framework that gives polluters a strong incentive to reduce the release of pollutants and the production of wastes. More emphasis should be placed on the principle that the polluter pays the cost of pollution damage, including damage to health. Although there are many operational difficulties in this principle, not least that of estimating the health cost of pollutants, it provides an important incentive for industries to reduce pollution by ensuring that they are charged the full health and environmental costs of the wastes they generate.

- The requirement that the producers of hazardous products should be responsible for them "from cradle to grave", i.e., from production to safe disposal. A number of international organizations are developing this approach to comprehensive control of hazardous wastes.

Recommendations

These recommendations do not concern particular technologies but are aimed at developing within each nation the knowledge and capacity for action to reduce the adverse environmental and health effects of industrial development.

The effectiveness of regulatory systems to control pollution should be improved. In most countries it is not lack of regulatory mechanisms but failure to use them properly that lies at the root of the government's failure to control pollution. More resources are required to build up institutional capacity and strengthen training, monitoring, and enforcement, with special reference to urban areas, industrial zones, and regions targeted for rapid development. Environmental audits should be carried out in existing industries, designed in such a way as to educate plant managers and workers, pinpoint plant conditions that need improvement, and indicate remedial action to improve plant safety.

In national and local strategies and action, special attention must be paid to susceptible populations. These include people who are particularly at risk from some environmental factor (pollutant or pathogen) because of their age, gender, existing disease or disablement, or genetic predisposition.

Environmental monitoring should be part of any industrial programme. Stack emissions and effluent discharges should be carefully monitored. The exposure of workers should be monitored and evaluated periodically; this provides a form of early warning, since excessive exposure levels for workers may also mean excessive exposure for wider populations. Such monitoring should be the joint responsibility of industry and the government.

Environmental and health considerations should be included in the planning of new developments and cover design, siting, and performance. At each stage in the planning and development of new industries and energy facilities—for instance in choice of technology, siting, construction, operation, and level of preparedness in the event of an accident—there are opportunities to minimize the risk of adverse health and environmental effects. Environmental impact analysis is a valuable tool in determining the costs and benefits of development and should be widely applied. New techniques are being developed to incorporate more accurate health risk analysis. Taking their results systematically into account will require that health agency experts participate in the planning of new industrial, agricultural and energy projects.

Ways should be sought to reduce the health risks of enterprises in the informal sector, especially in countries where governments lack the institutional capacity to be effective in this sector. People who are adequately informed about health risks in their work and homes can be a powerful force for promoting more healthy practices and rectifying hazardous conditions. Community associations and trade unions can also press for improvements in health and safety.

Governments should develop ways of reducing accidents and minimizing their adverse health and environmental effects. For this purpose the maintenance and continued operation of control equipment within industries and power stations should be ensured. Emergency plans should be prepared for each potentially hazardous plant to prevent or mitigate the adverse environmental health effects of any malfunction. Governments should collect data on the nature and consequences of accidents, and at the international level data on accidents should be collated and analysed, and made available to national and local authorities.

Increased priority should be given to education and training at all levels. People need to be informed about the environmental health hazards from industrial activities so that they can contribute to informed decisions about the installation of plant, siting, regulations, environmental and health surveillance, etc. It is important to make public all the aspects of the risks including the results of scientific analysis of the risks and the alternatives to the action proposed. Understanding the risks and benefits of the proposed activity and the relevant socioeconomic factors will aid in acceptance or at least tolerance of the risks.

National and local authorities should be encouraged to develop and disseminate information on health-related and environment-related problems concerning industry and energy systems. International organizations have a major role in the collection and evaluation of environmental health data related to industry and energy, in improving their quality and relevance, and in ensuring their availability.

Recommendations for research

Because the measurement of the health risks associated with more industrialized societies has deficiencies, experimental research should be pursued vigorously to identify the causative environmental factors in adverse health effects, the mechanism of action, and the dose-effect and dose-response relationships, especially in the following areas:

- An improved methodology to assess the toxicity of chemical mixtures, including those found in the environment, and of mixtures of chemical, physical, and microbiological agents.
- Development of quantitative risk assessment techniques, including methods for extrapolating the results from experimental animals exposed during short periods to relatively high doses to human populations exposed for long periods of time to low levels of chemical or physical agents.
- The development of *in vivo* and *in vitro* techniques for predictive risk assessment of new chemicals before they are used or give rise to exposure.
- Analyses of the responses of different species to chemical and physical agents so as to facilitate the extrapolation to humans of test results on experimental animals.
- Improvement of understanding of the pathways by which pollutants reach human targets and are taken up by the body.
- Development of techniques to measure percutaneous absorption, cell proliferation, and allergic reaction of the skin; to detect and quantify immune responses (including the use of biochemical processes); to identify and quantify the behavioural effects of chemical exposure; and to identify possible pulmonary, cardiovascular, renal, endocrine, haematological, reproductive, and developmental effects.

Epidemiological investigations should be carried out to establish the link between chronic disease and long-term exposure to low levels of pollutants and contaminants.

In most developing countries the problem of the virtual absence of information concerning the prevalence, trends, and causes of chronic diseases needs to be tackled. One way is through the development of area profiles, as described in Box 58.

Box 58. Area profiles

Area profiles are meant to provide descriptive data on the relations between acute and chronic poisoning and environmental data. Such profiles would need to be developed in a considerable range of different areas to represent different levels of industrial and urban development and energy use.

These profiles should include information on:
— demographic characteristics of the population
— leading causes of mortality and morbidity as well as data on birth rates
— perinatal mortality, congenital anomalies, and miscarriages
— industrial, agricultural, energy-use, and geographical characteristics
— levels of chemicals in the environment, their industrial origin and the corresponding human exposure
— long-term surveillance of industrial poisoning incidents
— case studies of illness caused by environmental and industrial contamination.

Source: WHO Commission on Health and Environment. *Report of the Panel on Industry.* Geneva, World Health Organization, 1991 (unpublished document WHO/EHE/92.4).

The existence of identifiable long-term relatively high-level exposure in a working population provides an opportunity to investigate the cause-and-effect relationship between chemical and physical agents and chronic disease. As there is often continuity between the extent of exposure at the workplace and in the general population, studies of populations could be of great value in defining, predicting, and preventing chronic disease in the general public that is attributable to industrial activity.

The development of new biological markers makes it possible to obtain important insights into the actual extent of human exposure and the relationship between exposure and adverse effects, which are essential for effective prevention and identification of subpopulations at particular risk. The development and use of these new biological markers should be actively supported, especially of those which can be measured using technology appropriate to the developing countries. Other biological indices of exposure to chemicals, such as changes in enzyme activity, cytogenetic alterations, disturbed physiological function, and mutagenicity of body fluids also deserve further study for their applicability in monitoring the exposure of populations to chemicals.

Methodologies that integrate exposure from all routes into a total dose need to be developed and validated, since no generally accepted procedures exist.

Most data on exposure to chemicals have been obtained in the temperate zones of the world, but most exposure to chemicals and their effects occurs in the semitropical and tropical zones. Research is required to ascertain whether and to what extent the toxicology, metabolism, and environmental behaviour of chemicals are affected by climatic conditions.

Health and environmental improvement entails costs, and there is often a trade-off between such improvements and economic growth. Awareness of this has already led to resistance to environmental control in countries at all levels of development by many manufacturers and governments who argue that people are more interested in economic growth than in better health. Research is needed on:

— the cost and effectiveness of different technologies and strategies to improve environmental conditions and health in urban and rural communities

— the adequacy of legislative and regulatory frameworks to provide incentives and sanctions, to promote health through fiscal and other policies

— the effectiveness of existing and alternative governmental and non-governmental financing sources as instruments of a policy for improved health

— the linkages and spillover effects of technologies and control strategies at national and international level

— the benefits of prevention as compared with cure and the implications for funding and the agencies or individuals responsible for funding.

More emphasis should be placed on developing ways and means of following up groups exposed to toxic agents over a long period of time since little is known about the health effects of long-term chronic exposure. Environmental epidemiology should receive high priority in relation to high-level exposure.

Research on improving systems and technologies for handling wastes, for recycling or reusing them, or for reclaiming materials for reuse elsewhere deserves higher priority.

References and notes

1. Corn, J.K. & Corn, M. The control of health problems related to industrialization. In: Wechler, H. et al., eds. *The social context of research*, Cambridge, MA, Ballinger Publishing Company, 1981, pp. 193–231.

2. *Global estimates for health situation assessments and projections 1990.* Geneva, World Health Organization, 1990 (unpublished WHO document WHO/HST/90.2; available on request from Division of Epidemiological Surveillance and Health Situation and Trend Assessment, World Health Organization, 1211 Geneva 27, Switzerland).

3. Matte, T.D. et al. Lead poisoning among household members exposed to lead-acid battery repair shops in Kingston, Jamaica (West Indies). *International journal of epidemiology*, **18**: 874–881 (1989).

4. See for instance: Consumers Association of Penang. *Development and the environment crisis—a Malaysian case*, Penang, Malaysia, 1982; Hamza, A. An appraisal of environmental consequences of urban development in Alexandria, Egypt. *Environment and urbanization*, **1** (1): 22–30 (1989); Beg, M.A.A. et al. Land-based pollution and the marine environment of the Karachi coast. *Pakistan journal of science, industry and resources*, **27** (4): 199–205 (1984); *The state of India's environment 1982: a citizen's report.* Delhi, Centre for Science and Environment, 1982; *The state of India's environment: a second citizen's report.* Delhi, Centre for Science and Environment, 1985; Smil, V. *The bad earth: environmental degradation in China*, New York, M.E. Sharpe, 1984; Jimenez, R.D. & Velasquez, A. Metropolitan Manila: a framework for its sustained development. *Environment and urbanization*, **1** (1): 51–58 (1989).

5. *The state of India's environment: a second citizen's report.* Delhi, Centre for Science and Environment, 1985.

6. *The state of the environment.* Paris, Organisation for Economic Co-operation and Development, 1991.

7. Phantumvanit, D. & Liengcharernsit, W. Coming to terms with Bangkok's environmental problems. *Environment and urbanization*, **1** (1): 31–39 (1989).

8. Hamza, A. Management of industrial hazardous wastes in Egypt. *Industry and environment*, **4**: 28–32 (1983).

9. Lopez, J.M. The Caribbean and Gulf of Mexico. *The Siren*, No. 36: 30–31 (1988).

10. Ruddle, K. Inshore marine pollution in Southeast Asia. *Mazingira*, **7** (2): 32–44 (1983).

11. Street, A. Nicaraguans cite Pennwalt, U.S. company has poisoned its workers and Lake Managua. *Multinational monitor*, **2** (5): 25–26 (1981).

12. Leonard, H.J. *Confronting industrial pollution in rapidly industrializing countries—myths, pitfalls and opportunities.* Washington, DC, Conservation Foundation, 1984.

13. Office of Housing and Urban Programs. *Ranking environmental health risks in Bangkok, Thailand*. Washington, DC, US Agency for International Development, 1990.

14. *The state of India's environment 1982: a citizen's report*. Delhi, Centre for Science and Environment, 1982.

15. Escobar, J. The south-east Pacific. *The Siren*, No. 36: 28–29 (1988).

16. Global Environment Monitoring System. *Global pollution and health—results of health-related environmental monitoring*. Geneva, WHO/UNEP, 1987.

17. Smil, V. *The bad earth: environmental degradation in China*. New York, M.E. Sharpe, 1984.

18. Anderson, I. Isotopes from machine imperil Brazilians. *New scientist*, 15 October 1987, page 19.

19. Tsubaki, T. & Takahashi, H., eds. *Recent advances in Minamata disease studies*. Tokyo, Kodansha Ltd, 1986.

20. Upton, A.C. et al. Public health aspects of toxic chemical disposal sites. *Annual review of public health*, **10**: 1–25 (1989).

21. Cooper Weil, D.E. et al. *The impact of development policies on health: a review of the literature*. Geneva, World Health Organization, 1990.

22. Nogueira, D.P. Prevention of accidents and injuries in Brazil. *Ergonomics*, **30** (2): 387–393 (1987).

23. Michaels, D. et al. Economic development and occupational health in Latin America: new directions for public health in less developed countries. *American journal of public health*, **75** (5): 536–542 (1985).

24. Rossiter, C. & El Batawi, M.A. The working environment. *Industry and environment*, **10**: 3–11 (1987).

25. Leonard, H.J. Hazardous wastes: the crisis spreads. *Asian national development*, pp. 33–42, April 1986.

26. Rosencranz, A. Bhopal, transnational corporations and hazardous technologies. *Ambio*, **17** (5): 336–341 (1988).

27. *Control of environmental health hazards*. Geneva, World Health Organization, 1987 (unpublished document WHO/EHE/87.1; available on request from Division of Environmental Health, World Health Organization, 1211 Geneva 27, Switzerland).

28. Castleman, B.I. The export of hazardous factories to developing countries. *International journal of health sciences*, **9** (4): 569–597 (1979).

29. Castleman, B.I. & Navarro, V. International mobility of hazardous products, industries and wastes. *International journal of health sciences*, **17** (4): 617–633 (1987).

30. Asogwa, S.E. Prevention of accidents and injuries in developing countries. *Ergonomics*, **30** (2): 370–386 (1987).

7.

Human settlements and urbanization

Introduction

Human settlements provide a living and working environment for virtually all the world's population; only a tiny proportion live in isolated homesteads or as nomads. Here the term human settlements is understood to include not only the physical elements of the environment but also the social and cultural activities located there (*1*). As such, their form and content have a major influence on human health.

Environmental management is needed in all settlements to ensure a healthy environment, and the need rises in proportion to the scale of industrial production concentrated in a settlement, the size of the settlement's population, and the extent to which resources are used for both production and consumption. Even in a small predominantly agrarian village, there is a need to ensure that water sources are protected, contact with human (and very often animal) excreta is reduced to the minimum, roads remain passable during rainy periods, and storm and surface run-off do not pose a threat to the inhabitants. The need for safeguards against the pollution of water sources from agricultural chemicals and wastes has been noted. The scale and complexity of environmental management is much greater for a city, where population densities are much higher and waste generation levels per person larger. In densely built-up areas, environmental management is needed to ensure a balance between public and private space, and, among other things, ensure that all urban dwellers have access to land for sport, recreation, and children's play.

Rapidly growing urban centres pose a particular challenge for environmental health. As well as being an essential part of economic development, urbanization can bring major benefits to health and the environment. The concentration of production and of population lowers unit costs for the supply of piped water and health services, for many forms of sanitation system, and for the collection and treatment of household and commercial wastes. But in the absence of government action to provide the infrastructure, services, and control of pollution on which health and the environment depend, environmental health problems are greatly increased, because of the

197

high concentration of industrial, commercial, and residential wastes. These problems are particularly apparent in developing countries; urban change has outpaced the capacity of most of them to develop the institutional means to cope with these environmental health problems. Virtually all urban governments in developing countries lack the power, resources, and technical personnel needed. In many the structure of government has remained little changed over the past 30 years, even though the population may have increased severalfold (2–4).

This chapter concentrates on such aspects of health promotion and environmental management in human settlements as housing, basic services, the links between the living environment and psychosocial health problems, noise, and transport.

Housing and basic services

In virtually all countries, the needs of a proportion of the population for shelter and basic services are not met. Some 600 million urban dwellers and more than 1000 million rural inhabitants live in life-threatening and health-threatening houses and conditions characterized by overcrowding and lack of basic services such as piped water, sanitation, and health care.

In considering the link between housing and health, housing is taken to mean more than the house's physical structure. It includes such elements as whether the housing has piped water and adequate provision for cooking, washing, laundry, food storage, and the removal of human wastes and wastewater. Other elements are the site and neighbourhood within which each housing unit is located, which should provide much of the defence against injury and disease vectors.

In developed countries, the health and safety aspects of housing are concentrated in the design, physical structure, building materials, and building performance (light, ventilation, insulation). Possible links between housing deficiencies and psychosocial problems are also a matter of concern. Water, sanitation, solid waste removal, and drainage are taken for granted since it is assumed that they are available. It is also assumed that the buildings themselves are legally there and that building and planning codes and norms and other regulations have covered most of the health and safety aspects of the buildings.

In most developing countries, however, the majority of residential buildings fall outside any health and safety regulations, and their siting and construction were never subject to any building or planning codes. Most continue to be built outside such regulations; only a small minority of the houses built in developing countries today are designed and supervised by architects, and seldom are the designs and materials subject to building and planning regulations (5). This is so even for most new housing in urban centres.

New commercial, industrial, and residential buildings constructed by the formal sector in the cities of developing countries in the tropics seem to copy the design of similar buildings in the developed countries in temperate regions, little consideration being given to the climatic and cultural differences. This also seems apparent in much of the planning of settlements and choice of building materials. Yet knowledge exists in most countries about the design and construction of buildings that make good use of local materials, maximize human comfort, moderate extremes of heat and cold, and minimize energy needs for heating and cooling.

Housing and health

WHO has singled out nine features of the housing environment that have important direct or indirect effects on the physical and mental health of the occupants:

(a) the structure of the shelter (which includes the extent to which the shelter protects the occupants from extremes of heat or cold, noise, and invasion by dust, rain, insects, and rodents);

(b) the extent to which the provision for water supplies is adequate, from both a qualitative and a quantitative point of view;

(c) the effectiveness of provision for the disposal (and subsequent management) of excreta and liquid and solid wastes;

(d) the quality of the housing site, including the extent to which it is structurally safe for housing and provision is made to protect it from contamination (of which, provision for drainage is among the most important aspects);

(e) the consequences of overcrowding, including household accidents, air-borne infection, acute respiratory disease, pneumonia, and tuberculosis;

(f) the presence of indoor air pollution associated with fuel used for cooking and heating;

(g) food safety standards, including the extent to which the dwelling has adequate provision for storing food to protect it against spoilage and contamination;

(h) vectors and hosts of disease associated with the domestic and peri-domestic environment;

(i) the home as a workplace, where occupational health questions such as the use and storage of toxic or hazardous chemicals and health and safety aspects of equipment need consideration (6).

Other features of housing also have an important bearing on the state of health of the occupants. The cost is one of the most important, since it affects their income. The nature of their tenure may have an influence on health, for two reasons: the stress caused by insecure tenure, which for tenants or squatters often includes a constant fear of eviction; and the disincentive for tenants or illegal occupiers to invest in improvements to the structure and services since the owners would benefit more than they themselves would.

Housing also has important social aspects that influence the safety and the sense of well-being of the occupants. Dissatisfaction with housing in terms both of its internal characteristics and of the quality and safety of the neighbourhood, and with its inadequacy to meet the social needs of the occupants may have an important bearing on mental illness and psychosocial problems.

Housing and health in developed countries

In the developed world, the health risks associated with housing have been much reduced for most of the population. While there may be deficiencies in the legal and institutional structures ensuring that buildings meet health and safety standards, the existing regulations, duly applied, limit the proportion of housing in which communicable diseases tend to flourish. Serious problems remain unsolved in regard to homelessness and to inadequate housing in specific areas (for instance in many rundown inner city districts), but the proportion of national population affected has been reduced in recent decades. The proportion of the population with piped water and sanitation approaches 100% in most instances. Infants and children in developed countries are several hundred times less likely to die from diarrhoeal or respiratory disease than those in developing countries. The emphasis in developed countries is therefore on the health and safety aspects of the structure and building materials.

Among the materials used in housing (and in commercial and industrial buildings) with a potential health risk are those which contain asbestos (usually used for insulation) and lead (in paint and waterpipes). Organic compounds that may also pose a risk include formaldehyde, chloroform, and perchloroethylene, found in building materials, furnishings, space heaters, wood preservatives, cleaning agents, glues, and other solvents (7). Exposure to radon, a radioactive gas occurring naturally in many rocks and soils, is possibly the leading cause of lung cancer among nonsmokers and may be responsible for as many as 5000–20 000 lung cancer deaths per year in the United States (7). Many of these pollutants may have greater effects on health where lack of ventilation results in higher concentrations in the air.

Another health problem related to building is the sick building syndrome, which commonly occurs inside highly insulated buildings in cold climates where air renewal and ventilation have been limited to save energy or heating costs. It has been recognized as a serious occupational health problem for office workers in both Northern Europe and North America. The syndrome is characterized by chronic fatigue, a stuffy nose, a feeling of discomfort, coughing fits, headache, burning eyes, breathing difficulties, and dizziness. The effects on health include increased morbidity (with diagnoses of respiratory conditions and allergies, hypersensitivity reactions, and psychosocial stress). The sick building syndrome may also give rise to high absenteeism rates. The causes are complex and the symptoms are modified by psychosocial factors.

Enough is known to prevent most of the problems associated with the sick building syndrome, while also promoting energy-efficient buildings. Preventive measures include the setting of minimum standards for air renewal, a better balance between temperature and humidity, and the use of "low-emittant" materials in building, lining, insulation, and painting. It is also recognized that aspects other than indoor air quality must be considered in promoting a healthy indoor environment, including attention to lighting and reduction or control of noise.

Housing and health in developing countries

The links between housing and health are both more common and stronger in developing countries, where "recent analyses ... show a strong association between ill-health and both quantitative and qualitative shortcomings in water supply, food supply, and sanitation. Inadequate shelter, poor ventilation, lack of facilities for solid waste disposal, air and noise pollution and overcrowding are also likely to have negative consequences for health" (8). A comparable association may be found between ill health and poor-quality housing in developed countries as well, especially among particular population groups such as ethnic minorities or temporary immigrant workers in particular locations (for instance rundown inner cities in declining industrial centres).

It is impossible to estimate with any precision what proportion of urban and rural dwellers in the developing countries live in inadequate housing with inadequate provision for water, sanitation, and other basic needs. Case studies of specific cities in Africa, Asia, and Latin America show that it is common for between 30% and 60% of the population to live either in illegal settlements with little or no infrastructure or services or in overcrowded and often deteriorating tenements and cheap boarding-houses (5, 9). Most of these case studies are concerned with large cities, whereas in fact a high proportion of the urban inhabitants in most developing countries live in relatively small urban centres. Estimates for 1990 suggest that less than 2.5% of the urban population of the developing countries live in cities with

10 million or more inhabitants, and less than 25% in cities with 100 000 or more inhabitants (5).

Three generalizations relating to housing and health are valid for the low-income majority in most of these countries. The first is that the accommodation in which they live is inadequate to protect them from health risks. The second is that most have too low an income to afford to buy, rent, or build even the cheapest adequate apartment or house with sufficient space, security, services, and facilities. The third, more characteristic of urban than of rural areas, is that the tenure is insecure. Fear of eviction is a constant worry for most tenants, temporary boarders in cheap rooming-houses, *de facto* owners in illegal settlements, or renters of land on which a house has been built.

Virtually all the homes and neighbourhoods of poorer groups share two characteristics with serious adverse effects on health: the presence in the living environment of pathogenic microorganisms and disease vectors, and crowded cramped housing conditions. The pathogenic microorganisms linked with contaminated food and water in the home and their health impacts have been considered in earlier chapters.

Many health problems affecting poorer groups are associated with overcrowding; they include household accidents, airborne infections, acute respiratory infections, pneumonia, and tuberculosis. Most poorer groups live in overcrowded conditions. The average number of persons per room is between 2 and 3.5 in most developing countries, as against 0.5 to 1.0 in most developed countries (1). It is common for this number to rise to 4 or more among poorer groups; it is also common for poor households to live in one room in both rural and urban areas. In many poor urban districts, households may have less than one square metre of interior space per person (10) and beds are often shared; in the most extreme cases even small rooms are subdivided to allow multiple occupancy. In Hong Kong many people live in beds stacked three high in dormitories, each bed being surrounded by a cage for privacy and protection against robbery. In one dormitory, 130 persons were found living in this way (11). In Calcutta, bunks stacked one above the other in tiny rooms are available for rent by the hour, two or more persons renting the bed within any 24-hour period (5).

Such overcrowding ensures that diseases such as tuberculosis, influenza, and meningitis are easily transmitted from one person to another. Several studies have recorded links between respiratory infections generally, dampness, and indoor air pollution, but the extent to which the infections are aggravated by environmental conditions is not fully brought out in any of the studies (12). Acute respiratory infections, the most common of all the illnesses, are increasingly recognized as a major cause of mortality and morbidity. Acute bacterial and viral respiratory infection, together with tuberculosis, account for some 5 million deaths annually. Tuberculosis (mostly pulmonary) is responsible for more than half of these deaths (Box 59).

Box 59. Tuberculosis: impact on health and association with housing

About 20 million people worldwide have active pulmonary tuberculosis (TB), a communicable disease of the lungs caused by a bacterium transmitted through the air when infected people cough or sneeze. If untreated, the fatality is close to 50%, mostly among young adults. Nearly 3 million people die each year from TB, more than from any other infectious disease. Virtually all of these deaths are in developing countries, over 60% of them in Asia and over 20% in Africa; 1.4% are in developed countries, mostly among the elderly, ethnic minorities, and immigrants.

Each year there are 8 million new cases of TB, 4 million of which are infectious. The countries with the largest number of cases are Bangladesh, Brazil, China, India, Indonesia, Nigeria, Pakistan, the Philippines, and Viet Nam. The highest proportion of the population with TB tends to be found in sub-Saharan Africa.

In most developing countries, the incidence of TB has been declining, although it increases in absolute numbers as the population increases. In some East and Central African countries, reported cases have grown rapidly, almost doubling in the last 4–5 years. One of the main reasons for this is the spread of infection with the human immunodeficiency virus (HIV); when people infected with TB are also infected with HIV, TB is more likely to become active. An estimated three million people with HIV infection are also TB-infected. In people with TB, the time it takes for AIDS to develop is dramatically shortened.

Household members living with an infectious case of TB are at greatest risk. The highest incidence of TB tends to be among populations living in the poorest areas, where families are usually large, housing inadequate and overcrowded, nutrition levels low, and health care limited or unavailable. Household or social or work contacts are at greatest risk of infection. Overcrowded housing conditions and poor ventilation often mean that TB infection is transmitted to more than half the family members.

The cost of immunization against TB is less than US$ 6 per person. The cost of drugs to treat TB is only some US$ 30–50 per patient and high cure rates are possible. In the United Republic of Tanzania a TB programme using short-course chemotherapy has achieved an 85% cure rate for diagnosed cases.

Sources: Cauthen, G.M. et al. *Annual risk of tuberculosis infection.* Geneva, World Health Organization, 1988 (unpublished document, WHO/TB/88.154); and *Global estimates for health situation assessment and projections 1990,* Geneva, World Health Organization, 1990 (unpublished document WHO/HST/90.2).

Acute respiratory infections tend to be endemic rather than epidemic, affect younger groups, and be more prevalent in urban than in rural areas. The frequency of contact, the density of the population, and the concentration and proximity of infective and susceptible people in an urban population promote the transmission of the infective organisms. Poorer groups in developing countries are much more at risk because of the greater proportion of younger age groups, limited health and financial resources, and over-crowded households in congested settlements with limited access to vaccines and antibacterial drugs. The constant influx of migrants susceptible to infection and possible carriers of new virulent strains of infective agents, together with the inevitable increase in household numbers, fosters the transfer of nasopharyngeal microorganisms.

Meningococcal meningitis is also an airborne infection in which over-crowding is probably a contributory factor. Outbreaks in developing countries commonly occur where there are large numbers of new arrivals living in overcrowded settlements. In Africa meningococcal meningitis is a serious health problem; in the Sudan, for instance, 38 805 cases and 2770 deaths were reported in epidemics in 1988 and 1989 (*13*).

Streptococcal infections are major contributors to morbidity. Streptococcal sore throat is extremely common in all populations and is readily passed from person to person within households; large-scale outbreaks often occur in schools and military establishments. The most serious sequel of oro-pharyngeal streptococcal infections is rheumatic fever, which in many developing countries accounts for about one-third of all cardiovascular diseases. Rheumatic fever occurs most commonly among children in the age group 5–9 years. The incidence of rheumatic fever in developed countries is reported to be below 5 per 100 000 population, whereas in many developing countries among children living in populations with overcrowded living conditions it may approach 300 per 100 000. Although acute streptococcal pharyngitis is widespread, only a small proportion of cases proceed to rheumatic fever (*13*).

The environment in and around human dwellings offers an important habitat for a wide range of disease vectors (*14*), which can be divided into arthropods (including insects, spiders, and mites) and vertebrates (including dogs, bats, birds, and rats). Arthropods can in turn be divided into four categories: those breeding on the body surface or in clothes (including lice and scabies mites); those breeding in the house (including fleas, cockroaches, bedbugs, triatomine bugs, and soft ticks); those breeding peridomestically or in containers and sewage (including various kinds of mosquito, midges, and flies); and those which are adventitious, entering the house to feed (including various kinds of mosquito, sand-flies, and scorpions).

The impact on health of these disease vectors is considerable. The diseases they cause or carry include bancroftian filariasis (mosquitos), Chagas disease (triatomine bugs), dengue fever (mosquitos), diarrhoeal disease (cockroaches, blowflies, houseflies), hepatitis A (houseflies, cockroaches), leishmaniasis (sandflies), plague (certain fleas), relapsing fever (body lice and soft ticks), relapsing fever (body lice and soft ticks), scabies (scabies mites), trachoma (face flies), typhus (body lice and fleas), yaws (face flies), and yellow fever (mosquitos) (*14*). Chagas disease should be highlighted because of the relation of its vectors to house structure and the scale of its impact on health (Box 60).

Environmental management has an important role in the control of such disease vectors in the domestic or peri-domestic environment and in lessening the risk of human infection. Four aspects of such control need stressing:

— the location of housing (for instance, exposed water often serves as a breeding site for a range of insects including malarial mosquitos)
— restricting the vectors' access to humans (for instance with nets and screens)
— restricting the vectors' food sources or breeding sites (for instance preventing access to stored foodstuffs, organic wastes, and excreta, keeping domestic animals away from houses, improving drainage, and draining pools and waterlogged sites)
— restriction of hiding-places (repairing cracks in walls, floors, and ceilings, and ensuring good ventilation and lighting) (*14*).

A high proportion of people in low-income settlements or districts also have intestinal worms. The scale of the problem can be seen from estimates for hookworm infestation, which suggest that, worldwide, some 700–900 million people are infested and there are 1.5 million cases of disease and 50 000 deaths a year (*15*). A survey of 238 slum children in Manila aged 8 months to 15 years found 92% with whipworm, 80% with roundworm, and 10% with hookworm, 84% having at least two species of parasite (*16*). Studies in poor urban communities in Kuala Lumpur and Allahabad also found a high prevalence of intestinal worms, especially in children (*17, 18*).

The health problems linked to unsafe or dangerous building structures include increased risk of fire, building collapse, and electrocution from faulty wiring. Much urban and rural housing in developing countries is constructed of flammable materials (wood, cardboard, plastic, canvas, straw) and the risk of fire is extremely high where open fires or mobile stoves are used for cooking and candles or paraffin lamps for heating. The fire risk is further increased where household wastes are burnt in the open and dwellings are constructed close together (*19*). Household accidents, including burns and scalds, are very common in overcrowded conditions. Injuries from falls are common in substandard housing and in settlements with no all-weather roads

---

Box 60. Chagas disease

Chagas disease (American trypanosomiasis) is a debilitating parasitic disease widespread in Latin America. Infection by the parasite *Trypanosoma cruzi* is from bites by the blood-sucking triatomid bugs, which are its natural vector, or through blood transfusion from infected donors. First described by Carlos Chagas in Brazil in the early twentieth century, there is still no effective treatment for the disease. An estimated 18 million people suffer from it and some 100 million are at risk. It is a leading cause of heart disease in several Central and South American countries and the mortality may be considerable; in many areas it is one of the chief causes of sudden death in apparently healthy young persons. However, there are no accurate figures, because it mostly affects poor rural areas that are often without access to health services and where there are many deficiencies and inaccuracies in the reporting of causes of death.

Infection most often occurs in low-income families in rural areas where poor housing conditions provide breeding sites for the disease vector. The risk of infection can be much reduced by preventive action to avoid or minimize contact between people and the vectors, as by regular spraying with insecticide, and housing improvement, for instance plastering walls to reduce the resting and breeding sites of the vectors.

Although it is considered a rural disease, the migration of many rural people infected with Chagas disease to urban areas has made it a significant cause of morbidity and mortality there. For instance, the Federal District in Brazil is considered to be free of the insect vector of Chagas disease. However, Chagas disease was found to be responsible for about one death in ten among people between 25 and 64 years of age. This places the disease roughly on a par with cancer, heart disease, and stroke in its contribution to causes of death.

Sources: Briceno-Leon, R., *La casa enferma: sociología de la enfermedad de Chagas.* Venezuela, Consorcio de Ediciones Capriles, 1990; Gomes Pereira, M. Characteristics of urban mortality from Chagas' disease in Brazil's Federal District. *Bulletin of the Pan American Health Organization,* **18** (1): 1–9 (1984); WHO Technical Report Series, No. 811, 1991 (*Control of Chagas disease:* report of a WHO Expert Committee).

---

or paths or sited on steep slopes. The elderly and children are likely to suffer most. A survey of 599 slum children in Rio de Janeiro found that accidents accounted for 19% of all health problems; those reported were falls (66%), cuts (17%) and burns (10%) (*20*). The age of the child is an important determinant of accidents; the peaks in accidents were between the second and fifth year of life. The authors noted that the hazardous physical environment is only one factor involved; another is limited parental child care and supervision when all the adults work.

Risks to health and risks of accidents are often further increased by danger from the sites on which houses are built. Large clusters of illegal dwellings often develop on steep hillsides, on flood plains, or in desert land. Poor groups build on such sites because they are cheap or because illegal occupation is less likely to be threatened since the land is unsuitable for commercial development. Health risks are also increased by the fact that domestic, and on occasion industrial, solid wastes are disposed of in open spaces within residential areas. Lack of sewers (or other sanitation systems) and of site drainage means that pools of contaminated water form close to the shelters and flooding brings additional health problems caused by over-flowing latrines. Storm and surface water drains are rarely installed in most new residential developments. Frequent flooding and waterlogged sites take a serious toll on health. Box 61 outlines the link between flooding and outbreaks of leptospirosis in São Paulo.

The effects of injuries are further magnified by lack of provision for first aid and the difficulty in rapidly transporting a sick or injured person to hospital and of ensuring that the person will receive rapid treatment once he or she arrives. The lack of paved roads and sites on steep slopes, waterlogged, or in other ways difficult to cross with motorized vehicles also mean that, in the event of fires or other emergencies, neither fire engines nor ambulances can reach the settlement, at least not without long delays (19).

Each settlement has its own range and mix of housing types, making it difficult to generalize about the precise nature of the linkages between housing and the health of occupants. The association between poor health and poor-quality housing and living conditions in many rural areas in developing countries has long been known. In urban settlements the extent of ill health and premature death in squatter settlements and other low-income areas in developing countries has certainly been underestimated. In such cities the range and form of each settlement are influenced by factors such as the city's employment structure, income distribution, structure of land ownership, and attitude to illegal housing development. The range of housing options open to lower-income groups can change rapidly in any city, for instance as a result of political or economic change (5). All such changes have effects on health. There is also a considerable variety of housing types in rural areas, each with its own range of health risks: the health risks associated with an agricultural labouring household living in employer-provided barracks are likely to be different from those associated with farmers living in their own self-constructed shack.

The health profiles of residents in particular settlements will reflect their different demographic structures. Some rural settlements or areas within a city may have a high concentration of old people with very low incomes. Certain areas within cities have relatively young populations, for instance

---

Box 61. Leptospirosis and flooding: the case of São Paulo

Outbreaks of leptospirosis have been recorded in São Paulo and Rio de Janeiro since the beginning of the century. The most recent epidemics occurred in São Paulo in 1983 (383 recorded cases) and 1987 (340 recorded cases). In Rio de Janeiro more than 700 cases were reported after heavy floods in 1988. The link between flooding and leptospirosis has been noted by several authors; the risk of an outbreak is increased substantially by the concurrence of several factors, including floods, high population density, the presence of rats, cats, and dogs, and the incidence of animal leptospirosis.

Large areas of former agricultural land covered by urban developments have promoted the uncontrolled channelling of rainwater. The deficient drainage is made worse by the sloping terrain and the fact that natural embankments towards the river Tiete have been filled and raised to increase building land. The Tiete river has been entirely canalized and a dam constructed that raises the level of the water. Following heavy rainfall, the city experiences frequent minor floods, especially in low-lying areas. An increase in the incidence of leptospirosis has been noted regularly following city flooding.

A study examined the domestic environment of 107 patients diagnosed as having leptospirosis who could be traced to their homes (13). About 90% were male, generally at increased risk of occupational exposure to contaminated waters. In the study nearly half the patients reported contact with floodwater in their place of domicile prior to the commencement of symptoms. Half lived on the edge of the principal roads leading out of the city, the rest in slum colonies or on the edge of unpaved roads. Nearly 70% lived less than 200 metres from a city or council garbage dump. The presence of rats and of stray dogs in both the lots and the garbage dumps was noted.

Source: WHO Commission on Health and Environment. *Report of the Panel on Urbanization.* Geneva, World Health Organization, 1992 (unpublished document WHO/EHE/92.5).

---

those areas which develop as centres for cheap boarding-houses for newly arrived migrants, who are generally young. Improved services and facilities are needed in virtually all instances, but the actual form in which they are needed and the way in which they should be provided must relate to the particular circumstances of each area and the needs of its residents. Improving conditions in rented accommodation can prove more problematic than in settlements where most occupiers are owners (or *de facto* owners in illegal settlements). Landlords may be the main beneficiaries of public investment to improve such areas and tenants the losers as they are pushed out by higher rents (21).

Basic services

The most important basic services for health are water and sanitation, education (including literacy), and health care. In urban areas in particular, garbage collection and disposal services are also important for health.

Health care

A substantial proportion of the world's population still lacks access to health care and to the cheap and effective preventive and curative interventions that such a service can provide. By 1990 only 61% of the population of developing countries had access to primary health care (22). Although the percentage of children and pregnant women covered by immunization has grown considerably in recent years, there are still hundreds of millions who remain unimmunized. By 1990 more than two-fifths of children in Africa still had not been immunized against measles, poliomyelitis, pertussis and diphtheria. The coverage was better in other regions, varying from 73% to 94%. In the same year only a third of pregnant women were fully immunized against tetanus. In regard to diarrhoeal diseases, there has been a rapid growth in the availability of oral rehydration therapy (ORT) in recent years, but by 1988 (the latest year for which figures are available) the estimated use rates for ORT in children of 0–4 years of age was 32% (22).

Three problems need to be stressed: the low priority given to primary health care in health budgets and by development assistance agencies; the difficulties that many health care systems have when seeking to expand coverage; and the cuts in funds available for health care. As regards the first of these, a recent World Bank report (23) noted that most health spending in developing countries goes to curative care and only a small proportion to health care centres:

> ...an estimated 70 to 85 percent of the developing world's total health spending, both public and private, goes for curative care. Between 10 and 20 percent is spent on preventive care and the remaining 5 to 10 percent on community services such as mosquito control and health education. Within the curative sector, hospitals often account for more than 80 percent of the cost. Yet it is well known that preventive and community services are far more effective in reducing morbidity and mortality. If public resources tied up in hospitals were redirected to the lower levels of the health care system, many diseases could be prevented altogether or treated earlier at less cost.

The proportion of health expenditure devoted to primary health care appears to have grown in recent years, even though the percentage of the GNP allocated to health expenditure has been stationary since an evaluation in 1985. A recent review of progress in the quality of health care (*22*) noted that the global and national efforts to promote and implement primary health care for all citizens had been successful in extending essential care to expanding segments of the population, including those most in need and with least access. When the particular element of primary health care has been supported with extensive technology, training and management development, as has been the case with the Expanded Programme on Immunization and the Control of Diarrhoeal Diseases, this extension in coverage has normally been accomplished while maintaining a minimum level of quality (even though problems are often encountered in ensuring essential supplies, maintaining the cold chain, etc.). When, however, the extension of coverage has been accomplished primarily through the development of health infrastructure (staff and facilities) alone, then, the review notes, the quality of care is likely to decline. This may be the case, for example, when the expanding infrastructure produces higher coverage with antenatal and delivery care. The quality of this care (in terms of delivering well what is most needed) and the resultant client satisfaction and health outcome seem to suffer, as the development investment needed to expand the infrastructure is often not followed by the necessary expansion of the operating budget for such items as drugs and other supplies, vehicle maintenance and travel allowances for supervision.

The economic crisis has also forced most governments to cut down social expenditure. The result is often a decline in what were already very inadequate levels of investment in water, sanitation, garbage collection, and health care. The per caput expenditure on health in developing countries was already very low at the beginning of the 1980s: an average of US$4 per person per year in 92 developing countries compared with an average of US$220 per person per year in 32 rich countries. In this same period, in a third of developing countries the spending per person per year was less than US$2 (*24*). The meagre resources allocated to health care often went largely to curative-care hospitals in one or two major cities that provided services for a very small proportion of the national population. This is one of the least cost-effective ways of improving health (*25*).

Health spending per person has declined in most countries since 1980. The 1990 edition of *The state of the world's children* (*26*) reported a decline in more than three-quarters of the countries of Africa and Latin America in recent years, a decline that is almost certainly more widespread than the statistics suggest. "Hundreds of health clinics have been closed down, and many which remain open are understaffed and lacking essential supplies." This report also stated that infant mortality is known to have risen in parts of Latin America and sub-Saharan Africa and that the incidence of low birth weight had increased in 7 of the 15 countries for which recent information was available (*26, 27*). Cuts by governments in social expenditure are often demanded by outside agencies before aid or balance-of-payments support is given. Most of the official bilateral and multilateral development assistance agencies give very low priority to funding primary health care (*28, 29*).

Education

Perhaps the two most important indicators of education for the promotion of health are the proportion of school-age children receiving primary education and the adult literacy rate (especially for women, since in most instances they have the principal role in promoting infant and child health and in nursing sick people within the family). Estimates for 1985 suggested a total of 900 million illiterate people worldwide. The literacy rate for men in developing countries rose from 53% in 1970 to 71% in the first half of the 1980s (*22*). Although the female literacy rate is much lower—only 50% in 1985—enrolment rates for girls have been increasing more rapidly than for boys (*22*).

Garbage collection and disposal

Garbage collection services are inadequate or non-existent in most residential areas of developing cities; an estimated 30–50% of the solid waste generated within urban centres is left uncollected (*30*). It accumulates on streets and in open spaces between houses, causing or contributing to serious health problems. The poorer households suffer most, since it is overwhelmingly in the poorer areas of cities that there are no services to collect garbage or the services are very inadequate (*30*).

Garbage left uncollected encourages fly-breeding, the flies promoting the transmission of infection. It can also promote diseases associated with rats such as plague, leptospirosis, salmonellosis, endemic typhus, rat-bite fever, and some arboviral infections (*31*). Uncollected garbage can be a serious fire hazard and a serious health hazard for children playing on the site (*32*). Uncollected garbage also blocks drainage channels, increasing health problems related to flooding and waterlogged soils.

Road accidents

Every year some 500 000 people are killed in automobile accidents, according to World Bank estimates (*33*). Of these, roughly 350 000 are in developing countries where, although the number of motor vehicles relative to the population is generally much lower, the available statistics suggest a higher number of road fatalities relative to the number of vehicles. Two-thirds of the accidents involve pedestrians, most of whom are children. Two-thirds of the accidents occur in cities or in surrounding areas. Given the rapid population growth in urban areas and the growth in the number of motor vehicles, the number of deaths from automobile accidents is likely, in the absence of effective intervention, to continue growing.

The number of injuries is many times the number of accidental deaths. Studies in different countries confirm that there are 10–20 times as many people injured as killed. Many have serious injuries and lasting disabilities. The injured are often not counted in national health statistical systems. A review of data from the United States concludes that out of 1000 people with road injuries (vehicle occupants, pedestrians, cyclists, motorcyclists), 11 will die (most within a day), 27 have injuries classified as life-threatening, 83 serious injuries, 163 moderate injuries, and 714 minor injuries (34).

Road accidents represent one of the most serious health problems in many countries, especially if the health effects are assessed taking into account the loss of productivity from premature death or disability. It is mostly young persons who are killed or disabled. In the age group 5–44 years, automobile accidents are the second most important cause of death in the world (22).

Noise

Noise is a common nuisance in everyday life and can give rise to serious health problems. Hearing loss is perhaps the best known and the most insidious, and is not uncommon as a result of occupational exposure. Temporary at first, it becomes irreversible after continued or repeated exposure. Studies of continued exposure have shown that the risk of a rise in the hearing threshold of 25 decibels (dB) doubles when the working lifetime exposure to noise increases from 85 to 90 dB, i.e., trebles. Depending on the studies, the percentage of subjects with a 25 dB threshold is 10, 12, or 15% after continued exposure to 85 dB, and 21, 22 and 29% after continued exposure to 90 dB. There is much less agreement on the quantitative effects of varying and intermittent noise and impulsive noise.

Night-time noise is a major disturbance to sleep above an indoor level of about 40 dB, especially for older people and in the early hours of the morning. While sleep may not always be affected, adverse effects on daytime performance, such as increased reaction times, have been recorded, the effects being more marked in older subjects. Subjectively, people often believe that they become used to night-time noise, but physiological tests point to the contrary, cardiovascular responses remaining unchanged after five years of exposure.

Noise affects performance in other ways. The performance of simple tasks remains unaffected at noise levels as high as 115 dB, but complex tasks are disrupted at much lower levels, some at intermittent exposure to 80 dB. Frequency of sound is also important, with high frequencies more disruptive than low frequencies. Impulsive noise is specially disruptive. Exposure to speech, whether irrelevant or meaningful, on the other hand, alters mental performance (reasoning, mental arithmetic, problem-solving) almost independently of intensity and pitch, but meaningful speech is more disruptive in reading tasks than meaningless speech. Behavioural after-effects have also been described. Even moderately high levels (80–90 dB) of noise over which people have no control raise anxiety levels and increase the risk of hostile reactions.

Community exposure

Background environmental noise levels rise in direct proportion to the population of a given area. Thus noise appears to be endemic in urban conditions. In the city the main causes of traffic noise are the motors, tyres, and exhaust systems of automobiles, trucks, buses, and motorcycles. This type of noise may be exacerbated in the narrow streets of older cities, where sound reverberates between the buildings. To this noise are added the sounds of compressors and drills used in road and construction work, railroad engines, horns, whistles, and aircraft.

Annoyance describes the community's collective feelings about excessive noise, as recorded by questionnaires inquiring about sleep disturbances, interference with communication, and disruption of the peaceful enjoyment of one's property. More than mere irritation, it signifies degradation in the quality of life. The sources of noise vary from place to place and involve aircraft, road, and railway traffic, building construction, entertainment, including sporting events, and the activities of neighbours. It is estimated that 130 million people in OECD countries are exposed to more than 65 dB in the daytime and 400 million to 55 dB, a level that most find disturbing (7). Within the OECD, however, levels of exposure vary, the proportion of people exposed to 65 dB from road traffic differing by a factor of six from country to country (7). Rail transport is a more significant source of noise in Germany and Switzerland than in other OECD countries.

Inadequate though the information for developed countries is, there is even less for developing countries. The variability of the noise level is likely to be even higher. In general, exposure to noise in cities is rather more intense than in the developed world, owing partly to lack or lax enforcement of anti-noise legislation, partly to climatic reasons encouraging people to keep their windows open. The multiplicity of small cottage industries, (e.g., weaving or panel-beating) scattered within a city may give rise to particularly high levels of noise.

City planning, soundproofing of buildings, noise control engineering solutions, strictly enforced anti-noise legislation and, for some sources, education campaigns and respect for neighbours are necessary to prevent transport and sound-emitting electronic devices from further raising the noise levels to which the public is exposed.

Occupational exposure

The most intense continued and frequent exposure to noise occurs in the working environment, especially in industry. Millions of workers throughout the world suffer to a varying extent from noise-induced hearing loss.

The energy-producing industry includes noisy processes, both underground and on the surface, workers being exposed to noise from blasting, drilling, cutting, and loading operations. The petroleum industry exposes workers to high noise levels from a variety of drills, compressors, motors, blowers, generators, pumps, and valves. Electricity and nuclear plants also expose workers to noise from large equipment such as air compressors and steam turbines.

Food processing, especially canning and bottling, creates problems not unlike those in other industries. Tree cutting and wood processing workers, including lumberjacks, are continually exposed to the high-pitched noise of chain-saws. Crop production equipment, mainly tractors, and other farming equipment, e.g., for threshing and winnowing, also involve recurring exposure to high noise levels unless the driver is protected by a soundproof cab or other device.

Manufacturing industries are the most significant source of occupational exposure in developed countries. In the USA, some of the noisiest have been ranked according to the percentage of workers exposed to average sound levels above 90 dB (35):

    lumber and wood products
    petroleum and coal
    textiles
    primary metals
    paper
    chemicals
    printing and publishing
    metal fabrication.

Protection of workers is not always possible, but engineering controls would be feasible in many circumstances. If these are difficult to install or cannot be installed immediately, hearing protectors and periodic audiometric monitoring of those exposed will ensure that hearing damage is reduced to a minimum.

Settlements and psychosocial health problems

Good housing and a suitable physical and social environment promote good mental and physical health. Where they are absent, psychosocial disorders can become a major cause of morbidity and death among adolescents and young adults (12). Among the most serious psychosocial health problems are depression, drug and alcohol abuse, suicide, child and spouse abuse, delinquency, and target violence (e.g., rape, teacher assault). Many social pathologies are associated with poor-quality housing, insecure tenure, or eviction from housing. Vandalism and violence contribute to a poor environment, also with adverse effects on health. It is difficult, however, to quantify the importance of environmental factors in relation to the many other contributory factors.

Personal violence, including homicide, assault, suicide, suicide attempts, sponse and child abuse, is a growing problem throughout the world and often primarily affects the poorer members of society. It has been suggested that the public health sector has a legitimate role with the justice, social, and educational sectors in reducing this problem. It is being increasingly recognized that the environment plays an important role in violent behaviour and that the public health initiatives that were so effective in combating infectious disease should be utilized for combating violent behaviour (36).

Many of the physical characteristics of the housing and living environment have a major influence on mental disorder and social pathology through such stressful factors as noise, air, soil, or water pollution, overcrowding, inappropriate design, inadequate maintenance of the physical structure and services, poor sanitation, or a high concentration of specific toxic substances. The precise link between the different elements of the physical environment and the manifestation of social pathology is difficult to ascertain and to separate from background or intervening factors.

One of the most important intervening factors is level of income or amount of capital assets, because of the obvious correlation between housing quality and price; studies have indicated a higher prevalence of mental illness in low-income, physically rundown areas (12). Other social and cultural variables may increase or diminish the health impact of physical factors; for instance, strong social networks and a sense of community organization in many rundown inner city districts in developed countries and squatter settlements in cities in developing countries might help to explain the remarkably low level of psychosocial problems. Such social networks often prove of major importance in survival strategies as well as in mitigating the effect of inadequate physical environments on psychosocial health problems. The importance of such networks has often been demonstrated when poor urban communities have been rehoused in buildings of better quality; the destruction of the social network, which is often combined with loss of income-earning possibilities, contributes to an increased incidence of both physical and mental ill health (*37*). The availability and acceptability of health care services, social welfare services, and other assistance programmes also influence the incidence of psychosocial problems.

The relationship between housing and mental disorder requires an understanding not only of the availability of housing but also of many other variables such as cost, structure, space/density, facilities, and location. Dwelling density and crowding have been the most notable variables in studies linking housing and social pathology. One study correlated the dwelling density with psychiatric symptoms in urban Filipino men and found positive correlations between three different patterns of disorder: withdrawal, aggression, and psychosomatic disorders (*38*).

Correlations between psychosocial problems and high-rise housing have also been studied. High-rise buildings have often proved particularly unpopular among poorer groups in Europe, although this may relate as much to lack of an alternative, inappropriate design, poor maintenance, and absence of security as to the fact that they live in high-rise buildings. Such buildings, which ill suit the needs of households with young children, may suit other groups. Middle- and upper-income groups living in high-rise housing appear to have fewer psychosocial problems linked to the housing. These differences need careful analysis; one may be that these groups have chosen to live in high-rise buildings and the buildings in which they live are better served in terms of maintenance and security. Other aspects of the relationship between living in high-rise buildings and health are poorly understood, for instance the health effects of measures such as sealed windows, which are routinely used, the greater difficulty of evacuating residents in the case of fire, and the reduced noise and air pollution levels in the higher storeys.

Many studies of psychosocial problems have sought differences between rural and urban areas, although the diversity of housing and living conditions limits the validity of comparisons (*39*). As for diseases or infant and child mortality rates associated with poverty, differences within cities are often high and may be greater than between rural and urban areas. The place of residence may be less important for psychiatric disorders than age, gender, education, income, mobility, ethnicity, or occupation, since these may affect the psychological outlook, coping strategies, and the utilization of psychiatric services (*40*). A review of the literature on rural-urban differences "cautiously conclude(s)… that in general, urban and rural populations now differ only marginally in regard to the prevalence of psychiatric impairment, but this is not to say that specific communities may not have exceptionally low or high rates, for any reason" (*40*).

Particular populations or age groups within specific urban or rural settings are likely to have a particularly high degree of social pathology. Deteriorating inner city areas or urban centres with declining economies are characterized by social disorganization and disintegration and create scores of high-risk populations—migrants, children, women, the handicapped, the elderly, the homeless, street children. The physical and economic deterioration is also accompanied by a feeling of entrapment among particular income, age, and ethnic groups, which can make the problems more difficult to resolve.

There is a growing recognition that certain patterns of mental disorder associated with urban life may be more a function of poverty than of urban residence *per se*. Studies that have considered social class have found that, while the poor do have high rates of particular disorders, the wealthy also suffer mental disorders although, as a group, of a different kind. When poverty implies social disorganization and social disintegration, the relationship to mental disorders appears to be much stronger.

Urban life may have more pernicious consequences for child behaviour because of the increased likelihood of family disintegration and negative peer and environmental influence (*41*). The psychosocial development of children may become a major problem in areas characterized by poor-quality housing and basic services and low-income inhabitants. If cognitive, sensory/motor, and social development is prevented or hindered, it may take a lifetime to reverse the consequences. The approach to these problems must be specific, since there are inner city areas and declining urban centres which, although poor, are neither degrading nor destructive of human health. Social processes rather than geographical residence may be the critical factor.

Children are especially vulnerable to deficiencies in the provision of space, facilities, and services. For instance, children's play is known to have a central role in learning, motor and communication skills, problem-solving and logical thinking, emotional development, and social behaviour (*42*). In most urban centres the public provision for safe and stimulating children's play is very inadequate, especially in poorer districts (*42*). In most countries, indeed, there are great inadequacies in the provision of services and support for children in difficult circumstances, for instance street children and the children of migrant workers (*43*).

Health impact of urbanization in developing countries

Virtually all governments in developing countries have failed to ensure that rapid urban growth is accompanied by the investment needed in the infrastructure and services, especially in residential areas with a predominance of poorer households. Few governments have given priority to increasing the power, resources, and trained personnel of the city and local authorities that have to cope with rapid urban growth. The result has been a rapid increase in the number of people living in very overcrowded conditions and in illegal or informal settlements. The health and environmental implications of over-crowding and inadequacies in the water supply, sanitation, and other parts of the infrastructure and services have already been described. The inadequa-cies may be more the result of the illegal nature of the settlements than of the lack of resources available to local governments and of the capacity of the inhabitants to pay the cost.

There are hundreds of studies describing the development of different illegal or informal settlements in cities in developing countries and it is in these settlements that most new urban housing has been developed over the last 30–40 years (44). The studies reveal the ingenuity with which new settlements have been built at low cost and with scarce resources, and they often demonstrate a sophisticated capacity among poorer groups to organize and plan (45, 46). But individual ingenuity and collective organization among low-income households cannot deal with problems such as no paved roads, no drains or sewers, no piped water, no services to collect garbage, no treatment of accidents, injuries, and illness in the absence of outside support. When the settlement does seek some solution, it is often undermined by the hostility of the public authorities to the settlement's very existence.

In most small urban centres and in many of the cities in the poorest developing countries, the proportion of people living in illegal settlements may be smaller partly because the market in land is less commercialized. In addition, in many of the least urbanized countries traditional land tenure systems limit the individual's right to own, buy, and sell land, and this has made it easier for poorer households to obtain land for housing (47). Despite the fewer numbers of people living in illegal settlements in such urban centres, the proportion living in areas with inadequate or no provision for an infrastructure and services may be as high as or higher than in the largest cities in richer developing countries, the inadequacies stemming less from their illegal status, and more from lower incomes and weaker local govern-ments.

The health impact of most public housing projects has to be seen in the light of the concentration of scarce government resources on building relatively few units, often not allocated to poorer groups. Even when governments have adopted cheaper, more flexible solutions, such as pro-vision for or improvement of the infrastructure and services within existing low-income settlements (slum or squatter upgrading) or the provision of housing sites or core units with basic services, the achievements in terms of health improvement have been more limited than anticipated. A review of the literature on this subject noted that the cost to health of the temporary or permanent displacement of poorer groups by public projects, the effect on household budgets, and the diversion of project resources to non-poor groups may be substantial (8). Moreover, most projects that sought to improve environmental health conditions for poorer groups neither undertook a prior health survey nor involved the inhabitants in the planning and implementation of the projects, often misunderstanding the scale and nature of ill health and its causes. The level of service provision was also often inadequate and assumptions as to the capacity to pay of the settlers inaccurate. A few studies have noted that the capacity and willingness to pay of poorer groups is often underestimated, especially for water supply and sanitation (48, 49).

A final aspect of urbanization with important health implications is the association of urban expansion with disease. The expansion of the built-up area, the construction of roads, reservoirs, and drains, land clearance, and deforestation may effect drastic changes in the local ecology. Natural foci for disease vectors may be trapped within the urban extension and new ecological niches for zoonotic animal reservoirs created (50). Within conurbations, synanthropic animal and arthropod vector populations may adapt to new habitats and introduce fresh infections to spread among the urban population. For instance in India, where the vector of lymphatic filariasis is a peridomestic mosquito, there has been rapid increase in the incidence of the disease and in the vector population, associated with the steady rise in the growth of human populations in endemic areas. Anopheline mosquitos generally shun polluted water, but *A. stephensi*, the principal vector of urban malaria, is also reported in India and in the Eastern Mediterranean Region to have adapted to the urban environment, and other species of anophelines now breed in swamps and ditches surrounding urban areas in Nigeria and Turkey. *Aedes aegypti*, the vector of dengue and urban yellow fever, proliferates in tropical urban settlements and has been frequently found breeding in polluted water sources such as soakaway pits, septic tanks, and other sites that contain a high amount of organic matter. *Aedes albopictus* was introduced into the United States from Asia around 1986, and within five years it had spread to 160 counties in 17 states. It was also introduced into Brazil, where it is reported to be present in four states (51) and in late 1991, it made its first appearance on the African continent, in Nigeria. This species is peridomestic, like *A. aegypti*, and is an efficient vector of dengue and other mosquito-borne viruses.

Trends

Three trends are worth highlighting: population growth in urban areas and its implications for health; the reduction in the purchasing power of poorer groups; and the cuts in government social expenditure, especially on health services.

The rate at which urbanization is occurring has perhaps been exaggerated, partly owing to the time-lag in obtaining census data on urban change (5). The trend towards an increasingly urbanized planet is, however, unlikely to change in the next few decades. Projections suggesting that a high proportion of the world's urban population will soon be concentrated in megacities are also unlikely to be fulfilled; many of the world's largest cities and metropolitan areas have been experiencing a decline in their growth rates in recent intercensal periods (52–54).

Many major cities in the developed world have experienced population decline as a result of economic stagnation; most of these cities first developed as industrial centres, and their economic role has lessened as national economies have moved away from heavy industry to services and high technology. Thus great centres of industry and innovation in earlier decades have witnessed economic decline, for instance Cleveland, Detroit, and Pittsburgh in the United States, Liverpool, Glasgow, and Belfast in the United Kingdom, St Etienne in France, Dortmund, Essen, and Duisburg in Germany, Rotterdam in the Netherlands, Bilbao in Spain, and Genoa in Italy (55). Intensive efforts by some local governments are succeeding in attracting new businesses, but most of these cities are unlikely ever to return to the economic prominence they once enjoyed. Solving their health and environmental problems will require concerted efforts and support by higher levels of government.

Many developing countries are no longer urbanizing rapidly, especially the more urban ones whose economies have stagnated. Many of the structural factors favouring rapid urban growth in the past are no longer present: in much of Asia and Africa, for instance, the need to build a national government after independence (entailing a rapid expansion of urban bureaucracies), removal of the colonial controls on population movements to cities, and large investments in the urban infrastructure (5). The economic crisis in Africa is also promoting new forms of urban development. As one commentator notes (56):

> ...as African cities continue to grow under conditions of economic stagnation or even absolute deterioration, they take on more of the qualities of their rural hinterlands. Some of the evidence for this ... includes the increasing importance of urban agriculture, the weakening of effective land use controls and the more diverse utilization of urban space, the spread of 'spontaneous' settlements and of petty commodity production, the deterioration of formerly high standards of urban infrastructure and services and the maintenance (perhaps even the strengthen-

ing) of rural economic links and regional cultural identities on the part of the urban migrants.

Even with slower growth rates, the population growth in most major cities and many smaller urban centres is likely to continue to overwhelm the capacity of the local authorities to provide the infrastructure and the services essential for health. The authorities usually have responsibility for the provision and maintenance of water, sanitation, garbage collection, emergency services, streets, and health care. Where some of these are the responsibility of central governments or are contracted out to private companies, local authorities usually have important supervisory roles. But it is rare for them to have sufficient funds to expand the infrastructure and services (2, 3). This helps to explain the increasing numbers of people lacking adequate services.

The current economic crisis affecting most developing countries is reducing the purchasing power of the poorer groups and their capacity to pay for improved housing or services. During the 1980s the average income is reported to have fallen by 10% in most of Latin America and by over 20% in sub-Saharan Africa. In many urban areas real minimum wages have declined as much as 50% (26, 27).

Strategies

A central feature of a strategy for the improvement of conditions in human settlements is the development of a partnership between public authorities, the private sector, and community or neighbourhood organizations. Such a partnership will permit agreement to be reached on the main health problems and the best use of existing resources for solving them. It also makes possible within each locality specific action to deal with health problems.

Major developments over the last 20 years in the application of new or revised older techniques in water supply, sanitation, drainage, and solid waste management have produced a range of cost-effective solutions appropriate to local conditions, cultures, and circumstances that will greatly improve health and environmental conditions for those currently ill-served. They have also produced more cost-effective techniques for preventing, controlling, and treating the diseases and injuries associated with poor housing, living, and working environments, and the development and refinement of primary health care systems have lowered costs and widened the coverage. Experience over the past ten years suggests that greater impact and cost-effectiveness can be achieved through multisectoral intervention—for instance by improved water supply and sanitation combined with health care, hygiene education and, where needed, drainage.

Effective promotion of health needs stronger links between the health care and social services and often between the health, justice, and education sectors. Health personnel should have the knowledge and skills to work with other social services, for instance in the provision of reliable child care for working and sick parents, shelter for the homeless, care for the handicapped, and services to cope with the consequences of alcohol and drug abuse and family violence.

The health services need to break away from their traditional concentration on limited curative care so as to provide care that meets other pressing needs in the community, such as mental health. The health services should be able to provide advice and assistance that is more social than medical.

What are needed are strategic and institutional frameworks to encourage and support this approach. Effective cooperation depends not only on an appropriate institutional and legislative framework and knowledge among health professionals and others working in social services about how to work together, but also on the ability of governments to support and catalyse action within each settlement or neighbourhood and coordinate sectoral contributions at this level.

This implies a change of emphasis in the role of government, with more attention given to its role as enabler and promoter, than to its more established roles as regulator and provider of an infrastructure and services. This is a change recommended by development specialists from many different sectors. Overconcentration by governments on provision and regulation rather than on the strategic framework within which the contributions of other actors are optimized is seen as a key factor in the poor performance of housing policies in many developing countries. Box 62 presents an example of this change in regard to shelter policies.

A comparable change from control to enablement is also under way in urban policy. Government programmes to slow down rapid urbanization by restricting rural-to-urban migration or urban investment are now recognized as of limited effect. They often have a high cost and they bring few benefits to poorer groups. They rarely tackle the underlying causes of rapid city growth, especially macroeconomic and pricing policies and centralized government structures, which are among the root causes of rapid urbanization. Urbanization is increasingly understood as an important part of the development of more productive economies. Strategic long-term policies can mitigate the negative effects of urbanization on health and the environment without high economic costs (49). Moreover, concentrated populations provide many economies of scale in the provision of most health-promoting infrastructures and services and in the control of pollution (57).

The growth of cities can be slowed down and urban problems lessened by more realistic prices charged to the consumers and businesses that use public services; by more effective pollution control preventing the polluters from passing on costs to others; and by the increased competence of local

---

Box 62. From provider to enabler—the changing nature of housing policies in developing countries

During the 1950s and 1960s many governments of developing countries launched programmes to improve housing conditions. Evaluations during the 1970s and 1980s suggested that most projects to build or finance houses or apartments for low-income groups not only had a high opportunity cost (few units built relative to need and high unit costs), but also produced houses that often ill met the needs of poorer groups in terms of site, space, cost, and mode of repayment. From the 1970s onwards an increasing number of specialists urged governments to change their role as provider to that of enabler. Instead of trying to build housing for poorer groups or directly finance such housing, an enabling policy concentrates on increasing the supply and reducing the cost of all the components of housing, for instance sites, building materials, and access to credit so as to enable people to buy, build, or improve their houses. The policy is supplemented by a greater commitment to the provision of water, sanitation, all-weather roads, drains, health centres, and other key infrastructure and services, including improvement of existing slums and squatter settlements. It is also supplemented by a more flexible approach to such provision, as by partnerships with community organizations formed by lower-income groups to install a water supply and drains and organize garbage collection. Many government projects moved from supply to enablement. From the late 1960s it became more common for governments to support the upgrading of inner city slums and squatter settlements rather than evict their inhabitants and redevelop the areas. Experience with upgrading frequently proved very positive, with a much improved housing and living environment at a very low per caput cost. Many city and municipal governments have entered into partnerships with community organizations formed by poorer groups and with nongovernmental organizations, and this has greatly reduced housing costs and ensured a better match between what is provided and the needs and priorities of low-income groups. Certain governments have made enabling strategies a central part of their housing programme, for instance Sri Lanka in its "million houses" programme, and Costa Rica in its 1986–1990 housing programme.

Sources: UNCHS (Habitat). *Global report on human settlements 1986.* Oxford, Oxford University Press, 1987; Hardoy, J.E. & Satterthwaite, D. *Squatter citizen: life in the urban Third World.* London, Earthscan Publications, 1989; World Bank. *Urban policy and economic development: an agenda for the 1990s.* Washington, DC, 1991.

---

governments. Many smaller urban centres in developing countries have been successful in attracting new investment away from major metropolitan centres (*58*), as they have for decades in many developed countries. Competent local governments in these smaller urban centres are a major factor in such urban deconcentration.

New approaches should be developed to improve housing, infrastructures, and services so that a far higher proportion of those in need are reached at a cost affordable both by the users and by the government. This involves:

— increasing the capacity of local governments to act and invest and to work with local populations in identifying local problems and devising the most appropriate local solutions

— changing or adjusting building and planning codes and norms so that they support and encourage local action that is health-promoting and does not lead to environmental degradation

— developing new ways for government agencies to work with community organizations to ensure that a basic infrastructure and basic services are provided and maintained and that provision for health care meets the most pressing needs.

A major programme promoting such new approaches is the Global Strategy for Shelter to the Year 2000, developed by the United Nations Centre for Human Settlements and adopted by the General Assembly of the United Nations in December 1988.

Environmental health cannot be the sole responsibility of government in policy formulation or implementation, especially in relation to settlements in developing countries. New partnerships should be developed so that the issue of environmental health becomes the joint responsibility of all individuals and groups working or living within the locality, including central and local government, NGOs, the private sector, schools and universities, and the media. The most important of the people to be organized, strengthened, and supported are those of the community-level organizations. There are also private sector organizations that could match community-based efforts with funds, contributions in kind, and expertise. Small-scale enterprises organized at the community level and aimed at improving the environmental conditions of neighbourhoods and settlements can be economically profitable and efficient in the delivery of services without being a burden on public funds and institutions.

Support for these people and the partnerships they form implies that government should decentralize decisions on the management of environmental health matters as much as possible, and let others participate, manage and develop their capabilities according to their potentialities and priorities. The government must therefore be flexible, providing people at the local level with crucial resources such as access to credit or grants, equipment, and technical advice. Box 63 describes the WHO Healthy Cities Project, which provides a framework for new partnerships and for intersectoral coordination.

To function effectively in health promotion and environmental protection, local authorities need broad, financially sustainable revenue bases,

Box 63. The Healthy Cities Project: mobilizing local action and city networking for health

The Healthy Cities Project is, above all, a project that gets all the key agents within a city (government, business, community organizations, professional groups, NGOs) to agree on what they can do jointly to improve the health and quality of the living environment in their city. The movement started as a European project to create action-oriented approaches to health in cities; the WHO European Office has had a healthy cities project in operation since 1986. In recent years all WHO regional offices have been developing healthy cities projects in collaboration with cities and municipalities in a large number of countries.

The primary objective of the healthy cities project in participating cities is to strengthen the capabilities of municipal governments and provide opportunities for individuals, families, and community groups to address their environmental and health problems. The project achieves this by providing a framework that combines several key elements:
— increased awareness of health and environment issues in urban development efforts by all municipal and national authorities
— a network of cities that provides information exchange and technology transfer
— linkage of technical programmes for health and the environment with political mobilization and community participation.

The healthy cities project actively promotes primary health care policies and programmes in urban areas, and counters the tendency for urban primary health care in some countries to remain a health department function with a strong curative orientation. In many countries the political commitment to intersectoral policies and activities to support health, improve environmental conditions and prevent disease has been inadequate, especially in view of the many major determinants of health in developing countries that lie outside the health sector in the social and physical environment. The project has been good at mobilizing intersectoral cooperation. It has also proved valuable in ensuring that mayors and other senior political or administrative staff grasp and support the concept of their city being a healthy city and are committed to providing the framework for the various agencies to cooperate.

The healthy cities project also taps people's attachment to and pride in their neighbourhood or city to win their participation in health and environmental projects. The cities in the project use intersectorality, participation, social support, information, and various strategies to attain the goal of a healthy city.

including the power to raise taxes and borrow from money markets to meet their responsibilities. The operations of local governments should not only be seen to be honest but should also be regularly subjected to auditing. Suitable staff should be recruited, trained and well remunerated to enable the local government to tackle environmental health matters and handle the appraisal and monitoring of projects, budget and accounting systems, and urban management. Health staff must have the ability to identify environmental factors causing poor health and communicate information to non-health staff.

There is a need in national and city governments and at the level of districts and communities for more accurate and more specific information on people's health status, to provide a basis for more effective action. Recent reviews of empirical studies on health differentials within particular cities or districts have revealed a surprisingly large range of health problems among poorer groups (59). These reviews have also highlighted the large range of social, economic, and political factors that influence such health problems. More accurate information on health problems is essential to ensure that health becomes more central in political choices, as it should be in effective preventive and curative action, especially if its ability to highlight susceptible and vulnerable groups is improved. Effective surveillance and monitoring systems are also crucial in the early identification of epidemics and in rapid action to control them.

Waste reduction, reclamation, recycling, or reuse should be encouraged by using participatory community-based schemes of the kind recently initiated in a number of developing countries. When these bring personnel into close contact with wastes, special provision is often needed to limit the health risks and prevent or cure specific diseases (60).

Recommendations

Where communicable and easily preventable diseases are a major cause of mortality or morbidity, governments and international agencies should give priority to reducing the adverse health effects of pollutants and pathogens.
For individuals and households, this will mean:
— the provision of health care services accessible to all, including emergency services, immunization, and oral rehydration therapy
— water, sanitation, and hygiene education
— food and nutrition security programmes focused on the poor and especially on women and children
— knowledge, equipment, and incentives for fertility control
— health-promoting knowledge for citizens, including breast-feeding, child-spacing, and preventive health.
For districts and municipalities, it will mean:
— regular collection of garbage and full exploitation of opportunities for recycling and reclamation

— drainage and other measures to limit accidents and health risks from site hazards such as flooding or mud slides

— participatory organizations with which environment- and health-promoting action can be undertaken.

Governments and international agencies should also make a renewed commitment to increasing the proportion of the population covered by primary health care. Most international agencies allocate only a very small proportion of their funds to primary health care (28). As for water supply and sanitation, more attention needs to be given to cost-effectiveness and the establishment of institutional means to ensure that recurrent expenditure is met.

There is an urgent need for governments and development assistance agencies to develop a more sustainable institutional basis for health when sufficient provision is made to cover the costs of running and maintaining social and health services. WHO advocates the establishment of district health systems, both rural and urban, as a way of ensuring good, sustainable health action at local level. These can provide a basis for the many different sectoral activities at different levels to be planned, carried out, funded, managed, and supervised, so that resources are well applied and coordinated and the appropriate quality maintained.

Providing maximum access to services implies an affordable mix of permanent health care centres (clinics) and outreach activities, including home visits and home-based activities. For instance, community health workers, traditional birth attendants, trained nurses who will be available for consultation in their homes, and volunteers from within each community will all be needed.

Special attention should be given to increasing people's access to basic health care in low-income urban settlements, especially those on the periphery of cities, where the deficiencies in the provision of health care are often most serious. Given the continuing lack of resources in the poorest countries and the inequities in resource allocation, there will need to be a variety of health care providers—government, the municipality, NGOs, private practitioners of various types, volunteers, traditional practitioners, schoolteachers, and members of the community. The challenge is to organize these resources into a rational system.

All agencies and ministries whose work has some influence on the environment should review their norms, procedures, and institutional structures so as to optimize their contribution to health and the environment.

Suitable structures and processes should be developed for the coordinated intersectoral planning and implementation of urban and rural development projects. High-level consultative bodies linking government agencies, the private sector, NGOs, and community groups are necessary. The objective is to strengthen the capability of municipal governments and provide opportunities for individuals, families, and community groups to deal with their own environmental and health problems. As the WHO Expert Committee on Environmental Health in Urban Development said in its report (*61*), this includes:

— finding ways to develop community-based initiatives to address environmental health problems and related social problems (such as poor-quality housing and illegality) which detract from human well-being

— where needed, providing for salaried community facilitators to work with low-income communities in problem identification, group organization, and coordination with government agencies

— recruiting community volunteers to participate in information gathering, mobilization, and monitoring

— improving the preparation of professionals in environmental health and related fields to work with community groups

— involving the schools in educating children to become agents of change both in the home and in the neighbourhood with respect to hygiene and the care of the environment.

The health sector should become more active in contributing to the planning and day-to-day implementation of community development projects. Among the key areas are:

— inputs into local and national government urban development plans that go beyond conventional health care and ensure that plans and action outside the health sector enhance and do not harm health

— support for community-based initiatives, e.g., providing technical advice or expounding needs to higher authorities in such activities as slum and squatter upgrading and serviced sites

— the setting of, and ensuring of compliance with, standards of environmental health. This traditional role needs to be revived, but in ways that ensure that the standards are set in respect to those factors which really impinge on community health status and are maintained through supportive measures and not simply legal enforcement.

All governments should review the basic information they collect about environmental and health problems to consider whether it is sufficiently accurate and relevant as a basis for health promotion and environmentally sound management of urban and rural settlements. Box 64 gives an example of an initiative to develop a set of core indicators for urban management.

There is a crucial need to develop the capacity of city, municipal, and district authorities to make the best use of the available statistics and information in identifying the main environmental health hazards within their

---

Box 64. Core indicators of urban management

A technical working group convened by the World Bank, UNDP, and the United Nations Centre for Human Settlements as part of their urban management programme has suggested that practical indicators and data collection can be developed based on:
(a) disaggregation of national statistical data
(b) local surveys, including household surveys
(c) administrative records
(d) remote imagery
(e) environmental models
   Nine environmental problem categories were identified: water resources, supply and sanitation; municipal and industrial wastes; transportation; energy use; air pollution; noise pollution; land use; housing conditions; and health conditions. A core set of indicators is being developed for these nine categories and should be complemented by a set of baseline urban statistics on population, socioeconomic characteristics, and the natural environment.

---

jurisdiction and the groups most at risk. Development of such a capacity should include strengthening the collection of data on health.

The environmental conditions and health status of communities need to be monitored, with particular emphasis on health problems in informal or illegal settlements.

Recommendations for research

The health status of urban populations should be assessed in relation to the development of the urban environment. For that purpose a set of standard environmental indicators should be adopted that provide either quantitative or qualitative measures of accessible water quality, sanitation, housing, pollution levels, and access to educational, social, and health care facilities. Since most of the data available cover the aggregate of the urban population, the information needs to be broken down by locality to identify the high-risk sections of the urban population under study. Urban health studies may be (a) cross-sectional or (b) longitudinal, to permit comparison with other urban population groups in different urban environments and to measure the cost-benefit of the environmental changes introduced, such as the introduction of an urban air pollution control programme.

Studies are required on the incidence of mental illness and social pathology in the urban setting and on urban developments of increasing complexity. They should focus on the relationships between urban settlements and violence. The results of these studies should assist in determining what factors in the urban milieu are deleterious to mental health and whether they can be corrected in the future planning and operation of urban development projects. The pattern of onset, course, and outcome of pathological manifestations among different sections of the population, migrant or indigenous, should be studied by locality/neighbourhood and socioeconomic status to identify the high-risk groups and, where appropriate, the social networks concerned. WHO may have a role in convening regional conferences of social scientists, epidemiologists, and psychiatrists interested in these community studies, with the aim of establishing acceptable criteria for social and psychiatric variables.

To promote improvement in the health and living environment of disadvantaged communities, the local population should be encouraged to take part in local health surveys of their own communities. The findings of the surveys should be discussed with the participating communities and action programmes to deal with their environmental needs should be undertaken with their support and involvement.

Studies should be carried out to evaluate the methodology of successful community environmental health projects in rural and urban areas and to identify the skills and attributes that effective community workers should have. The data obtained could form a basis for training programmes for community workers.

Emphasis should be given to the development of low-cost and appropriate technology in relation to housing, water supply, sanitation, solid waste disposal, vector control, control of indoor and outdoor air pollution, and recycling or reuse of domestic and industrial waste.

Environmental decision-making models should be developed that offer a range of technical choices with appropriate costing for the disposal of domestic and industrial wastes. They will help in deciding the most appropriate action to be taken with regard to energy use, industrial development, and urban waste management. Public health practitioners in general possess substantial information about the technicalities of pollution control but have little knowledge about costing and cost-benefit analysis.

References and notes

1. United Nations Centre for Human Settlements. *Global report on human settlements 1986.* Oxford, Oxford University Press, 1987.

2. Cochrane, G. *Policies for strengthening local government in developing countries.* Washington, DC, World Bank, 1983 (Staff Working Paper No. 582).

3. Stren, R. E. Urban local government. In: Stren, R. E. & White, R. R., eds. *African cities in crisis,* Boulder, CO, Westview Press, 1989.

4. Rethinking local government: views from the Third World. *Environment and urbanization*, **3** (1): 1991.

5. Hardoy, J.E. & Satterthwaite, D. *Squatter citizen: life in the urban Third World*. London, Earthscan Publications, 1989.

6. *Shelter and health*. Geneva, World Health Organization, 1987 (unpublished document WHO/EHE/RUD/87.1; available on request from Division of Environmental Health, World Health Organization, 1211 Geneva 27, Switzerland).

7. *The state of the environment*. Paris, Organisation for Economic Co-operation and Development, 1991.

8. Cooper Weil, D.E. et al. *The impact of development policies on health: a review of the literature*. Geneva, World Health Organization, 1990.

9. *Urbanization and its implications for child health: potential for action*. Geneva, World Health Organization, 1989.

10. Aina, T.A. *Health, habitat and underdevelopment—with special reference to a low-income settlement in metropolitan Lagos*. London, International Institute for Environment and Development, 1989 (IIED Technical Report).

11. Murphy, D. *A decent place to live—urban poor in Asia*. Bangkok, Asian Coalition for Housing Rights, 1990.

12. Stephens, C. et al. *A review of the health impacts of environmental problems in urban areas of developing countries*. Paper prepared for the WHO Commission on Health and Environment, 1991 (available on request from Division of Environmental Health, World Health Organization, 1211 Geneva 27, Switzerland).

13. Sapir, D. *Infectious disease epidemics and urbanization: a critical review of the issues*. Paper prepared for the WHO Commission on Health and Environment, 1990 (available on request from Division of Environmental Health, World Health Organization, 1211 Geneva 27, Switzerland).

14. Schofield, C.J. et al. The role of house design in limiting vector-borne disease. In: Hardoy, J.E. et al., eds. *The poor die young: housing and health in Third World cities*. London, Earthscan Publications, 1990, pp. 189–212.

15. *Global estimates for health situation assessments and projections 1990*. Geneva, World Health Organization, 1990 (unpublished document WHO/HST/90.2; available on request from Division of Epidemiological Surveillance and Health Situation and Trend Assessment, World Health Organization, 1211 Geneva 27, Switzerland).

16. Auer, C. *Health problems (especially intestinal parasitoses) of children living in Smokey Mountain, a squatter area of Manila, Philippines*. Basel, Swiss Tropical Institute, Department of Public Health and Epidemiology, 1989 (MSc Thesis).

17. Bundey, D.A.P. et al. Age-related prevalence, intensity and frequency distribution of gastrointestinal helminth infection in urban slum children from Kuala

Lumpur, Malaysia. *Transactions of the Royal Society of Tropical Medicine and Hygiene*, **82**: 289–294 (1988).

18. Misra, H. Housing and health problems in three squatter settlements in Allahabad, India, In: Hardoy, J. E. et al., eds., *The poor die young: housing and health in Third World cities*. London, Earthscan Publications, 1990, pp. 89–108.

19. Goldstein, G. Access to life-saving services in urban areas. In: Hardoy, J.E. et al., eds. *The poor die young: housing and health in Third World cities*. London, Earthscan Publications, 1990, pp. 213–227.

20. Reichenheim, M. & Harpham, T. Child accidents and associated risk factors in a Brazilian squatter settlement. *Health policy and planning*, **4** (2): 162–167 (1989).

21. Amis, P. Squatters or tenants: the commercialization of unauthorized housing in Nairobi. *World development*, **12** (1): 87–96 (1984).

22. *Health trends and emerging issues in the 1990s and the twenty-first century*, Geneva, World Health Organization, 1991 (unpublished document; available on request from Division of Epidemiological Surveillance and Health Situation and Trend Assessment, World Health Organization, 1211 Geneva 27, Switzerland).

23. World Bank. *World development report 1990; poverty*. Oxford, Oxford University Press, 1990.

24. Figures given in Morley, D. & Lovel, H. *My name is today: an illustrated discussion of child health, society and poverty in less developed countries*. London, Macmillan, 1986, drawing from World Bank, *Health sector policy paper,* Washington, DC, 1980.

25. Tabibzadeh, I. et al. *Spotlight on the cities: improving urban health in developing countries*. Geneva, World Health Organization, 1989.

26. UNICEF. *The state of the world's children 1990*. Oxford, Oxford University Press, 1990.

27. Albanez, T. et al. *Economic decline and child survival: the plight of Latin America in the eighties*. Florence, International Child Development Centre, 1989 (Innocenti Occasional Papers No. 1).

28. United Nations Centre for Human Settlements. *Financial and other assistance provided to and among developing countries for human settlements—report of the Executive Director*. Biennial report presented to the Commission on Human Settlements at a meeting in Harare, April 1991 (UNCHS document HS/C/13/10).

29. Hardoy, J.E. & Satterthwaite, D. Environmental problems in Third World cities: a global issue ignored? *Public administration and development*, **11**: 341–361 (1991).

30. Cointreau, S. *Environmental management of urban solid waste in developing countries*. Washington, DC, World Bank, 1982 (Urban Development Technical Paper No 5).

31. Cairncross, S. & Feachem, R.G. *Environmental health engineering in the tropics—an introductory text*. Chichester, John Wiley and Sons, 1983.

32. *Surface water drainage in low-income communities*. Geneva, World Health Organization, 1991.

33. WHO Commission on Health and Environment. *Report of the Panel on Urbanization*. Geneva, World Health Organization, 1991 (unpublished document WHO/EHE/92.5).

34. Hartunian, N.S. et al. *The incidence of economic costs of major health improvements*. Lexington, MA, Lexington Books, 1981.

35. Occupational Safety and Health Administration. Occupational noise exposure: hearing conservation amendment. *Federal register*, **46**: 4078–4179 (1981).

36. See for instance special section on youth violence in *Public health reports*, **106** (3): 225–279 (1991).

37. Turner, J.F.C. *Housing by people—towards autonomy in building environments*. London, Marion Boyars, 1976 (Ideas in Progress).

38. Marsella, A. *Urbanization and mental disorders*. Background paper prepared for the WHO Commission on Health and Environment, 1990 (available on request from the Division of Environmental Health, World Health Organization, 1211 Geneva 27, Switzerland).

39. Cairncross, S. et al. The urban context. In: Hardoy, J.E. et al., eds. *The poor die young: housing and health in Third World cities*. London, Earthscan Publications, 1990, pp. 1–24.

40. Webb, L. Rural/urban differences in mental disorders. In: Freeman, H., ed., *Mental health and the environment*. London, Churchill Livingstone, 1984.

41. Cederblad, M. Behavioural disorders in children from different cultures. *Acta psychiatria scandinavica,* **78** (Suppl. 344): 85–92 (1988).

42. Hughes, B. Children's play—a forgotten right. *Environment and urbanization*, **2** (2): 58–64 (1990).

43. Patel, S. Street children, hotel boys and children of pavement dwellers and construction workers in Bombay: how they meet their daily needs. *Environment and urbanization*, **2** (2): 9–26 (1990).

44. Cairncross, S. et al. New partnerships for healthy cities. In: Hardoy, J. E. et al., eds. *The poor die young: housing and health in Third World cities*. London, Earthscan Publications, 1990, pp. 245–268.

45. Peattie, L. Participation: a case study of how invaders organize, negotiate and interact with government in Lima, Peru. *Environment and urbanization*, **2** (1): 19–30 (1990).

46. Turner, B., ed. *Building community—a Third World case book*. London, Habitat International Coalition, 1988.

47. McAuslan, P. *Urban land and shelter for the poor*. London, Earthscan Publications, 1984.

48. Cairncross, S. Water supply and the urban poor. In: Hardoy, J.E. et al., eds. *The poor die young: housing and health in Third World cities*. London, Earthscan Publications, 1990, pp. 109–126.

49. World Bank. *Urban policy and economic development: an agenda for the 1990s*. Washington, DC, 1991.

50. *Manual on environmental management for mosquito control: with special emphasis on malaria vectors*. Geneva, World Health Organization, 1982 (Offset Publication No. 66).

51. Freier, J.E. & Francy, D.B. A duplex core trap for the collection of adult *Aedes albopictus*. *Journal of the American Mosquito Control Association*, **7**: 73–79 (1991).

52. Rofman, A.B. Argentina: a mature urban pattern. *Cities*, **2** (1): 47–54 (1985).

53. Townroe, P.M. & Keen, D. Polarization reversal in the State of São Paulo, Brazil. *Regional studies*, **18** (1): 45–54 (1984).

54. Harris, N. Some trends in the evolution of big cities. *Habitat international*, **8** (1): 7–28 (1984).

55. Hay, D. On the development of cities. In: Cadman, D. & Payne, G., eds. *The living city—towards a sustainable future*. London, Routledge, 1990.

56. Stren, R.E. *The ruralization of African cities: learning to live with poverty*. Toronto, 1986 (Project Ecoville Working Paper No. 34).

57. United Nations Centre for Human Settlements. *Human settlements and sustainable development: the role of human settlements and of human settlements policies in meeting development goals and in addressing the issues of sustainability at global and local levels*. Nairobi, 1990.

58. Manzanal, M. & Vapnarsky, C. The development of the Upper Valley of Rio Negro and its periphery within the Comahue Region, Argentina. In: Hardoy, J.E. et al., eds. *Small and intermediate urban centres: their role in regional and national development in the Third World*. London, Hodder & Stoughton and Boulder, CO, Westview, 1986.

59. Harpham, T. et al., eds. *In the shadow of the city: community health and the urban poor*. Oxford, Oxford University Press, 1988.

60. Furedy, C. *Social aspects of solid waste recovery in Asian cities*. Bangkok, ENSIC Asian Institute of Technology, 1990 (Environmental sanitation reviews, No. 30), pp. 2–52.

61. WHO Technical Report Series, No. 807, 1991 (*Environmental health in urban development*: report of a WHO Expert Committee).

8.
Transboundary and international problems

Preceding chapters have dealt with problems that are essentially local in their health and environmental consequences. Here, six issues are considered that all have such international dimensions that their solution has been or is being sought through the adoption of international legal instruments. The treatment is brief because the concern these issues raise is essentially environmental and their health effects indirect or marginal.

Long-range transport of air pollutants

Oxides of sulfur and nitrogen, besides having local effects, can be transported by atmospheric circulation over long distances when emitted high above ground. Coal-fired, and to a lesser extent oil-fired, power stations are major emitters. In Europe natural sources of sulfur dioxide contribute only 10% of total sulfur emissions to the atmosphere. Large modern fossil-fuelled power stations are generally built away from population centres, and high chimneys disperse the pollutants; this lowers the exposure of local populations to sulfur dioxide but favours the long-distance transport of pollutants. In the atmosphere, sulfur and nitrogen oxides are converted to sulfuric and nitric acid, which give rise to acidic precipitation far away from the emission point.

As a result, poorly buffered waters in lakes and streams have been acidified over large areas of the northern hemisphere and their productivity reduced. Poorly buffered soils have been chemically altered with adverse consequences to vegetation, particularly conifers, damaged as well by the direct deposition on their leaves of sulfates and nitrates and a host of other pollutants (some of local origin, particularly from motor vehicles). The resulting forest dieback can clearly be seen in a number of places in Central Europe.

While the adverse effects of acid precipitation on ecosystems are clear, there are uncertainties about associated indirect effects on health. Acidification of soils mobilizes the metals they contain, making them more readily available to enter fresh water and the food chain, with the possibility that they may reach people through the ingestion of food. Thus enhanced levels of mercury have been detected in freshwater fish from acidified Swedish lakes, leading to increased and potentially harmful levels of methylmercury in people who consume large amounts of fish.

Acidic waters may corrode piping and plumbing and give rise to dangerous levels of lead in drinking-water, with a potential risk of impaired neurophysiological development in children (see Box 49, page 154). Much of the evidence for this comes from areas of Scotland with a high natural acidity of soils and water. While acid precipitation may contribute to such an effect, its contribution is unknown. Cadmium in plumbing solder may be mobilized into drinking-water supplies and result in increased intake, which if sustained over a long time may lead to kidney damage. A report from the International Programme on Chemical Safety (IPCS) points to the possibility of such population effects from daily intakes of cadmium only a few times larger than those that normally occur (1). For households supplied by individual or small-scale systems without routine neutralization, there is a possibility of dissolution of cadmium and other metals. In the northern United States, it has been estimated that more than 200 000 persons use such water supplies (2).

Levels of copper in acidic drinking-water are often elevated because of the extensive use of copper pipes. Increased copper concentrations can give rise to gastrointestinal symptoms. A few cases of childhood liver cirrhosis have recently been reported in Europe, and the possibility of a relationship to excessive intake of copper from copper-containing water has been suggested (3). However, further evidence is needed to support this hypothesis.

Concentrations of aluminium in natural waters are dependent on the pH; clearly increased concentrations (up to 2000 µg/l) have been found in water from shallow wells in acidified areas. A statistical association in the general population between concentration of aluminium in drinking-water and the occurrence of Alzheimer disease and dementia has been reported (4), but a causal relationship has not yet been established.

Thus it is possible that human exposure to metals is increased by mobilization of the metals as a result of acidification. If increased exposure occurs in populations where some health effects caused by metals already occur, an increased occurrence of adverse health effects is to be expected. Further studies are needed to define such increased exposure, the contribution of acid deposition (as opposed to naturally occurring organic acids in soils) to acidification, and the importance of such changes in inducing adverse health effects.

Adding lime to water and soils is effective in reversing acidification, but it is difficult to consider it as a long-term solution on the scale at which it would be required. There is thus no alternative to the reduction of emissions at source. This can be achieved through a combination of technical solutions, including a change of fuel, pre-treatment of fuel, change in the combustion process itself, and cleaning of the flue gases. Some of these options are being taken up in a few developed countries on a limited scale, but they are costly, especially when they involve modification of existing plants or major energy policy changes. In developing countries choices would be more difficult still. With coal, especially cheaper types with a high sulfur content, meeting an increasing share of their energy needs over the next two decades, the problems of long-range transport of pollutants and of acid precipitation will tend to affect the whole of the northern hemisphere and certain areas in the south with high industrial and urban concentrations of pollutants.

Reduction of transboundary pollution by sulfur dioxide is being achieved through the 1987 Protocol to the 1979 Convention on Long-Range Transboundary Pollution. Under this Protocol a number of European states undertook to reduce their emissions or transboundary fluxes of sulfur dioxide by at least 30% by 1993. An additional protocol, which is not yet in force, provides among other things for a reduction by 1994 in the levels of nitrogen oxide emissions or transboundary fluxes to the levels they had reached in 1987. Similar instruments may soon become necessary in other areas.

Transboundary movement of hazardous products and wastes

The growth in transport capacity, in global communication systems, and in consumer demand has led to global markets for food, energy, medicines, and many other products that influence both human health and the environment. Thus the availability of fish caught in tropical waters has resulted in the occurrence of ciguatera poisoning in temperate areas, as mentioned in Chapter 3.

One particular area of concern is the transboundary movement of wastes. The increasing difficulty and cost of disposing of hazardous wastes in developed countries has led to the development of a trade in waste involving transport, mostly to developing countries, that has so far not been regulated internationally. A number of European and North American industries and municipal authorities, faced with stringent national regulations and public opposition to the disposal of wastes in their home countries, have been shipping them to precarious and poorly protected dumping sites abroad for a fraction of the cost that their disposal would otherwise have entailed. The possible consequences of exposure to leaks from the sites for the people living in their vicinity is hardly considered either by the exporting firm or by local authorities at the disposal site, who are often unaware of the composition of the wastes and the hazards they present. Examples of such practices are given in Box 65. Some reports suggest that this problem has existed for

Box 65. Export of toxic wastes: some examples

Thailand

Large quantities of chemical wastes have been stored in Bangkok's main port, Keong Tuey. Most come from unknown shippers in Singapore, although some also come from China (Province of Taiwan), Germany, Japan, and the United States. Officials from the Government's National Environment Board have expressed fears that the barrels may contain polychlorinated biphenyls or dioxin, which can only be destroyed in high-temperature incinerators, which Thailand does not possess.

Benin

European firms were seeking a contract to send 5 million tonnes of wastes each year from Sesco, a company registered in Gibraltar. It was reported that Benin was to receive US$ 2.50 for each tonne received, while Sesco would charge firms up to US$ 1000 a tonne or more to dispose of the wastes. Benin is one of the poorest countries in the world and lacks virtually all the infrastructure and the facilities needed to handle and manage even a small fraction of the 5 million tonnes a year proposed.

Guinea-Bissau

It was reported that Lindaco, a firm based in Detroit, applied to the United States Government to ship up to 6 million tonnes of chemical waste to Guinea Bissau, another of the world's poorest countries. Other contracts have been signed in Guinea-Bissau for importing chemical and industrial wastes from developed countries.

Nigeria

3800 tonnes of European chemical wastes were dumped by Italian ships in the southern port of Koko on the Niger river with a payment to the landowner of the equivalent of around US$ 100 a month; the cost of disposing of these in Europe would have been of the order of US$ 350–1750 a tonne. The toxic wastes were incorrectly labeled as building materials and the small port of entry did not have customs officers with sufficient knowledge of chemistry to identify the risk. The wastes were stored in 200-litre drums, many of them leaking and most in poor condition. Many drums contained volatile chemicals which, in a hot climate, present a serious risk of spontaneous fire or explosion. Although the dumping had been carried out without the knowledge of the Italian Government, the wastes were subsequently removed and the dumping area reclaimed by the Italian Government in collaboration with the local authorities.

Venezuela

In October 1987, 11 000 barrels of chemical wastes were returned to Italy after a private Italian company had tried to store them in a warehouse in Puerto Cabello.

Sources: See note 6.

some years, for instance in Northern Mexico with illegal transboundary dumping of toxic wastes produced by United States firms (5).

The effects of exposure to such wastes in the importing countries are unrecorded or poorly reported. Growing concern about the rising trend in the traffic has led a number of countries to prohibit the export of hazardous wastes and the international community to adopt the Basel Convention on the Control of Transboundary Movements of Hazardous Wastes and their Disposal in 1989. The Convention is expected to enter into force early in 1992 and will be a major step towards reducing the risks arising from such movements.

Stratospheric ozone depletion

Ozone is continuously produced and destroyed in the stratosphere through complex photochemical reactions. In the absence of human interference the balance between production and destruction results in a constant amount of stratospheric ozone around the globe. This amount would seem to be minor in quantitative terms, but it plays an extremely important role in absorbing part of the biologically damaging fraction of the ultraviolet rays coming from the sun, thus shielding the earth from a major portion of radiation which, if received in full, would be incompatible with life as we know it.

Such ultraviolet radiation as is currently received at the surface of the earth has beneficial effects. It converts 7-dehydrocholesterol to vitamin D_3 in the skin, thus contributing to the prevention of rickets. Excessive exposure to sunlight, however, has adverse effects. The best known is the increased incidence of skin cancer in fair-skinned individuals. Squamous cell carcinoma and malignant melanoma have been increasing by factors of between three and four in the western United States between 1960 and 1984, probably as a result of changed lifestyles which, since the Second World War, have involved prolonged exposure to sunlight, especially in childhood. It is also known that some forms of cataract are associated with prolonged exposure to intense sunlight.

When human exposure is unnecessary, the risk of such effects can easily be reduced by minor changes in recreational habits, for instance by avoiding sunbathing in the middle of the day and using protective means. This is all the more important because human activities are currently reducing the stratospheric ozone, thereby increasing the flux of biologically damaging components of sunlight.

The reduction in the ozone is caused by the release of chlorofluorocarbons (CFCs), which are widely used as refrigerants, propellants, plastic foam blowers, and cleaning agents for electronic circuitry. Other substances, including fire-fighting halons and solvents such as carbon tetrachloride, also contribute by interacting photochemically with ozone in the stratosphere. All are extremely stable substances and are now in widespread use. Once released into the environment they diffuse through the lower atmosphere and into the stratosphere, where they interact chemically with ozone and destroy it.

The seasonal depletion of the ozone layer above Antarctica has been expanding over the years since its discovery in 1985. The trend is attributed with reasonable confidence to increasing releases of CFCs and other ozone-damaging chemicals transported there by diffusion and atmospheric movements. Their interactions with ozone are specially marked in the Antarctic stratospheric environment during the southern spring.

While the formation of increasingly large ozone holes, with local reductions of the ozone layer of over 50%, is the most spectacular phenomenon associated with the presence of CFCs and other active gases in the stratosphere, there is now increasing evidence of a much smaller (a few per cent) but steady thinning of the ozone layer in the northern hemisphere. This is likely to be associated with increased ultraviolet radiation fluxes on the ground and ultimately with an increased incidence of skin cancers and cataract. However, measurements of these fluxes at ground level are very difficult, have so far been few, and have given inconsistent results. But the possibility that the biologically active component of sunlight may be increasing should discourage people from indulging in unnecessary exposure. Unavoidable exposure, e.g., of farmers, shepherds, construction workers, or sailors, should be reduced by suitable clothing, sunscreens, and sunglasses.

International action is under way to achieve a concerted reduction of the use of CFCs and other compounds with similar action on stratospheric ozone (1987 Montreal Protocol to the Vienna Convention on the Protection of the Ozone Layer and its 1990 amendment). These efforts must be strongly supported, since restoring the integrity of the layer will avoid adverse effects not only on human health but, more importantly, on a number of life-supporting systems that have no other protection against ultraviolet radiation. Morever, some of the gases whose emissions the Convention and its Protocol seek to reduce to protect stratospheric ozone are among those that contribute most to the greenhouse effect.

Climatic change

The atmospheric concentration of carbon dioxide has been rising since the early nineteenth century, to a large extent as a result of the increasing use of fossil fuels but more recently also owing to the growing resort to slash-and-burn agricultural practices in the tropics. Emissions of nitrous oxide have also been rising fast in this century, owing mainly to the growing use of nitrogen fertilizers. There is a growing concentration of methane in the atmosphere, linked with the increasing number of cattle being raised, the expansion of rice paddies, leakages from coal mine seams and from oil wells, and seepage from domestic and other waste tips. As noted above, the use of halocarbons for a range of purposes accounts for their accumulation in the atmosphere in recent decades. Box 66 lists the gases that were the main contributors to global warming during the 1980s.

Box 66. The major contributors to global warming, 1980–90

	Proportion of total warming effect (%)
Carbon dioxide	61
Methane	15
Nitrous oxide	4
Other nitrogen oxides	6
CFC-11 and CFC-12	9
Others	5

Source: Intergovernmental Panel on Climate Change. *Scientific assessment of climate change.* Geneva, UNEP/WMO, 1990.

All these gases have the property of absorbing the energy re-emitted by the earth's surface, while being transparent to incoming solar radiation. They therefore act as an energy trap and preserve the heat in the atmosphere. The presence of carbon dioxide in the atmosphere has made possible the temperature at which we have evolved to be maintained relatively constant for millennia. But the currently increasing concentrations of carbon dioxide and other "greenhouse gases" are higher than in the past 160 000 years and may lead to a substantial warming of the atmosphere.

The Intergovernmental Panel on Climate Change has forecast that, if present emissions of greenhouse gases continue, the global average atmospheric equilibrium temperature at ground level may rise by 1.5–4.5 °C, but the time scale and the actual extent of the increase are still uncertain.

The consequences of such a rise will depend on what changes in temperature and precipitation take place in different parts of the globe, but current climate models do not provide sufficient detail to say more than that the warming is expected to be greater at higher latitudes. Warming of the oceans, which will result in expansion of the volume of their waters, coupled with melting of glaciers will lead to a rise of the sea level, by up to 60 cm if the maximum warming mentioned above is reached. Box 67 gives an example of the range of environmental changes (excluding health effects) predicted in

Box 67. Possible environmental changes in the Mediterranean associated with global warming

With an assumed temperature increase of 1.5 °C by the year 2025, evapotranspiration will increase throughout the Mediterranean, leading to a possible decrease in precipitation in the south and an increase in the north. Hot dry summers, exceptional drought or rainfall, floods, storms, tidal surges, water stagnation, and eutrophication could increase in frequency.

Such an increase in temperature would also lead to increased land degradation, deterioration of water resources, decline in agricultural production, and damage to natural terrestrial and aquatic ecosystems. It could alter marine circulation both in the Mediterranean and the Atlantic, affecting marine productivity and the pattern of pollutant dispersal.

The future impact on Mediterranean society of non-climatic factors such as population increase and development may far exceed the direct impact of climatic change. Non-climatic factors will cause a continuous increase in vulnerability to climatic stress, particularly in the south. Together, these demographic and climatic changes are likely to increase the probability and hasten the occurrence of catastrophic events.

It is particularly difficult to forecast the effects of climatic change on agriculture, other than that irrigation systems will suffer increasing stress and that soil degradation will reduce yields in rain-fed systems. Salinization of irrigation water would have adverse effects on sensitive grain yields. Consequently, new varieties of crops may need to be introduced.

A eustatic rise in the mean sea level of about 20 cm by 2025 would not, in itself, have a significant impact on the Mediterranean except locally (e.g. in lagoons). However, the local sea-level changes could be as much as five times this amount because of natural land subsidence enhanced by excessive groundwater withdrawal. The negative effects of this would be felt in low-lying areas, deltas, and coastal cities.

Most of the deltaic lowlands of the Mediterranean Sea are experiencing serious environmental problems because of agricultural, industrial, urban, and tourist developments over the past two decades. The problems range from water pollution and salinization to land subsidence, shoreline erosion, and restriction and deterioration of wildlife habitats. These problems would be increased by adverse socioeconomic conditions, the effects of which would be superimposed on those of climatic change.

Generally, marine and land weeds would be expected to benefit from a warmer atmosphere richer in CO_2. The flora and fauna of the wetlands would be forced to adapt gradually to changed conditions and this might be crucial for species that possess reduced tolerance to high salinity. As bioclimatic zonation gradually shifted north, several species would migrate to the north and insect populations might increase. There would be favourable conditions for an increased risk from agricultural pests, bacteria, and diseases, especially in the swamps.

Source: Sestini, G. et al. *Implications of expected climate change in the Mediterranean Region: an overview*. Athens, UNEP, 1989 (MAP Technical Reports Series No. 27).

the next decades in one geographical area, the Mediterranean, on the assumption that by the year 2025 the average surface temperature of the atmosphere will have risen 1.5 °C and the sea level by 30 cm.

On the same assumptions, environmental effects could be expected to be far more destructive in island countries at present only a few metres above sea level at their highest point, such as the Maldive Islands, or where large dense populations live on low ground. Cyclones of the kind that recently ravaged the coastal areas of Bangladesh would be increasingly devastating in proportion to the rise in the sea level.

Because of the uncertainties about the magnitude, rate, and distribution of any future warming of the earth, it is not possible to anticipate the health implications of the changes. Their occurrence and significance would depend on a number of factors, including age structure and state of health, layout and resources of the land, and reliance on local or on imported food. The degree of economic development of a country, other things being equal, would be an overriding factor in its ability to mitigate the damaging effects of climatic change.

The indirect health effects of global climatic change could be very significant. Alterations in agricultural and animal husbandry practices might affect food production. Food supplies could be threatened by shifts in climatic zones and by changes in crop, livestock and fish-farming productivity, reduced availability of water for irrigation, and loss of arable land owing to desertification or a rise in the sea level. In semi-arid areas hit by droughts or floods, a substantial reduction in agricultural productivity has often resulted. Although higher crop yields might result from an increase in the rainfall in temperate or cold zones and from the greater availability of carbon dioxide for photosynthesis, in general climatic changes would be likely to diminish the variety of crops available and restrict the diet. The most widespread effect would probably be local shortages of food supplies resulting in deprivation and malnutrition affecting children and pregnant women in particular and possibly leading to large-scale migration. The adverse effects would be especially serious in developing countries, aggravating already existing problems, and in those where human, financial, and technical resources are lacking.

Direct effects on health from climatic change are also possible, but less important on the global scale. A direct health consequence of atmospheric warming would be increased human exposure to exceptional heat waves. While people can adapt to gradual increases in temperature, the greater the increase in the suddenness, frequency, intensity, and duration of heat waves the more profound the consequences for health, especially in the elderly, the very young, and those with incapacitating diseases. For them even minor heat stress may cause illness. Severe heat stress may lead to a rapid deterioration in health, with effects ranging from mild syncope to fatal heat stroke. High relative humidity in these circumstances considerably amplifies heat strain by reducing heat loss through evaporation. Extreme increases in temperature, especially in densely populated urban areas, carry the greatest risk.

Another indirect effect of atmospheric warming could be a change in the distribution of communicable diseases. Those transmitted by vectors dependent for their survival on tropical or subtropical environments would spread as their traditional areas of distribution expanded. Malaria (particularly falciparum malaria, which depends on higher temperatures for its survival) and schistosomiasis might thus threaten areas where they are so far unknown or from which they have been eradicated. Shortages of water, damage to coastal waste treatment or waste disposal facilities, and inability to adjust to the inflow of immigrants abandoning flooded homes would increase the risk of waterborne disease.

Climatic changes resulting from modifications of the chemical composition of the atmosphere are predicted on the basis of models that need validation but that no observations have so far disproved. Such changes are likely to have major consequences, and not only on health; safeguarding against them will also involve costs that only the richest developed countries would be able to afford. A number of human activities that give rise to significant emissions of greenhouse gases, especially those involving the use of fossil fuels, could be carried out in a less wasteful way, in developed countries in particular. Chlorofluorocarbons could be phased out altogether or their use reduced drastically. How this could be achieved is under active consideration by the United Nations, UNEP, and WMO.

Ocean pollution

Except for those trapped in geological formations or kept in tightly monitored repositories and those readily degradable before they reach the sea, all wastes eventually reach the oceans through atmospheric deposition, land run-off, outfall discharges, and accidental spills. The resulting contamination of seawater is widespread but varies from one area to another.

Coastal waters, particularly those along thickly settled or heavily industrialized shores that are poorly flushed by tidal movements, are in general the most polluted by untreated sewage reaching them through rivers or outfalls. Domestic and industrial effluents release to the sea both microbial and chemical agents.

Bacteria and viruses can contaminate seafood caught in areas near outfalls or river mouths and cause gastrointestinal and other disease outbreaks. Bathers are directly exposed to microorganisms, including fungi, on the beach or in the water. Monitoring of marketed seafood and shellfish beds, and also of the water quality of the beaches, is necessary to ensure health safety.

Chemical effluents affect coastal waters, adding (a) nutrients, leading to greater productivity and occasionally transient and sometimes toxic algal blooms (Chapter 3) and often resulting in a reduction of the number of species dwelling near the point of release; (b) organic material increasing the biochemical oxygen demand of the recipient waters and eventually bringing about changes in the local flora and fauna; (c) toxic chemicals that may directly affect organisms in the water and, their levels being magnified through the food chain, result in undesirably high human intake.

The contamination of seafood by bacteria and viruses and of beaches by fungi is now a matter of almost universal concern, although data on the frequency and severity of outbreaks are few and unreliable, except for major epidemics such as the 1991 cholera epidemics in Latin America and west Africa (Chapter 4). Chemical contamination of seafood is a source of concern around industrial outfalls and shallow waste-dumping sites. Although there are fears that people may be exposed to high intakes of heavy metals (especially mercury) and chlorinated hydrocarbons (e.g., polychlorinated biphenyls) through the consumption of seafood, cases of poisoning have rarely been recorded, a major exception being Minamata (Box 54, page 182). But the possible continued accumulation of such substances in human tissues cannot be discounted. It warrants the monitoring of seafood and of human tissue samples and human milk in groups with a high consumption of fish.

While microbiological pollution is largely confined to coastal waters, man-made or released chemicals are found in the open ocean as well. Currents carry them offshore from coastal waters. Winds deposit them in gaseous form or as dust on the surface, from where they sink to deeper layers. As a result, "man's fingerprint is found everywhere in the oceans. Chemical contamination and litter can be observed from the poles to the tropics and from beaches to abyssal depths. But ... the open sea is still relatively clean. Low levels of lead, synthetic organic compounds and artificial radionuclides, though widely detectable, are biologically insignificant. Oil slicks and litter are common along sea lanes, but are, at present, of minor consequence to communities of organisms living in open-ocean waters" (7). Levels of contaminants in open ocean fish are still too low to be a source of hazard to consumers, with the exception of certain long-lived predator fish such as tunny, which may accumulate high levels of mercury, acquired mostly from geological sources.

A number of international conventions and other regional and global instruments aimed at protecting the seas from pollution have been adopted within the general framework of the Law of the Sea. While it is premature to assess the effectiveness of international regulations, they reflect the widen-

245

ing and widely shared concern that, unless action is taken now, the oceans may be irreversibly damaged by the continuation of certain human activities.

Biodiversity

The environment is a complex of ecosystems made up of a variety of species, themselves represented by a number of strains, each with its own genetic identity. This diversity is acknowledged to be a condition for the long-term sustainability of the environment, and the maintenance of its integrity is therefore recognized as being indispensable to sustain human health.

There are more specific reasons why biodiversity is of great concern in the protection of human health. Because taxonomic knowledge of species is far from complete, it is essential to guard against the extinction of the largest possible number of species and strains, among which are some that may in the future provide us with food and medicine or be used in the biological control of pests and pathogens.

The protection of biodiversity, which forms the subject of a draft convention on biodiversity, cannot be unconditional. Biodiversity and health protection may come into conflict, for instance when an organism highly pathogenic to humans or a pest threatening food supplies can be successfully eradicated. The need to maintain diversity must be carefully weighed against the health cost that its survival would involve (Box 68).

Strategies

The global nature of the issues considered in this chapter requires that strategies for tackling them be adopted worldwide. This can best be achieved through the development of international legal instruments, a number of which are already in force. Their aims being primarily environmental, those instruments have only an indirect bearing on matters of health. It is the responsibility of the health authorities to ensure that health considerations are given the importance they deserve in legislation, lest essential aspects of the action prescribed fail to recognize them, to the detriment of human health.

With respect to ozone destruction, the Montreal Protocol to the Vienna Convention provides for worldwide reduction in the production and emission of certain CFCs. The latest observations in the stratosphere suggest that the phasing out of those products must be further accelerated because CFCs not only reduce stratospheric ozone (with possible direct effects on human health) but also contribute to atmospheric warming.

The long-range transport of sulfur dioxide and nitrogen dioxide is subject to a European Convention whose efforts at curbing their emissions

---

Box 68. Biodiversity—conflict recognition and resolution

In every sector involved in the exploitation of the environment and natural resources, including public health, there is a need for guidance in recognizing and dealing with conflict situations arising in the application of the principles of conservation of biodiversity. The draft Convention on Biodiversity recognizes the need for species and ecosystems to be preserved independently of their worth to people, and the obligation on the part of people to take this need into consideration. Such an obligation is at odds with human interests if the species concerned is harmful to people, for instance by endangering human health or survival. Such conflicts must be recognized, analysed and resolved.

If the species concerned is an obligatory human pathogen (i.e., not present in any other host species), and responsible for considerable loss of human life, poor health, and disability, there is universal agreement that it is morally justified to eradicate it, although this may not be technically possible. Examples are the human immunodeficiency viruses, smallpox virus, poliomyelitis virus, *Plasmodium falciparum* (the cause of cerebral malaria), and the guinea worm.

Although the ethical dilemma is considerably more difficult if the species is a pathogen of moderate or low virulence, a vector of a human pathogen, a zoonotic pathogen, or a reservoir host of a zoonotic pathogen, there is still little disagreement that eradication of such a species is ethically acceptable if this proves to be the only way to save human lives. If, however, an effective, safe, and stable vaccine or drug is available, and if there are no logistic or economic obstacles to making it widely available, this is obviously the most appropriate weapon and may permanently eliminate the disease.

If drugs or vaccines have undesirable side-effects or are expensive, they are unacceptable because their use is not medically ethical or economically sustainable. In the search for alternative methods a conflict may then arise with the need to preserve biodiversity. Its nature will depend on the range of alternatives available and on whether these produce adverse environmental effects.

Examples of health measures already subject to such deliberations are: vector control either with pesticides or by environmental management of aquatic habitats in the control of diseases such as malaria or schistosomiasis; either extermination or vaccination of foxes in the control of rabies; either elimination of game animals in the control of sleeping sickness in people and nagana in cattle, or tsetse control with pesticides or traps.

---

or transboundary fluxes should be strongly encouraged. The possibility of developing similar approaches in other geographical areas exposed to acid precipitation must be explored. Strong support must be given to the Basel Convention on the movement of hazardous wastes across borders. The possibility and advisability of controlling the international movement of other hazardous products, or of perishable commodities that may become hazardous during transport, will need to be explored.

Climatic change being potentially the most pernicious environmental development over the next decades, efforts to develop an international convention on it must be welcome.

Because the quality of open sea waters is still good, it is essential that international measures be taken to ensure that human activities likely to involve discharges of wastes from seaborne as well as land-based sources are tightly regulated on a global, regional, or national basis, as necessary, so as to prevent major ocean deterioration with unpredictable consequences for human health. Current legal instruments are patchy in their geographical coverage and consider only certain types of pollution from certain sources. It is urgent that their coverage should be made global and include provision for the control of releases of all significant pollutants from all sources.

An international convention on the protection of biological diversity is currently being considered. While this is a most welcome development, health authorities should make sure that none of its provisions, by precluding certain action, in any way limit the adoption of reasonable measures towards the achievement of health for all.

Recommendations

Governments should give high priority to energy conservation and to improving efficiency in energy generation and uses (including end uses) to decrease the production of carbon dioxide. Although the degree and rate of climatic change are uncertain, the adverse effects on health that may follow (for example from loss of agricultural land, inundation of urban centres, spread of vector-borne diseases, or heat stress) are potentially of widespread importance and capable of creating environmental refugees on a large scale.

Energy conservation and efficiency are in the long-term interests of all countries. Even developing ones should therefore adopt energy-saving approaches in meeting their development goals, although it is recognized that achieving these will be highly dependent on the use of fossil fuel, especially coal, and will therefore inevitably generate increasing amounts of carbon dioxide.

The countries with the highest per caput consumption of fossil fuel should, as a matter of priority, plan now for a substantial reduction in greenhouse gas emissions. It is technically feasible to reduce current levels of fossil fuel use (and therefore levels of air pollution) without endangering prosperity and standards of living, through better energy conservation, the introduction of more energy-efficient technologies, and wider use of public transport systems.

Incentives should be provided for reducing the release of CFCs through, for instance, the reuse of those serving as refrigerants and the adoption of closed-circuit systems for their use as cleaning agents.

Excessive exposure of fair-skinned people to sunlight should be discouraged. Those who must work in the sun should routinely adopt protective measures.

Recommendations for research

Extensive research is required in all the areas discussed in this chapter. Most, however, are only indirectly related to health. For instance, the responsibility for removing uncertainties about the effects of continued greenhouse gas releases must remain with climatologists, and progress in this area should continue to be reviewed by the International Panel on Climate Change. In this section, only three major needs will be identified as being of immediate relevance to the health sector.

Research should be undertaken to determine the significance for human health of the increased presence of heavy metals resulting from their mobilization in soils and piping systems, as a consequence of water acidification owing to the long-range atmospheric transport and deposition of nitrates and sulfates.

Methods should be developed to determine reliably and on a systematic basis the flux of ultraviolet light in the relevant wave bands and its trends at appropriate locations on the earth's surface.

The sensitivity of pathogenic agents and their vectors to long-term changes of temperature and moisture and to changes in the species composition of their habitat should be determined. This will contribute to making action against their further spread possible when significant climatic or ecological changes have been recognized to be impending or under way.

References and notes

1. International Programme on Chemical Safety. *Methylmercury*. Geneva, World Health Organization (Environmental Health Criteria, in press).

2. Moskowitz, P.D. et al. *Identifying human populations at risk from acid deposition mobilized materials in drinking water supplies: a preliminary pilot study*. Sweden, International Conference on Acid Precipitation, Water Quality Control and Human Health, August 1985.

3. Muller-Hocker, J. et al. Copper storage disease of the liver and chronic dietary copper intoxication in two further German infants, mimicking Indian childhood cirrhosis. *Pathological residents practice*, **183**: 39–45 (1988).

4. Martyn, C.N. et al. Geographical relation between Alzheimer's disease and aluminium in drinking water. *Lancet*, **1**: 59 (1989).

5. Consumer Information and Documentation Centre. *Consumer currents*, **109**: 6 (1988).

6. Consumer Information and Documentation Centre, *Consumer Currents*, **105**: 3 (1988); Kone, S. Stop Africa from becoming the dumping ground of the world. *The siren*, No. 37, July 1988, pp. 2–3; MacKenzie, D. & Mpinga, J. Africa wages war on dumpers of poisonous waste. *New scientist*, 23 June 1988, pp. 30–31; Phantumvanit, D. & Liengcharernsit, W. Coming to terms with Bangkok's environmental problems. *Environment and urbanization*, **1** (1): 31–39 (1989); Secrett, C. Deadly offer poor countries find hard to refuse, *The Guardian*, 15 July 1988, p. 11.

7. Group of Experts on the Scientific Aspects of Marine Pollution (GESAMP). *The state of the marine environment*. Nairobi, United Nations Environment Programme, 1990.

9.
Strategies

Introduction

Health requires a good environment. People need to live in an environment that is conducive to healthy physical, mental, and social development. Above all they must have the means to acquire those resources on which their survival depends, including water, food, fuel, and shelter. All share responsibility for ensuring that this need, recognized as a right in the Universal Declaration of Human Rights, is met, and accordingly that the environment is preserved and natural cycles protected.

However, protection of the environment must not be regarded as having priority over health, unless the very basis of life on the planet is endangered, since the impending threat to the environment then inevitably involves long-term risks to human health and may even impair the prospects of human survival.

Governments have the main responsibility for the creation of a strategic and institutional framework to ensure that all their citizens have a healthy environment and that the levels of consumption and waste generation within their boundaries do not deplete the world's environmental capital and damage global systems. The essential aim of any government's long-term strategy is to put in place the services, incentives, and controls that encourage individuals, households, communities, businesses, and bureaucracies to promote health and the sustainable use of resources and also protect the natural and the human environment. To achieve this requires:

— identification of the major health and environmental problems, their causes, and their interrelationships
— identification of the actions needed, especially those that prevent or diminish hazards to health, and definition of the role of government and other sectors in such action
— fostering of individual, household, neighbourhood, district, provincial, national, and international knowledge, capacity, and motivation to act effectively, especially in addressing the needs of the poorer and least healthy groups and in safeguarding the environment against pollution or degradation.

Global objectives

Objective 1: to achieve a sustainable basis for health for all. This demands a slowing down of, and eventually a halt to, population growth and the promotion of lifestyles and patterns of consumption consistent with ecological sustainability.

Objective 2: to provide a health-promoting environment for all. This involves:

— reducing the risk of biological, physical, and chemical hazards
— ensuring that all people have the means to acquire those resources on which health depends
— planning in all sectors to minimize adverse effects on health and the environment from all new undertakings, products, investments.

Objective 3: to develop awareness in all individuals and organizations, including all sectors and all levels of government, community organization, and business, of their roles and responsibilities for health and the environment.

Principles

Two principles guide both strategy and action: a more equitable access to resources within and between countries; and full participation of the people in the formulation, implementation, and evaluation of plans and projects.

Principle 1. Equity: A more equitable access to resources is needed to provide all people and countries with the economic and technical basis for a health-promoting environment. Good health and a good environment do not need high per caput incomes and high resource consumption levels, but all individuals require sufficient income or land to meet their basic needs, and governments must ensure that poorer groups can acquire these necessities. This calls for the development of more stable and prosperous economies in poorer countries since poverty and economic instability undermine health and militate against any long-term strategy for sustainable development. The changes needed in the world's economic system include the transfer of resources, reductions in trade barriers and more generous development assistance on the part of the richer countries; without such changes the poorer countries will not achieve the economic and technical base that they need for a healthy population and sound environmental management.

Principle 2. Participation: Public participation is crucial for both strategy and action. The right to participate in the political process is one of the most fundamental human rights. But participation also serves the promotion of health and environmental quality in two other respects: first, as a means of promoting action and motivating individuals and communities to contri-

252

bute to the improvement of health and a good environment; second, as a check on abuse of the environment, since citizens with clear rights and knowledge and access to a legal system that makes speedy redress possible are a powerful restraint on the contravention of health and environmental regulations.

Effective participation also requires greater openness and credibility on the part of government and business. The opposition of citizen groups to such important technological advances in health protection as the use of irradiation for food preservation may owe much to public distrust of government, business, and scientists in regard to any issue in which radiation is involved. A new sense of responsibility on the part of the private sector must be generated or encouraged by the government, for example in relation to industries that sell hazardous products or industrial processes to developing countries to ensure that they are safe and not detrimental to health. That many companies now support more healthy and environment-friendly working practices shows some progress in this area (1).

Strategic elements

Four strategic elements are:
— changing the planning process and the institutional and regulatory structure within countries to give stronger emphasis to prevention and participation
— strengthening the knowledge and ability to act at all levels in regard to the environment, health, and development;
— broadening the role of the health profession and clarifying the responsibilities for health of all other people, institutions, and professions
— working towards an international consensus on transboundary and global problems.

1. Preventive planning. A planning process and institutional and regulatory structure with a much stronger emphasis on prevention will have at least two components:
— planning processes in which health concerns are given more attention in new industrial, commercial, agricultural, residential, and infrastructural developments by optimizing health and environmental aspects across sectors
— a structure of incentives and controls within which the economy can flourish and innovate while ensuring that short-term and long-term environmental health considerations are systematically taken into account in the design, siting and functioning of new developments.

The development of incentives and controls to promote the protection of health and the environment requires that the government expand its role not only as a provider and regulator but also as an enabler and promoter in such different sectors as housing, basic services, rural and urban development, and pollution control.

2. Strengthening the ability to understand and act. Strengthening the ability to act effectively to reduce health risks and improve environmental management calls for all people, from private citizens to those involved in developing macroeconomic policies, to be better informed. This implies a commitment to education and literacy in general, aimed at providing people with the ability to understand their roles and responsibilities in regard to health and the environment. Training is required for all professionals whose decisions affect health and the environment. It should not only increase the awareness of the professionals and teach them how their work interacts with health and the environment, but also furnish techniques for working with individuals and communities to identify health risks and the best means of dealing with them. Hygiene education and the full involvement of low-income communities in choices about the design, implementation, and maintenance of new water and sanitation systems are often neglected components of water and health development support programmes in developing countries (2). Within workplaces, adult education courses and radio and television campaigns are important.

Strengthening the ability to act also requires incentives such as macro-economic, pricing and fiscal policies that support health and environment goals and minimize conflicts between them.

3. Broadening the role of health professionals and authorities. Health professionals must assume a central role in helping individuals, community organizations, businesses, and others concerned to meet their responsibility for health and a healthy environment. They should be at the forefront of moves to improve the environment and to inform the government and the public of the health implications of development policies and of the costs and benefits to health and the environment of different options.

Effective environmental health interventions involve far more than the direct action traditionally within the mandate of health and environmental management authorities. Since protecting and promoting human health is a major goal of society, all individual and organized activities that make a positive or negative contribution to the state of the environment and have a direct or indirect effect on health are a matter of concern. These are the boundaries within which environmental action by health authorities must be considered.

Governments should ensure that health authorities take an active role in:

— ensuring that health considerations are taken fully into account in the formulation, implementation, and evaluation of public policy

— increasing the awareness of environmental health issues in other ministries and departments of government, in private enterprise, and among the public, and encouraging behaviour and environmental modifications that have beneficial health effects

— fostering local capacity to manage environmental health by strengthening the ability of local authorities to fulfil decentralized functions, encouraging the private sector, and supporting the development of community self-help programmes

— carrying out assessments to identify threats to health from existing conditions and environmental practices and from proposed changes related to shelter, urban development, occupation, industrial processes, energy generation, water resource management, etc., including evaluation of the health implications of environmental data originating from the monitoring programmes of other agencies

— conducting epidemiological surveillance of environment-related diseases and informing decision-makers about conditions and trends in the health status of populations and communities

— working with universities and training institutions to ensure that personnel in all sectors are trained to work with health professionals to identify, prevent or, alternatively, control environmental health hazards

— developing interagency emergency response capabilities for natural disasters and accidents, including medical treatment for disaster victims

— developing or modifying norms, standards, and legislation so that environmental health concerns are always considered.

It is obvious that health authorities can only prove effective in this wider role if national governments give higher priority to health and to ensuring effective intersectoral cooperation between the health and other ministries and agencies.

4. Working towards an international consensus. A major challenge facing the world in the next few decades is to reach international agreement on how to achieve a healthier and more sustainable interaction between people and the environment and how to implement such agreement.

Initiatives are being taken in two areas.

International legal instruments. The aim is agreement on the action each country must take within its own domestic sphere to modify patterns of production and consumption so that the total production and consumption of all countries is sustainable. International agreement is urgently needed to maintain biodiversity, to protect the atmosphere and the oceans, and to regulate the transboundary transport of hazardous wastes. In some of these areas—including the transport of wastes and protection of the atmosphere and oceans—considerable progress has already been made.

Trade. Consensus is sought on changes in the terms of trade and the removal of trade barriers to foster more stable and prosperous economies, in particular those of the poorer countries. There have been long-standing international discussions on the liberalization of international trade. Progress to date has been slow.

Tools and methods

Perhaps the most important basis for more effective action is a continuous process within each country to improve understanding of how best to act for health and the environment. Three general aspects are worth stressing: incorporation of health and environmental considerations in macroeconomic policies, cost-benefit analysis, and primary environmental care. The latter two techniques provide a better understanding of how to incorporate health and environmental considerations in decisions about specific projects or investment programmes.

The macroeconomic basis for health

Macroeconomic and sector policies, typically established without consideration of their health consequences, may in fact be major determinants of health status. For example, trade and fiscal policy or agricultural or energy pricing may influence health either directly, through their effects on income and its distribution, or indirectly, through their effects on the quantity and quality of the land, air, and water resources upon which human health depends.

Structural adjustment is a special case of macroeconomic policy reform. The adjustment process is widely accepted as a necessary condition for economic development and must therefore in the long run be beneficial to health. But the free market cannot be left entirely to itself; it must be complemented by government intervention to control abuses and ensure a more equitable distribution of the social and economic benefits of the market process. This clearly applies to the achievement of both health and environmental objectives.

These kinds of decision—how far to encourage market liberalization and when and how governments should intervene—count greatly in environmental and health outcomes. Yet it is only lately that health agencies have had a part in the decisions. It is clearly for the health agencies themselves to take the lead in (a) demonstrating the priority that health should have at the macro and sector levels, (b) fostering understanding of the relationships between macroeconomic, social, and sectoral policies on health, and (c) expressing their views to other government agencies so that appropriate action is undertaken.

Developing the skills to understand and act on the root causes of hazards to health and the environment calls for a multidisciplinary effort to ensure that health and environmental considerations influence macroeconomic policy-making and the determining of priorities and policies within sectors. Engineers, ecologists, economists, financial analysts, and behavioural and other scientists must complement the skills of the health practitioner and biomedical scientist.

Cost-benefit analysis

In specific projects or investment programmes, cost-benefit analysis techniques must be used both to assist decision-making within the field of environmental health and to incorporate environmental and health considerations in their formulation and implementation.

Primary environmental care

Primary environmental care is a newly developed tool for decision-making in the design and implementation of new projects. Developed as a methodology for promoting sustainable development at the community level (3), it is a process by which local groups or communities organize themselves, often with outside support, so as to apply their skills and knowledge to the care of their natural resources and environment while also satisfying their livelihood needs. Participatory and community-based in origin, it draws much from primary health care. It explicitly seeks to complement primary health care by focusing attention on natural resource management as a means of promoting simultaneously health and a sustainable environment.

References and notes

1. Cairncross, F. Cleaning up—a survey of industry and the environment. *The Economist*, 8 September 1990.

2. Warner, D. B. & Laugeri, L. Health for all: the legacy of the water decade. *Water international*, **16**: 135–141 (1991).

3. Borrini, G., ed. *Lessons learnt in community-based environmental management*. Rome, Istituto Superiore di Sanità, 1991.

10.
Recommendations

General recommendations

1. All governments and international agencies should give higher priority
    to developing a sustainable basis for the health of their people and
    countries. This includes identifying and acting on health risks and
    environmental degradation at all levels, from macroeconomic policies
    and pricing structures to decisions concerning particular projects.
2. To achieve a sustainable basis for health for all, high priority should be
    given to reducing population growth, overconsumption, and waste
    generation.

    Rapid and sustained falls in population growth rates are best achieved by
    dealing simultaneously with the economic, social, and cultural causes of
    large families. A key element is strong support for development, with
    high priority given to health and education for all groups, especially
    women. Reducing the population growth rates in countries with rapidly
    increasing populations requires:
    — removing the economic need for poorer groups to have large families
    — reducing the cultural barriers to reduced fertility by improving
      women's access to education and employment
    — ensuring that everyone has access to primary health care and family
      planning facilities in keeping with each country's and household's
      needs and cultural traditions.

    Reducing overconsumption and the generation of wastes, especially
    those with serious adverse health and environmental effects, requires
    responsible action at all levels from the individual to the government.
    High priority should be given to creating awareness and to providing
    economic and other incentives to encourage conservation and efficient
    resource use. The long-term goal is the promotion of lifestyles and
    patterns of consumption that are consistent with sustainability and with
    health for all.
3. Official bodies and scientific advisers should apply new, more participa-
    tory ways of working with low-income groups and their community
    organizations, both in identifying needs and priorities and in drawing on

their knowledge and social organization in designing, implementing, and monitoring interventions. This will ensure more effective action in dealing with many of the health and environmental problems that have most effect on poorer groups. Examples of new modes of government intervention that work with individuals, community organizations, and NGOs are: agricultural extension services, which make widespread use of participatory techniques in working with farmers; national shelter programmes based on supporting the self-help efforts of households and communities; and environmental protection guided by community-based primary environmental care.

4. Organizational changes should be made within government structures to give greater priority to the support of community-based initiatives and participation, especially by granting increased power, resources, trained personnel, and accountability at the local or municipal government level.

5. To achieve more accurate diagnoses and more effective action in regard to health and the environment, modifications should be made to existing decision-making mechanisms within international agencies and at all levels of government in order to ensure that:
   — health and environmental quality are assigned the value that people give to them
   — greater priority is given to preventing or limiting environmental health risks in all sectors and at all levels
   — cost-benefit and accounting methodologies ascribe realistic values to the capital represented by the environment, to provide a rational basis for limiting the depletion or degradation of finite resources.

6. High priority should be given by governments and aid and development assistance agencies to strengthening each country's capabilities. The promotion of health and environmental quality within each locality and country should make the best use of local knowledge, skills, resources, and ability to act and to organize, not only because it often ensures more appropriate solutions but also because significant increases in the volume of development assistance are unlikely to materialize. The last forty years of development assistance have highlighted the limitations of external aid in the absence of local institutions.

7. Scientific considerations should be given more weight in the decision-making process and the public must be kept informed about the current state of knowledge in regard to health and environment. Scientists should seek to meet the information needs of governments and the public, and develop more accurate diagnoses of problems, better analyses of causal or contributory factors, and more rigorous methodologies for diagnosis and analysis. This can be achieved only if those who work in health and environmental sciences seek new ways of cooperating with

international agencies, national, regional, and local governments, the business sector, NGOs, and community organizations in tackling health and environmental problems. It also requires a commitment by governments to support the continuous process by which countries can increase their knowledge of the complex links between health, the environment, and development and of the most effective means of promoting health and the sustainable use of resources.

8. Governments and intergovernmental agencies should give higher priority to laying the foundation of international consensus on a large range of environmental, health, and economic issues. A more healthy and sustainable interaction between people and the environment will depend on such consensus.

9. Information on the circumstances and consequences of major accidents involving significant exposure to chemicals and on the nature and effectiveness of remedial action should be carefully collected, where appropriate through epidemiological investigations, reviewed internationally, and stored in a readily accessible central data bank.

10. Each country should develop and implement an action programme to address its most immediate and pressing health and environmental problems. Much of what has been suggested above will take time to have an effect. Until the world's population is stabilized and high living standards and a high quality of life are dissociated from unsustainable levels of consumption and waste generation, deterioration of the environment will continue in most countries and be added to what has been inherited from the past, the impact of which on health and the environment may only now be becoming apparent. Short-term action is therefore needed now to protect people from the harmful effects on health of the environmental changes that will develop in the next two decades.

11. WHO should cooperate closely with other international organizations concerned specifically with development or the environment. Through a continuous flow of information from those agencies on the environmental changes associated with particular types of development in different countries, WHO will develop the capability to determine and assess the significance of the health consequences of these changes and, if so requested, provide advice to the countries concerned.

Sectoral recommendations

Earlier chapters include sections on strategies and recommendations. Only the main points are summarized here.

Food and agriculture

Equal access to an adequate diet must be assured to all citizens on a long-term environmentally sustainable basis. This calls for distribution policies providing food at reasonable cost in the amount and of the quality required to ensure health, and policies for increasing the income of poorer households so that they can meet the cost. In some areas it also involves changes in land tenure. It requires everywhere the adoption of good agricultural practice and the integration of health goals within agricultural, nutrition, food, and water development schemes.

Food safety is a paramount consideration. Priority should be given to the reduction of biological contamination which, even in developed countries, is responsible for an increasing number of bacterial and viral gastrointestinal diseases, and to the reduction of risks from chemical contamination through rationalization of the use of chemicals in agriculture.

To increase the availability of food to meet the challenge of population growth requires the concentration of efforts on the reduction of losses after harvest, spoilage during storage and distribution, and wastage by consumers.

Water

Because fresh water is limited in quantity, there is a need for comprehensive water planning and management, with the participation of all the users (domestic, industrial, agricultural), so that the best use is made of the water, equitable access to it is ensured, conflicts are minimized, and pollution control measures meet the requirements of each user. Pricing structures that reflect real costs and encourage efficient use are a major element of management. All parts of the community should be involved in decisions concerning the management and distribution of fresh water and the collection and disposal of wastewater.

Control of waterborne bacteria, viruses, and parasites remains the first health priority, especially in developing countries, but contamination of water by heavy metals and organic chemicals must also be prevented or minimized.

The reuse of wastewater and the prevention of losses from the distribution system by proper maintenance and repair are essential to ensure the sustainability of freshwater supplies.

Renewed commitment of governments and aid agencies to the improvement of water supply and sanitation is now needed in order to achieve the goals of the International Decade for Drinking Water Supply and Sanitation. This will require better integration of water supply, sanitation, drainage, and hygiene education and greater attention to maintaining water and sanitation infrastructures.

Energy

Countries should implement national energy strategies that give full consideration to their health and environmental implications and promote the most efficient use of fossil fuels. In implementing the strategies, countries should seek to achieve as a matter of priority: reduction of the adverse health effects of indoor air pollution from the domestic use of coal and biomass fuel; reduction of urban air pollution from fossil fuel use; control of the emissions of carbon dioxide to the atmosphere; development and use of renewable energy sources, including the use of power from waste incineration; and prevention of accidents, especially in mines and at dams and nuclear power plants.

The priorities will be different in different countries, depending on their economic, environmental, and cultural circumstances. Thus, a vital need in countries where cooking is done indoors on open fires would be to improve the ventilation of cooking stoves. In cities with heavy traffic, a switch to cars equipped with catalytic converters would greatly reduce emissions of nitrogen oxides, carbon monoxide, and volatile organic compounds, which are a major component of total air pollution. The adoption of pollution control devices for fossil-fueled power plants would similarly reduce emissions of sulfur dioxide and particulates. Energy saving at all levels, for instance through the adoption of convenient and efficient public transport systems, would significantly reduce emissions and at the same time reduce energy costs. Preparedness would reduce the impact of the accidents that occur in spite of all the preventive measures taken.

Industry

Foreknowledge of the problems, planning, and prevention are the keys to an industrial development that would have minimal adverse consequences for health and the environment, thus maximizing the benefits of industrialization. Foremost among the requirements in all manufacturing industries is improved knowledge of the adverse effects of chemical and other agents released to the environment, including the working environment, so that rational risk management schemes can be developed. This makes possible better design, siting, and planning and more rational primary prevention within and outside the factory, through the application of cost-effective control technologies and adequate regulatory mechanisms. None of this is possible without close coordination between all the sectors involved, adequate resources, and adjustment of technologies and legislation to the socio-economic context within which they must be applied. An essential requirement is the will, at factory, community, and national level, to see the development succeed.

The principle that the polluter pays should increasingly guide the approach to pollution control, despite the difficulty of applying it in all cases. Proper maintenance of all equipment should be ensured. Waste generation should be minimized through recycling and the adoption of low-waste technology. The responsibility of the producer of wastes should remain throughout the life cycle of the wastes from their generation to their ultimate safe disposal.

The effectiveness of regulatory systems should be improved by (1) strengthening the relevant institutional structures, (2) making environmental monitoring part of any industrial programme, and (3) carrying out environmental audits of all operational installations. Special attention should be paid to the hazards of small enterprises in the informal sector, where control is more difficult to achieve and enforcement tends to be less rigorous.

Human settlements and urbanization

The development of a strong partnership between public authorities, the private sector, and community or neighbourhood organizations is crucial for the improvement of conditions in human settlements, as is the tightening of the links between health care and social services, and between them and the judicial and education sectors. Institutional and legislative frameworks are required to encourage and support such a cooperative approach, which represents a switch of the government's main role from provider and regulator to enabler and promoter.

Action of this kind is especially necessary in urban areas. Central policies aimed at discouraging migration into cities and reducing urban investment have generally proved costly and have brought few benefits to poorer groups. They have seldom addressed the macroeconomic and pricing problems which may underlie rapid city growth, and they have failed to recognize that urbanization is an important component of the more productive economies. The growth of large cities can be slowed and urban problems lessened by more realistic prices for services and infrastructures, pollution control policies that prevent the polluter from passing on costs to others, and increased capacity of small centres to attract labour, thus diverting migrants from the major metropolitan areas.

Within this framework, priority should be given to reducing the health burden from pollutants and pathogens through the provision of a safe water supply, sanitation, regular collection and safe disposal or recycling of refuse, and adequate drainage. Primary health care, awareness, and education are essential ingredients. Building codes and city plans should be adjusted so that they promote health and preserve the quality of the environment.

Suitable structures and processes should be developed to ensure structural coherence in the planning and implementation of urban and rural development, and the health sector must become more actively involved.

The data collected on environmental and health conditions and problems, including the results of monitoring, should be reviewed to assess whether, in their relevance and quality, they provide a reliable basis for managing rural and urban settlements in a manner consistent with the promotion of health and the preservation of the environment.

Transboundary and international problems

The main approach to these problems is through international agreement and concerted action. The long-range movement of sulfur and nitrogen oxides in the atmosphere, the transport of hazardous wastes across borders, the destruction of stratospheric ozone, warming of the climate from greenhouse gases, ocean pollution, and the reduction of biological diversity all have been, or are planned to be, the subject of international conventions or protocols that jointly commit the contracting parties to preventing or prohibiting action that would worsen these problems and, ultimately, indirectly affect human health. Encouragement should be given to expanding the geographical coverage of agreements that cover limited areas only, to strengthening the provisions of those found to be inadequate, and to accelerating the development and adoption of those still in the stage of negotiation.

At the national level the main priorities are: achieving savings in energy consumption, especially from fossil fuel sources, thus reducing both local and global pollution; reducing the release of CFCs through reclamation and recycling of discarded refrigerators and other appliances, reducing their use as foaming agents, and utilizing them as cleaning agents for electronic components only under closed-cycle conditions; limiting the discharge of domestic and other wastes from both land-based and seaborne sources; and preserving the biological diversity on earth by being mindful of the need to protect species-rich habitats or habitats harbouring unique endemic species.

Recommendations for research

Most of the WHO Commission's recommendations for research come under sectoral headings at the end of chapters 3–8. Here they will be briefly recapitulated. Some general considerations, principles, and recommendations about research on health in relation to the environment and development are also included.

Principles guiding environmental health research

1. The diversity of environmental health issues and differences in their importance in different parts of the world should be recognized.
    For the majority of the world's population environment-related infectious diseases remain the most pressing health issue. For the developed world they play a lesser role, chronic diseases related to lifestyle (e.g., diet, smoking, and alcohol) and chemical pollution of the environment being more important. These diseases are also becoming increasingly important in developing countries.
2. Equal priority should be given to research aimed at preventing environmental health problems and to research aimed at their resolution or mitigation.
    There is a tendency for research on environmental health to concentrate too much on "cleaning up" and too little on prevention. In many instances there is also a failure to apply existing knowledge because it is not available to those making decisions or is not fully understood by them. Inadequate coordination between research groups often leads to duplication of research. The various reasons for the underutilization of existing knowledge should be investigated using social sciences approaches.
    Quantitative studies should be conducted to increase the precision with which it is possible to specify optimum levels of intervention and monitor environmental risk factors. Active exchange of relevant information and expertise should be organized at the international level, attention being paid to the need for international and regional databases.

Development-related health research and interaction with environmental issues

Development is recognized as a key issue in the improvement of human health. However, the precise interaction between development and health remains poorly understood; most of the conventional indicators used to measure development have at best only an indirect relationship to health. There is a need for development indicators at all levels (from community-based projects to national statistics) that ensure that the state of health of the people is included in development statistics and make easier the incorporation of health concerns in development plans.

An important subject of research should be exploration of significant and, as far as possible, causal relationships between development factors and health indicators, to quantify favourable links and detect possible adverse effects. In most circumstances the relationships are likely to be indirect and linked through environmental intermediaries.

- Research is needed on how to harmonize multiple goals ranging from economic efficiency to environmental health and ecological safety.
- Methodologies should be developed to assess the effectiveness of various environmental health policies.
- The discovery of more effective means of controlling diseases spread by biological vectors from reservoirs in the natural environment should remain a research priority in a large part of the world. Control can be expected to be achieved with minimal damage to the environment by the development (or further development) of:
  — integrated systems of environmental, biological and chemical control of vectors
  — vaccines against infectious agents or chemotherapeutic agents to interrupt their life cycle
  — biomedical methods of rendering vector species ineffective as carriers of disease.
- Research should be carried out to define and understand the complex functions of various ecosystems and so provide baseline information to assess potential pollution-induced changes that may affect human health.
- Research should study the deficiencies in our ability to identify and measure the health risks associated with more industrialized production. This will involve increased efforts at national and international levels to assess reliably the short-term and long-term toxicity and the environmental pathways of all chemicals likely to be released to the environment in significant amounts. It will also require a review of the transport and disposal of hazardous wastes in the light of local (e.g., climatic) circumstances, in order to devise rational strategies to reduce the risk of human exposure.
- Research is needed to assess the effect of human-induced environmental changes, including possible climatic changes, on the geographical distribution of certain tropical diseases. It should include retrospective studies of changes in their distribution that have already occurred, and indicate the kind of surveillance and preparedness needed to cope with these changes at an early stage.
- Research is needed to quantify the long-term effects of specific pollutants from the burning of biomass and fossil fuels in open fires indoors.

- Technical processes that result in the formation and/or discharge of toxic pollutants should be examined to see how they can be modified. Polluting processes must be changed to non-polluting processes. A comparable effort should be made in regard to biological and physical pollutants.
- Research is needed to develop low-cost methods to:
  — purify water
  — monitor water quality
  — develop food preservation and storage arrangements appropriate to conditions in developing countries.

General recommendations

1. Governments, international agencies, and public and private institutions should develop national capacities for systematic data collection and analysis, and for monitoring of environmental effects, with the objective of rapidly identifying potential health impacts, especially in the context of development.
2. Research priorities within each country should be established in the light of local or national needs, since problems and opportunities vary according to cultural, regional, climatic, economic, and other circumstances. For that purpose research and policy-making institutions and people should be associated.
3. Developing as well as developed countries should strengthen their research capabilities by training staff and strengthening the relevant institutions. Specialized institutions concerned with environmental health research should be asked to pay more attention to development factors. Partnerships between research and education institutions all over the world should help such efforts.
4. More attention should be given to improving understanding of individual and collective behaviour and motivation in relation to the environment and health, including the links between the urban environment and violence. Full involvement of the social sciences in research on health, development, and the environment is greatly needed.
5. Research should be carried out on improving knowledge of the costs and benefits of different strategies and actions to improve health and the environment in the context of development. Health economics should receive greater priority in such issues.
6. WHO should play a major role in developing and supporting this research, especially in encouraging biomedical researchers to work with environmental scientists to produce a better basis for understanding the health consequences of natural and human-induced environmental

change. A specific effort should be made to use existing knowledge intensively. WHO should help define relevant research strategies at the national and international level.

Sectoral research recommendations

In relation to **agriculture and food production**, research should aim at: determining the actual impact of traditional and new practices on the environment and, through it, on health; developing inexpensive, effective, reliable means of improving the storage of agricultural produce and food so as to enhance food safety and reduce losses due to spoilage; increasing agricultural yields without concomitant environmental degradation, including pollution; and developing a better understanding of individual and community behaviour in relation to new agricultural and food-processing technologies and their effects on health, nutrition, and the environment.

The **provision of fresh water**, especially drinking-water, and the **treatment of wastewater** for safe disposal or, better, reuse require the development of technically feasible systems using local skills, materials, and equipment and requiring limited financial resources for both installation and maintenance. Research should identify systems that, within these constraints, maximize health benefits and minimize risks and develop the databases that informed management of the systems will require.

In the sphere of **industry**, research should concentrate primarily on improving ability to assess the risks of industrialization. This will require epidemiological studies. The long-term relatively high level of exposure of certain groups of workers to environmental agents offers opportunities to improve our knowledge that must not be overlooked. Use of the biological markers that are now being developed will also provide an opportunity of gaining an insight into the extent of human exposure and the relationship between exposure and adverse effects.

Research in the field of **energy** should aim at: determining the possible effect of exposure to electromagnetic fields; devising pollution control methods appropriate to the requirements of developing countries; making possible the use of renewable energy on a significant scale; and accelerating the development of more efficient road vehicle engines, of vehicles that are not dependent on petrol, and of more convenient and efficient public transport systems.

There is a lack of information in a number of areas related to **human settlements and urbanization**. The health status of the population in relation to the development of the urban environment should be assessed by analysis of suitable sets of environmental indicators. Special attention should be given to the incidence of mental illness and social pathology (e.g., violence) in the urban setting. Health surveys should be conducted with the participation of the local community, particularly in disadvantaged areas, to make it aware of the health problems it faces and to encourage it to contribute to the solution of the problems. On the technical side, research should aim at designing appropriate low-cost technologies for housing, water supply, sanitation, and domestic and industrial solid and liquid waste disposal, vector control, and control of indoor and outdoor air pollution.

Transboundary and other international problems, although they have possible indirect effects on human health, require extensive research in areas that are largely outside the health sector. However, problems identified as requiring research that have implications for health relate to acid precipitation, ultraviolet radiation and changes in surface temperature and humidity, affecting the distribution of pathogenic organisms and their vectors.

Annex 1
Members of the WHO Commission on Health and Environment

Chairman

Mrs Simone Veil, France
> Member, European Parliament since 1979
> President, European Parliament, 1979–82
> Minister of Health 1974–79

Vice-Chairmen

Dr Emil Salim, Indonesia
> Minister of State for Population and the Environment since 1983
> Head of the Environmental Impact Management Agency since 1990
> Member of the Indonesian Academy of Sciences since 1981
> Member of the People's Consultative Assembly since 1987

Professor Nikolai F. Izmerov, USSR
> Director, Institute of Industrial Hygiene and Occupational Diseases,
>   USSR Academy of Medical Sciences since 1971
> Assistant Director-General of WHO, 1964–71
> Deputy Minister of Health of the Russian Federation, 1961–64
> Academician Secretary, USSR Academy of Medical Sciences

Members[a]

Dr Cheng Chunming, China
> President, Chinese Academy of Preventive Medicine since 1983
> Chairman, National Committee on Health Standards since 1984
> Professor of Nutrition, Chinese Academy of Preventive Medicine
>   since 1965

[a] Unable to attend: Professor Harald zur Hausen, Federal Republic of Germany (Director, German Cancer Research Centre); Dr Saburo Okita, Japan (Chairman, Institute for Domestic and International Policy Studies; President and Chancellor, International University of Japan; Minister for Foreign Affairs, 1979–80; Chairman, Japanese World Wide Fund for Nature).

Sir Richard Doll, United Kingdom
> Emeritus Professor, University of Oxford
> Member of Royal Commission on Environmental Pollution, 1973–79
> Regius Professor of Medicine, University of Oxford, 1969–79

Dr Abraham Horwitz, Chile
> Director Emeritus, Pan American Health Organization
> Director, Pan American Health Organization and WHO Regional Office for the Americas, 1959–75
> Chairman ACC Subcommittee on Nutrition since 1985
> Chairman of the Board of the Pan American Health and Education Foundation since 1988

Professor John M. Hunter, United States of America
> Professor, Departments of Geography and Community Health Sciences, and African Studies Centre, Michigan State University since 1967
> Lecturer on Geography, Durham University, United Kingdom 1964–67

Dr Mohammed Kassas, Egypt
> Emeritus Professor, Department of Botany, Cairo University
> President, International Union for the Conservation of Nature and Natural Resources, 1978–84
> Member of the Club of Rome
> Member of the Egyptian Academy of Science
> Recipient, United Nations Prize for Environment

Dr Roelof J.H. Kruisinga, The Netherlands
> President, Committee on Accreditation of Inspectorates and Laboratories since 1990
> Member of Senate, 1982–91
> Director-General of the Dutch Ministry of Public Health, 1979–82
> Minister of State for Public Health and Environment, 1967–71
> Minister of State for Transportation and Public Works, 1971–73

Dr Philippe Lazar, France
> Director-General, National Institute of Health and Medical Research since 1982

Dr Adetokunbo O. Lucas, United States of America
> Director, International Health Programs, Department of Population

and International Health, Harvard School of Public Health, since 1990

Director, UNDP/World Bank/WHO Special Programme for Research and Training in Tropical Diseases, 1976–86

Chairman, Medical Research Council of Nigeria, 1973–76

Professor Diogo Pupo Nogueira, Brazil

Professor Emeritus, School of Public Health, University of São Paulo

Chairman, Special Commission on Occupational Health, University of São Paulo

Secretary, Brazil International Commission on Occupational Health

Professor Sten Orrenius, Sweden

Director, Institute of Environmental Medicine, Karolinska Institute, since 1988

Professor and Chairman, Department of Toxicology, Karolinska Institute, since 1984

Dr David P. Rall, United States of America

Director, National Institute of Environmental Health, 1971–90

Director, National Toxicology Programme, 1978–90

Professor Vittorio Silano, Italy

Director-General for Food Hygiene and Nutrition, Ministry of Health, since 1990

Director-General for Prevention of Environmental Pollution and for Environmental Reclamation, Ministry of Environment, 1987–89

Director, Department of Comparative Toxicology and Ecotoxicology, Istituto Superiore di Sanità, 1982–87

Dr Frank E. Young, United States of America

Deputy Assistant Secretary for Health, Science and Environment since 1989

Commissioner, Food and Drug Administration 1984–89

Dean, School of Medicine and Dentistry, University of Rochester, New York 1979–84

Vice President for Health Affairs, University of Rochester, Rochester, New York 1981–84

Chairman, Department of Microbiology, University of Rochester, Rochester, New York, 1970–79

272

Chairmen of Panels

Dr Brian W. Christmas, New Zealand[a]
  Director, National Health Institute, 1972–75, 1987–89
  Deputy Director-General of Health, 1985–87
  Deputy Director-General of Health (Public Health), 1975–85
  Advocate-General of the Supreme Court
  Minister of Public Works, Transport and Town Planning

Dr Bernard D. Goldstein, United States of America
  Director, Environmental and Occupational Health Sciences Institute
    since 1986
  Professor and Chairman, Department of Environmental and Commu-
    nity Medicine, University of Medicine and Dentistry of New Jersey,
    Robert Wood Johnson Medical School, since 1980
  Assistant Administrator for Research and Development, Environmen-
    tal Protection Agency, 1983–85

Professor E.H. Kampelmacher, The Netherlands
  Deputy Director General, National Institute for Public Health and
    Environmental Hygiene, 1984–86
  Scientific Director, National Institute for Public Health and Environ-
    mental Hygiene, 1973–84
  Professor of Food Microbiology and Hygiene, Agricultural Uni-
    versity, Wageningen, 1971–85

Dr Barbara H. MacGibbon, United Kingdom
  Assistant Director (Medical), National Radiological Protection Board,
    since 1988
  Senior Principal Medical Officer, Division of Toxicology and En-
    vironmental Health, Department of Health, 1983–88
  Senior Lecturer/Senior Research Fellow, St Thomas Hospital Medical
    School, London

Representatives of other organizations

Commission of the European Communities (CEC), Brussels, Belgium
  Professor G. Aresini
  Dr A. Berlin
  Professor P. Bourdeau
Commonwealth Secretariat, London, England
  Dr H.M. Bichan

---

[a] Dr B.W. Christmas served as Chairman of the Panel on Urbanization in the absence of Mr
M. Diop (see Annex 2).

Council for International Organizations of Medical Sciences (CIOMS), Geneva, Switzerland
Dr Z. Bankowski

Food and Agriculture Organization of the United Nations (FAO), Rome, Italy
Mr R. J. Dawson
Mr P. J. Mahler
Ms W. Mann

International Atomic Energy Agency (IAEA), Vienna, Austria
Mr S. Haddad
Mrs M. S. Opelz

International Chamber of Commerce, Geneva, Switzerland
Mr A. E. Fry

International Group of National Associations of Manufacturers of Agro-chemical Products (GIFAP), Basel, Switzerland
Dr P. Brenneisen
Dr F. Mühlebach

International Labour Organisation (ILO), Geneva, Switzerland
Dr C. Pinnagoda
Mr S. Machida

International Life Sciences Institute (ILSI), Washington, DC, USA
Dr R. Buzina

International Union for the Conservation of Nature and Natural Resources (IUCN), Gland, Switzerland
Ms Ock-Kyung Kim

Organisation for Economic Co-operation and Development (OECD), Paris, France
Mr G. Bernier
Mr J. Brydon
Dr R. Visser

United Nations Centre for Human Settlements (UNCHS), UNHABITAT, Office Europe, Geneva, Switzerland
Dr P. S. Towfighi
Mr J. Lorentzen
Mr L. P. Ludvigsen

United Nations Children's Fund (UNICEF), New York, USA
Dr R. Atapattu

United Nations Conference on Environment and Development (UNCED), Conches, Switzerland
Dr N. Htun
Dr R. Helmer

United Nations Development Programme (UNDP), Geneva, Switzerland
  Mr T. Delbreuve
  Mr. A. Rotival
United Nations Environment Programme (UNEP)/International Register of
  Potentially Toxic Chemicals (IRPTC), Geneva, Switzerland
  Dr J.W. Huismans
  Mrs M. Laurijssen
United Nations High Commissioner for Refugees (HCR), Geneva, Switzer-
  land
  Dr M.W. Dualeh
United Nations Industrial Development Organization (UNIDO), Vienna,
  Austria
  Mr E. Burmistrov
  Mrs I. Lorenzo
  Mr D. Rakotopare
United Nations Population Fund (UNFPA), New York, USA
  Dr P. Severyns
  Mr P. Shaw
United States Environmental Protection Agency, Washington, DC, USA
  Dr J.A. Stober
World Bank, Washington, DC, USA
  Mr J. Warford
World Meteorological Organization (WMO), Geneva, Switzerland
  Dr R.D. Bojkov
  Dr L. Olsson
  Dr A.V. Soudine
World Federation of United Nations Associations (WFUNA), Geneva,
  Switzerland
  Mr M. Weydert
World Veterinary Association (WVA)/World Association of Veterinary
  Food Hygienists, Dublin, Ireland
  Professor J. Hannan

Secretariat

Dr B. Armstrong, International Agency for Research on Cancer (IARC),
  Lyon, France
Dr D.B. Bisht, Director, Programme Management, WHO Regional Office
  for South-East Asia, New Delhi, India
Mr X. Bonnefoy, Regional Adviser, Environmental Health, WHO Regional
  Office for Europe, Copenhagen, Denmark

Dr P. Guo, Director, Western Pacific Regional Centre for the Promotion of Environmental Planning and Applied Studies (PEPAS), Kuala Lumpur, Malaysia

Mr M.L. Gupta, Chief, Promotion of Environmental Health, WHO Regional Office for South-East Asia, New Delhi, India

Dr D. Kello, Chief, Toxicology and Food Safety, Environmental Health, WHO Regional Office for Europe, Copenhagen, Denmark

Mr G.O. Kermode, formerly Chief, Joint FAO/WHO Food Standards Programme, Rome, Italy (*Consultant*)

Dr H. de Koning, Regional Adviser, Environmental Health, WHO Regional Office for the Americas/Pan American Sanitary Bureau, Washington, DC, USA

Mr M. Koussitassev, Regional Adviser, Environmental Health, WHO Regional Office for Africa, Brazzaville, Congo

Dr W. Kreisel, Director, Division of Environmental Health, WHO, Geneva, Switzerland (*Secretary*)

Mr D.E. Satterthwaite, International Institute for Environment and Development, London, England (*Temporary Adviser*)

Dr F. Sella, formerly Director, Global Environment Monitoring System Programme Activity Centre, UNEP, Nairobi, Kenya (*Technical Secretary*)

Dr M.I. Sheikh, Director, Environmental Health Programme, WHO Regional Office for the Eastern Mediterranean, Alexandria, Egypt

Mr S.A. Tamplin, Regional Adviser, Environmental Health, WHO Regional Office for the Western Pacific, Manila, Philippines

Dr S. Tarkowski, Director, Environmental Health, WHO Regional Office for Europe, Copenhagen, Denmark

Dr L. Tomatis, International Agency for Research on Cancer, Lyon, France

Annex 2
Members of Technical Panels

Panel on Energy

Members[a]

Professor L. Hamilton, Biomedical and Environmental Assessment Division, Brookhaven National Laboratory, National Center for Analysis of Energy, Upton, Long Island, NY, USA

Professor S.R. Kamat, B-2 Shree Dattaguru Cooperative Housing Society, Deonar, Bombay, India

Professor J. Liniecki, Institute of Radiology, Department of Nuclear Medicine, Institute of Occupational Medicine of Lodz, Lodz, Poland

Dr B.H. MacGibbon, National Radiological Protection Board, Chilton, Didcot, England (*Chairman*)

Professor G. Nordberg, Department of Environmental Medicine, University of Umea, Umea, Sweden

Dr H.O. Sandoval, Hospital del Trabajador, Santiago, Chile

Dr I. Shigematsu, Radiation Effects Research Foundation, Hiroshima, Japan

Dr E.B. Torres, Department of Environmental and Occupational Health, College of Public Health, University of the Philippines, Manila, Philippines (*Vice-Chairman*)

Representatives of other organizations

International Atomic Energy Agency (IAEA), Vienna, Austria
    Mr S. Haddad
    Dr T. Müller

United Nations Environment Programme (UNEP)/International Register of Potentially Toxic Chemicals (IRPTC), Geneva, Switzerland
    Dr J.W. Huismans

United Nations Population Fund (UNFPA), New York, USA
    Dr M. Sabwa

---

[a] Unable to attend: Dr E. Bretthauer, Office of Research and Development, Environmental Protection Agency, Washington, DC, USA. Dr Bretthauer was represented by Dr Carl Gerber.

Secretariat

Mr G. Ozolins, Manager, Prevention of Environmental Pollution, Division of Environmental Health, WHO, Geneva, Switzerland (*Co-Secretary*)

Dr J. Szczerban, Chief, Office of Research Promotion and Development, WHO, Geneva, Switzerland (*Co-Secretary*)

Dr F. Sella, formerly Director, Global Environment Monitoring System Programme Activity Centre, UNEP, Nairobi, Kenya

Panel on Food and Agriculture

Members[a]

Dr C.L. Angst, Industry Council for Development, New York, USA

Professor I. Beghin, Institute of Tropical Medicine, Antwerp, Belgium

Professor D. J. Bradley, London School of Hygiene and Tropical Medicine, University of London, London, England

Professor E.H. Kampelmacher, Bilthoven, Netherlands (*Chairman*)

Professor S.A. Miller, Graduate School of Biomedical Sciences, University of Texas, San Antonio, TX, USA

Professor K. J. Netter, Department of Pharmacology and Toxicology, University of Marburg, Marburg, Germany

Professor P. Pinstrup-Andersen, Division of Nutritional Sciences, Cornell University, Ithaca, NY, USA

Dr V. Sergiev, Martsinovsky Institute of Medical Parasitology and Tropical Medicine, Moscow, USSR

Dr N.W. Tape, Director, Food Research Centre, Agriculture Canada, Ottawa, Ontario, Canada

Representatives of other organizations

Food and Agriculture Organization of the United Nations (FAO), Rome, Italy
   Mr R. J. Dawson

International Group of National Associations of Manufacturers of Agrochemical Products (GIFAP), Basel, Switzerland
   Dr P. Brenneisen
   Dr F. Mühlebach

International Life Sciences Institute (ILSI), Washington, DC, USA
   Dr R. Buzina

United Nations Population Fund (UNFPA), New York, USA
   Dr P. Shaw

---

[a] Unable to attend: Professor O. Soemarwoto, Padjadjaran University, Institute of Ecology, Bandung, Indonesia; Dr M.S. Swaminathan, Teynampet Chennai, Madras, India.

Secretariat

Dr I. Hespanhol, Community Water Supply and Sanitation, Division of Environmental Health, WHO, Geneva, Switzerland (*Co-Secretary*)

Dr F. Käferstein, Chief, Food Safety, Division of Health Promotion and Protection, WHO, Geneva, Switzerland (*Co-Secretary*)

Dr Y. Motarjemi, Scientist, Food Safety, Division of Health Promotion and Protection, WHO, Geneva, Switzerland

Dr A.G. Pradilla, Chief, Nutrition, Division of Health Promotion and Protection, WHO, Geneva, Switzerland (*Co-Secretary*)

Dr F.G. Quevedo, Scientist, Food Safety, Division of Health Promotion and Protection, WHO, Geneva, Switzerland

Dr R. Slooff, Scientist, Division of Environmental Health, WHO, Geneva, Switzerland

Panel on Industry

Members[a]

Dr N.P. Bochkov, Institute of Medical Genetics, Academy of Medical Sciences, Moscow, USSR

Dr P. Bourdeau, Directorate General for Science Research and Development, Commission of the European Communities, Brussels, Belgium

Dr B.D. Goldstein, Environmental and Occupational Health Sciences Institute, New Jersey, USA (*Chairman*)

Professor C. Hogstedt, Department of Occupational Medicine, Karolinksa Hospital and National Institute of Occupational Health, Ekelund-svaagen, Solna, Sweden

Dr K. Lokan, Australian Radiation Laboratory, Yallambie, Victoria, Melbourne, Australia

Profesor Niu Shi-ru, Institute of Environmental Health and Engineering, Chinese Academy of Preventive Medicine, Beijing, China

Dr E. Somers, Drugs Directorate, Health and Welfare Canada, Health Protection Branch, Ottawa, Ontario, Canada

Dr Malinee Wongphanich, Occupational Health Department, Faculty of Public Health, Mahidol University, Bangkok, Thailand (*Vice-Chairman*)

---

[a] Unable to attend: Professor M. Corn, Johns Hopkins University, School of Hygiene and Public Health, Division of Environmental Engineering, Baltimore, MD, USA; Professor J. Rantanen, Institute of Occupational Health, Topeliuksenkatu, Helsinki, Finland. Professor Rantanen was represented by Professor A. Aitio.

Representatives of other organizations

Commission of the European Communities (CEC), Luxembourg
  Professor G. Aresini
  Mr R. Haigh
  Mr A. Sors
International Federation of Chemical, Energy, and General Workers' Unions
  (ICEF), Geneva, Switzerland
  Mrs A. Rice
United Nations Environment Programme (UNEP), Geneva, Switzerland
  Dr J.W. Huismans
United Nations Population Fund (UNFPA), New York, USA
  Dr M. Sabwa

Secretariat

Mrs B. Goelzer, Occupational Hygienist, Office of Occupational Health,
  Division of Health Protection and Promotion, WHO, Geneva, Swit-
  zerland (*Co-Secretary*)
Dr M. Mercier, Manager, International Programme on Chemical Safety,
  Division of Environmental Health, WHO, Geneva, Switzerland (*Co-
  Secretary*)
Dr L. Tomatis, International Agency for Research on Cancer, Lyon, France

Panel on Urbanization

Members[a]

Mrs S. Boonyabancha, Asian Coalition for Housing Rights, Bangkok, Thai-
  land
Dr B.W. Christmas, Roseneath, Wellington, New Zealand (*Co-Chairman*)
Professor J. Duhl, School of Public Health and City Planning, University of
  California, Berkeley, CA, USA
Dr El-Mohamady Eid, Egyptian Environment Affairs Agency, Cairo, Egypt
Dr P. Khanna, National Environmental Engineering Research Institute,
  Nagpur, India
Dr O.O. Oladapo, Alaska Estate, Surulere-Lagos, Lagos, Nigeria
Mr D.E. Satterthwaite, International Institute for Environment and De-
  velopment, London, England

---

[a] Unable to attend: Dr Anil Agarwal, Centre for Science and Environment, New Delhi, India;
Mr Mamadou Diop, Mayor of Dakar, Dakar, Senegal (Chairman); Comrade G. Negussie, Addis
Ababa Administrative Region, Addis Ababa, Ethiopia. Comrade Negussie was represented by
Comrade Wendmu Dejene.

Dr H. Vertio, Cancer Society of Finland, National Board of Health, Helsinki, Finland

Representatives of other organizations

United Nations Centre for Human Settlements (UNCHS), UNHABITAT, Office Europe, Geneva, Switzerland
    Mr A. Dzikus
    Dr G. Sinnatamby
    Dr P.S. Towfighi
United Nations Development Programme (UNDP), Geneva, Switzerland
    Mr S. Cheema
United Nations Environment Programme (UNEP), Geneva, Switzerland
    Mr N. Gebremedhin
United Nations Population Fund (UNFPA), New York, USA
    Dr M. Sabwa
United Nations Volunteers (UNV), Geneva, Switzerland
    Mr A. Drucker

Secretariat

Dr G. Goldstein, Responsible Officer, Environmental Health in Rural and Urban Development and Housing, Division of Environmental Health, WHO, Geneva, Switzerland
Dr I. Tabibzadeh, Responsible Officer, District Health Systems, Division of Strengthening of Health Services, WHO, Geneva, Switzerland

Annex 3
Members of the WHO Task Force of the WHO Commission on Health and Environment

Dr P. Beales, Chief, Training Unit, Division of Control of Tropical Diseases

Mrs B. Goelzer, Occupational Hygienist, Office of Occupational Health, Division of Health Protection and Promotion

Dr G. Goldstein, Responsible Officer, Environmental Health in Rural and Urban Development and Housing, Division of Environmental Health

Dr A. El-Bindari Hammad, Adviser to the Director-General on Health and Development Policies

Dr F. Käferstein, Chief, Food Safety, Division of Health Protection and Promotion

Dr W. Kreisel, Director, Division of Environmental Health (*Chairman*)

Dr M. Mercier, Manager, International Programme on Chemical Safety, Division of Environmental Health

Dr K. Mott, Chief, Schistosomiasis and other Trematode Infections, Division of Control of Tropical Diseases

Dr T.K.W. Ng, Medical Officer, Office of Occupational Health, Division of Health Protection and Promotion

Mr G. Ozolins, Manager, Prevention of Environmental Pollution, Division of Environmental Health

Dr A. Pradilla, Food and Nutrition Programme, Division of Health Protection and Promotion

Dr A. Prost, Acting Director, Programme Development and Monitoring

Dr F. Sella, formerly Director, Global Environment Monitoring System Programme Activity Centre, UNEP, Nairobi, Kenya (*Technical Secretary to the Commission*)

Dr R. Slooff, Scientist, Division of Environmental Health

Dr J. Szczerban, Chief, Office of Research Promotion and Development

Dr I. Tabibzadeh, Responsible Officer, District Health Systems, Division of Strengthening of Health Services

Mr K. Uchida, Scientist, Division of Environmental Health

Dr D. Warner, Manager, Community Water Supply and Sanitation, Division of Environmental Health